Sierra Nevada Ecosystem Project

FINAL REPORT TO CONGRESS

Status of the Sierra Nevada

VOLUME I

*Assessment Summaries and
Management Strategies*

Written and Edited by the SNEP Science Team and Special Consultants

Wildland Resources Center Report No. 36

CENTERS FOR WATER AND WILDLAND RESOURCES
UNIVERSITY OF CALIFORNIA, DAVIS

June 1996

Sierra Nevada Ecosystem Project: Final Report to Congress
Volume I: *Assessment Summaries and Management Strategies*
Wildland Resources Center Report No. 36
ISBN 1-887673-00-8

Support for this research was provided by cooperative research agreement with the United States Forest Service Pacific Southwest Research Station and the University of California.

This publication is a continuation in the Wildland Resources Center Reports series. It is published and distributed by the Director's Office of the Centers for Water and Wildland Resources. The Centers sponsor projects in water and wildland resources and related research within the state of California with funds provided by various state and federal agencies and private industry. Copies of this and other reports published by the Centers may be obtained from:

Centers for Water and Wildland Resources
University of California
1323 Academic Surge
Davis, CA 95616-8750
916-752-8070

Copies of the Centers' publications may be examined at the Water Resources Center Archives at 410 O'Brien Hall, Berkeley Campus; 510-642-2666.

Please cite this volume as: *Sierra Nevada Ecosystem Project, Final Report to Congress,* vol. I, *Assessment Summaries and Management Strategies* (Davis: University of California, Centers for Water and Wildland Resources, 1996).

Photographs: Dwight M. Collins, cover, title page, chapters 1, 2, 5, 8, 9, 11, 12; Jerry F. Franklin, chapters 3, 6, 7, 10; B. Knight, chapter 4; Neil Michaels, appendixes.

Errat

December 17, 199

Revised Figure 9.5 for Volume I
Revised Figure 48.21 for Volum

Note: The figure labels in both figures 9.5 left to right. Please note the correc Errata.

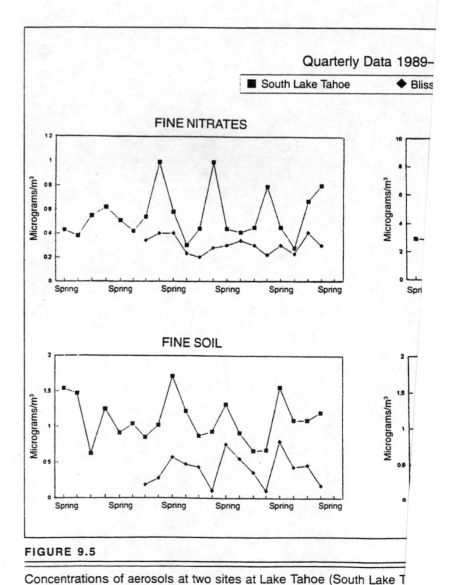

FIGURE 9.5

Concentrations of aerosols at two sites at Lake Tahoe (South Lake T 94. (From volume II, chapter 48.)

Revised Errata

December 18, 1996
This Errata replaces "Errata, Sierra Nevada Ecosystem Project, June 27, 1996"

Corrections to Summary

Page 1, right column, 3rd complete paragraph, line 2.
   Replace "Seventy people..." with "Ninety people..."

Corrections to Volume I

Page 81, left column, 2nd complete paragraph.
   Replace entire paragraph with,
   "In the Sierra, eighty-three terrestrial vertebrate species are considered to be dependent on riparian habitat to sustain viable populations; 24% of these are listed as species "at risk" (see next section). Seventeen species are similarly dependent on late successional foothill savannah, woodland, chaparral, or riparian habitat (some are double-counted with species requiring riparian habitat) for Sierran population viability; 16% of these species are at risk. This last number is misleadingly low because many species at risk in the Sierra are more widely distributed elsewhere, such as in the Coast Range".

Page 179, left column, Chapter 55, and Table of Contents in Volume II, page v.
   Replace title and author with "Ecology and Management of Giant Sequoia Groves, Nathan L. Stephenson".

Page 185, left column, 20th line from top
   Replace "Nate Stephenson" with "Nathan L. Stephenson".

Page 205, left column, 5th complete paragraph, 2nd line from bottom.
   Replace "seventy individuals..." with "ninety individuals...".

Page 209, left column, 1st complete paragraph after "Quincy Library Group...".
   Move entire paragraph beginning with "Case study workshops..." to page 209, right column, after "June 1995, Sierra Country, second meeting (Sierraville)".

Plate 4.2 caption, line 1
   After "Fire recurrence map" add "(1908-1993)".

Plate 4.3, in legend
   After "Grass" add "low hazard"; after "Pine with grass and shrubs" add "high hazard"; after "Mature Chaparral" add extreme hazard"; after "Intermediate brush" add "high hazard"; after "Lodgepole pine/red fir" add "low hazard"; after "Logging slash" add "high hazard"; after "Dense true fir" add "low hazard"; after "Pine/mixed conifer" add "high hazard"; after "Plantations/burned areas" add "low hazard".

Fig. 9.5, Volume I, page 141, and Fig. 48.21, Volume II, page 1252
   The figure labels in the diagrams were switched, left to right. Exchange labels "Fine Organic matter" with "Fine Nitrates", "Fine Sulfates" with "Fine Soil". Revised visually on Errata, December 17, 1996.

Corrections to Volume III—This Errata replaces Volume III, Statement of Errata

The Authorship of Chapter 19, "Assessment of Current Risks, Fuels, and Potential Fire Behavior in the Sierra Nevada" in the Table of Contents should read as follows:

David Sapsis, Berni Bahro, James Spero, John Gabriel, Russell Jones, and Gregory Greenwood

Corrections to Volume III (continued from front page)

Chapter 24, page 1065 and in the Table of Contents page iv.
   Replace title, "Coordinated Resource Management" with "Applied Ecosystem Management: Coordinated Resource Management in the Feather River Watershed". The authorship should read as follows:

Jonathan London
Department of Environmental Science,
   Policy and Management
University of California
Berkeley, California

Jonathan Kusel
Forest Community Research
and
Department of Environmental Science,
   Policy and Management
University of California
Berkeley, California

Contents

The SNEP Science Team and Special Consultants

Science Team

Don C. Erman, Team Leader, University of California, Davis, CA

Michael Barbour, University of California, Davis, CA

Norman Christensen, Duke University, Durham, NC

Frank W. Davis, University of California, Santa Barbara, CA

Harrison Dunning, University of California, Davis, CA

Deborah L. Elliott-Fisk, University of California, Davis, CA (former team leader)

Jerry F. Franklin, University of Washington, Seattle, WA

David Graber, National Biological Service, Three Rivers, CA

K. Norman Johnson, Oregon State University, Corvallis, OR

John W. Menke, University of California, Davis, CA

Constance I. Millar, U.S. Forest Service, Pacific Southwest Research Station, Albany, CA

Janet H. Momsen, University of California, Davis, CA

Peter B. Moyle, University of California, Davis, CA

David J. Parsons, U.S. Forest Service, Aldo Leopold Wilderness Research Institute, Missoula, MT

Rowan A. Rowntree, U.S. Forest Service, Northeastern Forest Experiment Station, Albany, CA

John Sessions, Oregon State University, Corvallis, OR

John C. Tappeiner, National Biological Service, Corvallis, OR

Susan L. Ustin, University of California, Davis, CA

Special Consultants

Philip S. Aune, U.S. Forest Service, Pacific Southwest Research Station, Redding, CA

Joan Brenchley-Jackson, University of California, Davis, CA

Tom Cahill, University of California, Davis, CA

Gary Darling, State of California Resources Agency, Sacramento, CA

Michael F. Diggles, U.S. Geological Survey, Menlo Park, CA

Timothy P. Duane, University of California, Berkeley, CA

Robert Ewing, Weyerhaeuser Corporation, Tacoma, WA

Gregory Greenwood, California Department of Forestry and Fire Protection, Sacramento, CA

Richard Kattelmann, University of California, Santa Barbara, Mammoth Lakes, CA

Jon Kennedy, U.S. Forest Service, Sacramento, CA

Jonathan Kusel, Forest Community Research and University of California, Westwood, CA

Douglas Leisz, Placerville, CA

Dennis Machida, California Tahoe Conservancy, South Lake Tahoe, CA

Kevin S. McKelvey, U.S. Forest Service, Pacific Southwest Research Station, Arcata, CA

Larry Ruth, University of California, Berkeley, CA

James R. Shevock, U.S. Forest Service, Regional Office, San Francisco, CA

Carl N. Skinner, U.S. Forest Service, Pacific Southwest Research Station, Redding, CA

William Stewart, Pacific Institute, Oakland, CA

C. Phillip Weatherspoon, U.S. Forest Service, Pacific Southwest Research Station, Redding, CA

Introduction

Background

In a few lines contained in the Conference Report for Interior and Related Agencies 1993 Appropriation Act (HR 5503), Congress authorized funds for a

> scientific review of the remaining old growth in the national forests of the Sierra Nevada in California, and for a study of the entire Sierra Nevada ecosystem by an independent panel of scientists, with expertise in diverse areas related to this issue.

This act created the Sierra Nevada Ecosystem Project (SNEP). The primary emphasis of the project was to assemble and assess the comprehensive data necessary to assist Congress and others in making important policy decisions for the future management of the Sierra Nevada. The other emphasis was to examine alternative management strategies that could help meet the broad goal for which the study was undertaken. That goal was to maintain the health and sustainability of the Sierra Nevada ecosystem while providing resources to meet human needs. Concern over conservation and use of the Sierra Nevada is not new. Some of the more recent issues connect to general concern over forest conditions in the Pacific Northwest and to specific concerns raised by a series of articles in the *Sacramento Bee* ("The Sierra in Peril") and subsequent conferences ("Sierra Summit," "Sierra Now").

More congressional direction on the scope of the SNEP study and the structure of the independent team was provided by a second bill. It was not passed before adjournment but was later read into the *Congressional Record* as a guide to the study. Letters from various members of the House of Representatives to the Chief of the U.S. Department of Agriculture, Forest Service, gave additional explanation of the intended legislation. The Forest Service supplemented the $150,000 provided in HR 5503 to conduct the study by committing $6.5 million over the three years of project work.

The first step in the study was formation of a Steering Committee (appendix 4) composed of a representative each from Forest Service Research, Washington Office; Forest Service Research, Pacific Southwest Station; U.S. Department of the Interior, National Park Service; University of California; and California Academy of Sciences, plus a "scientist of eminent standing" and member of the National Academy of Sciences. The Steering Committee selected a Science Team leader, worked with the team leader to select the team, developed the charge for the team in keeping with congressional intent, and provided overall guidance and advice throughout the study. The charge to the team and the congressional bills and letters were included in the *SNEP Progress Report,* May 1994.

The Science Team, eventually composed of eighteen members, was augmented by nineteen special consultants (both groups are listed after the table of contents). In addition, many other scientists worked closely with team members (one hun-

Team leader Don C. Erman (right) discussing SNEP with Ken Roby of the U.S. Forest Service, Donna Lindquist of Pacific Gas and Electric Company, and other participants at a public meeting to report progress. (Photo by Neil Michaels.)

dred seven as authors or coauthors of chapters and reports), some throughout the project; their contributions appear in volume II or III or are acknowledged elsewhere (appendix 4). Overall management of the project was the responsibility of the University of California Centers for Water and Wildland Resources, through a research agreement with the Forest Service, Pacific Southwest Research Station.

Approach

In broad outline, the Science Team divided its energy into (1) a period of data gathering and evaluation of data quality, (2) a period of assessment of the past and current status of the ecosystem, and (3) a final period of projecting and evaluating future trends under different possible strategies. The project devoted most of its effort to analyzing existing information rather than conducting new studies or experiments. The integration of this accumulated information became a primary objective, as the team sought a range of options for future directions of management. The study used geographic information systems (GISs) extensively as a primary means of synthesizing data, displaying information, and considering options for further analysis.

The Science Team identified the primary questions to examine by involving a wider group of scientists to assist in data gathering and evaluation and by discussing the findings and implications of all the assessments. This process quickly showed the integral role of people, including their communities and institutions, as important ecosystem components equal to the flora, fauna, and other natural features. The team also recognized that dialogue with the public was necessary. A group of seventy people with diverse interests and responsibilities in the Sierra was assembled as "key contacts." This group met with the team to review progress, ask questions, help in framing scenarios, assist in review of assessments, and plan larger public involvement. The team held

Team member William Stewart (center) listens to input from Mono County Supervisor Andrea Lawrence (left), Mike Albrecht of TUCARE (right), and others at a public meeting. (Photo by Neil Michaels.)

smaller work sessions and reported on progress several times at announced public meetings called by the Steering Committee. Throughout the study, many team members met with individuals and local and regional groups, presented reports at professional and technical meetings, briefed county, state, and federal agency personnel, and held local workshops. These interactions between scientists and the public helped refine our process, content, approach, and scope.

The charge of this study was not confined by the jurisdictions of ownership and management but rather followed the realities of the landscape. Data from both public and private lands were examined to the limit of time and resources; however, the 60% of the range in federal lands is highlighted because of availability of information.

The team found that much has been studied in the Sierra Nevada, although, in many areas vital to understanding the future, essential knowledge was unavailable or tests of ideas have yet to be done. Science Team members were asked to draw reasonable inferences from their assessment of existing information, including their own observations. They have been explicit about the basis of this knowledge and these data and about where they are making assumptions or giving personal judgments.

Assessments

Assessment of the individual components of the system involved teams of various sizes, contacts with other scientists, requests for commissioned reports, review of published and unpublished literature, workshops, individual knowledge and observation, and in some cases original analysis of data or field evaluations. Assessment projects were guided by five questions:

1. What were historic ecological, social, and economic conditions, trends, and variability?

2. What are current ecological, social, and economic conditions?

3. What are trends and risks under current policies and management?

4. What policy choices will achieve ecological sustainability consistent with social well-being?

5. What are the implications of these choices?

In many places our assessments have used historical data as a guide to understanding natural ecological processes and conditions. These data have been as varied as ice cores from the poles, tree rings from thousand-year-old trees, diaries of early explorers, and photographs taken at the turn of the century. The past is always imperfectly known and understood, partly because the data are imperfect and because alternative explanations of processes and conditions may fit the same data. Supporting information from experimental research and from observations of conditions at select locations (such as parks) have been used to strengthen inferences from the past. But these approaches aim at understanding the present, not setting a fixed benchmark of what the future should be. The assessment summaries focus on those aspects of the ecosystem in which either existing conditions or present trends are in need of remedial action. Possible actions are given as alternative management strategies for improving conditions.

What volume I presents is a brief summary of only some of the more important findings from these assessments. Practical limits of summarizing the substantial body of knowledge assembled by the study required us to omit much of the depth and richness. We have worked to avoid oversimplification or generalization without presenting the detailed methods and literature common to science reports. Thus, the full context, citation to sources, justification, and supporting data must be examined in the complete assessment reports. We have further summarized the assessments in a series of critical findings that are presented at the beginning of each chapter in this volume. These represent *new* findings, findings that *confirm* what has been generally believed about the Sierra, and *emergent* or *synthesizing* ideas that arose from SNEP's integrated analysis of individual reports.

Strategies

Ecosystem assessment findings provide a basis for evaluating where conditions may be heading and how much the Sierra Nevada has changed. The congressional language and background for this study emphasized that the report was to advise Congress on existing and possible future conditions of the old-growth and late successional forests and the ecosystems of the Sierra Nevada. Thus, the team was not asked to prepare a single plan, a range of options for implementation, or preferred alternatives, as in an environmental impact statement process required under the National Environmental Policy Act.

Improvements in conditions through remedial actions usually imply a definition of the goals of alternative strategies. SNEP was not charged with selecting the goals for society or the Sierra Nevada ecosystem. However, to devise strategies one must have goals. The team selected goals within the overall charge to the project, to be explicit and to suggest how conditions and trends revealed by the assessments could be changed. Many of our goals were chosen through input from public interaction. Discussions with the public, which continued over the course of the project, became a mutual search for strategies for improved management—not to find a finite set of the best alternatives but rather to understand better the connections among so many complex parts of the Sierra Nevada ecosystem.

Such an exercise may quickly overwhelm easy summary or comprehension because of the infinite combinations or variations of factors that make up the ecosystem. Thus, we chose a small sample of strategies to demonstrate broad choices and implications for meeting the stated goals. The strategies should also educate us on the ways in which parts of the system

Science team member Constance I. Millar (left) discusses assessment findings with Joan Reiss, environmental consultant. (Photo by Neil Michaels.)

interact and should lead to a better understanding of unexpected ramifications brought about by human action. No single model of the Sierra that encompasses all interacting parts is possible. We have deliberately chosen several models—mathematical and nonmathematical, quantitative and qualitative—to illustrate our strategies. Models are only one way to organize and display a thought process. Their utility is to aid in understanding the implications of choices, in suggesting other choices, and in opening up the territory for informed decision making. Some of the strategies required development of new methods or interpretations of scientific knowledge (e.g., areas of late successional emphasis, fuels management). The details and background for these strategies are given in full in the other volumes.

The SNEP Reports

The complete report of SNEP is contained in four volumes: Volume I contains critical findings, the context for the study, summaries of the major points from the assessments and case studies in the other volumes, and a presentation of alternative strategies and their implications for the future health and sustainability of the ecosystem.

Volume II contains the technical assessments of historical, physical, biological, ecological, social, and institutional conditions in the Sierra Nevada, selected case studies, details on the scientific basis and methods used in strategies, and references

At a September 1995 public workshop in Sacramento, SNEP team member John Sessions (standing) fields questions about simulation models. (Photo by Neil Michaels.)

to the literature and data sources. All chapters in volume II were reviewed extensively, including anonymous peer review secured by the Steering Committee.

Volume III includes late submissions of peer-reviewed papers from volume II, additional commissioned reports, and summary listings of workshops and participants. A list of the contents of volumes II and III is included in volume I (appendix 1).

Volume IV is a computer-based catalogue of all public databases, maps, and other digitally stored information used in the project. A major goal of the project was to leave an accessible and usable database containing information, approaches to analysis, and a framework for future study and decision making. These materials are listed under the SNEP name and available on the Internet from the Alexandria Project at the University of California at Santa Barbara and the California Environmental Resource Evaluation System (CERES) project of the Resources Agency of the State of California. A directory of the GIS portion and available data is in appendix 3.

The project was conceived as a scientific study by independent scientists. Thus, the reports presented in volumes II and III (and summarized in volume I) are attributable to the authors and follow the usual standards for citation, accuracy, and statement of opinion. Throughout the study, the team fostered debate and welcomed diversity of ideas. At the end, some issues remained in contention among team members and are so noted in the report. Assessment chapters, as in the journals of science, are not intended or written as consensus documents. Understanding complex ideas and recognizing areas of uncertainty come about as much by seeing different views as by studying a single, dominant perspective. But we have made every effort to document the basis in facts, assumptions, knowledge, and inferences that we used in reaching our conclusions. Readers of our reports, by their own analyses of our information, may reach new conclusions. We have intended that the bases for our conclusions and the process of our reasoning be open and available to alternative analyses.

No single strategy that we explore is considered comprehensive for all components of the ecosystem or the entire range, and all need specific information on local conditions to be fully useful. If our understanding of the scientific relationships within the ecosystem is correct, then the same understanding may be employed to develop other strategies and even reach other ends. This study has shown us that options are available that could lead to better management. Before a different management policy for the Sierra Nevada ecosystem proceeds, society must define the future vision, the charter for the future Sierra Nevada.

Having before us a summing up of this knowledge should help us all make informed choices in the give-and-take of the democratic process.

CHAPTER 1

Sierra Nevada Ecosystems

Climate Change   During the period of recent human settlement in the Sierra Nevada, climate was much wetter, warmer, and more stable than climates of the past two millennia; successful ecosystem evaluations and planning for the future must factor climate change into analyses.

INTRODUCTION

The Sierra Nevada evokes images particular to each individual's experience of the range. These images take on the quality of immutability, and we expect to find the range basically unchanged from one year to the next. The Sierra Ne-

FIGURE 1.1

Northern Sierra montane aerial view. (Photo by Jerry F. Franklin.)

vada, however, including its rocky foundations and the plants and animals that inhabit it, changes continually through time. Ecosystems respond to cumulative effects from the past; the old-growth forests in the Sierra today evolved under different conditions from those of the present. To understand how the landscapes of the Sierra Nevada are changing, and what role humans have in shaping the future, we benefit by knowing what makes up the current Sierra as well as key factors influencing change. This was the point of departure for the Sierra Nevada Ecosystem Project. A brief introduction to the Sierra Nevada and the context of the study are presented here; subsequent chapters summarize the study's findings.

ROCK AND SOIL

At its foundation, the Sierra Nevada is an enormous deposit of granitic rock whose exposed slopes are readily visible at the crest of the range. The gradual west slope rising from the expansive Central Valley to the Sierra crest is dissected by deep, west-trending river canyons. At the eastern edge of the uplift, the high peaks dominate the uppermost elevations, forming rolling highlands in the north—with elevations mostly less than 9,000 feet (figure 1.1)—and expansive, highly dissected mountains in the broad southern alpine zones, where Mount Whitney (highest peak in the contiguous forty-eight states) rises to 14,495 feet. The range ends abruptly at the eastern escarpment, dropping with a shallow gradient in the north, but in the south plunging more than 10,000 feet from the Sierran crest to the floor of the Great Basin.

❄ *The SNEP Study Area*

The core area boundary for the Sierra Nevada Ecosystem Project was the area containing the headwaters of twenty-four major river basins and extending through the foothill zone on the west side and the base of the escarpment on the east side (figure 1.2). No single boundary adequately defines all the ecological components, but watersheds are in many ways the most discernible and to many biota the most meaningful ecological units in the Sierra. At the request of Congress, a larger study area for the project included portions north of the physiographic Sierra Nevada and extensions beyond the core area to the south and east. Appropriate adjustments to these boundaries were considered in SNEP analyses pertinent to the needs of each issue.

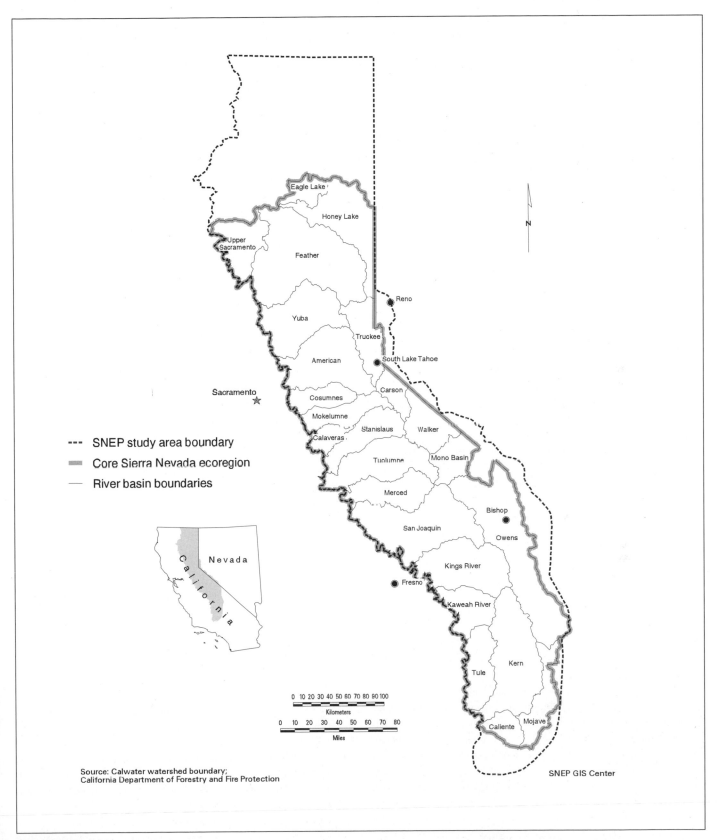

FIGURE 1.2

Boundaries of the core Sierra Nevada ecoregion, the study area, and the twenty-four river basins used by SNEP in its assessments.

As a geological feature, the Sierra Nevada is relatively distinct. The western boundary is defined as a contact between old, harder rocks of the Sierra Nevada and their eroded and redeposited younger by-products at the edge of the Central Valley. At the north, the older rocks of the Sierra Nevada are overlain by younger volcanic rocks of the southern Cascades in the Mount Lassen area. The eastern edge of the range follows the base of the Sierran escarpment. At the south, the geologic Sierra Nevada abuts the structurally distinct Tehachapi Mountains, forming a discernible boundary in southern Kern County.

The Sierra Nevada's environmental history has been shaped over several hundred million years by varying intensities and forms of uplift, erosion, volcanism, and glaciation. Plate tectonics and climate variations acting at millennial, decadal, and annual timescales interact to influence the intensity of these events and their impacts on the landscape. These diverse geological activities have produced a broad suite of rock formations in the Sierra Nevada, dominated by granite but including many types of igneous, sedimentary, and metamorphic rocks, with ages from Cambrian (about 500 million years ago) to Quaternary (the past 2 million years). Most evidence suggests that the modern range is about 10 million years old, although very recent and controversial evidence suggests a much older age.

Rocks of the Sierra Nevada interact with climate, topography, surface processes, and biota to create Sierra Nevada soils. Because the Sierra Nevada is underlain by mostly granitic rocks, soils that develop from these foundations are thin and rocky. Although the nutrient capital (fertility) of the soil in general over the Sierra Nevada is rather low, the range contains some of the most productive sites for conifers in the world. Soil types form a mosaic across the Sierra, influencing vegetation, erosion, wildlife distribution, water quality, fertility, and a myriad of human uses.

Such a complex geological and soil foundation has dramatic implications for human uses of Sierra Nevada ecosystems. Mesozoic deposits (more than 100 million years old), altered through pressure and heat and exposed through erosion or buried deep underground, form the gold and silver that attracted a rush of miners and began the period of Euro-American settlement. Abundant sediments from ancient seafloors, lake beds, and water-carried deposits create the ore and gravel resources that are the contemporary valuable rocks of the Sierra (plate 1.1). Persistent seismic activities, especially along volcanic vents of the eastern escarpment near Mammoth Lakes and Markleeville, are a focus of concern for urban development in these areas, yet those same vents provide geothermal power for existing communities. The rich and fertile soils that have formed on the western edges of the Sierra Nevada continue to support a diverse agriculture that had its origins in the Native American communities that occupied the region.

Volcanic and seismic activity is highly localized but ongoing in the Sierra Nevada. New volcanic craters have been built, vents have erupted, hot springs have formed, faults have slipped, and volcanic-induced mud slides have occurred as recently as the past hundred years in a few regions. Volcanic events will undoubtedly persist as agents of change affecting local ecological and human elements of Sierran ecosystems and demanding local attention.

CLIMATE

Major climate change has occurred at millennial, decadal, and annual scales in the history of the Sierra Nevada (figure 1.3). The regional climate developed from warm, wet, tropical conditions about 65 million years ago through a cycle of at least eight major glacial and interglacial periods of the last million years to the winter-wet, summer-dry pattern of the last 10,000 years. These climatic periods have greatly influenced vegetation, animals, and human populations; their effects are observable today and influence how people manage resources. For instance, two extensive droughts, each lasting 100 to 200 years, occurred within the last 1,200 years. During the cold phase of the Little Ice Age (about A.D. 1650–1850), glaciers in the Sierra Nevada advanced to positions they had not occupied since the end of the last major ice age more than 10,000 years ago. The period of modern settlement in the Sierra Nevada (about the last 150 years), by contrast, has been relatively warm and wet, containing one of the wettest half-century intervals of the past 1,000 years. Many of the forests that stand today were established under different climates—generally wetter ones—from the present regime.

The current Sierran climate is dominated by a "mediterranean" pattern of a cool, wet winter followed by a long dry period in summer. High yearly variability in temperature and precipitation is also characteristic. Because of the influence of the Pacific Ocean and storm tracks from the west, strong climatic gradients develop with elevation from west to east. At foothill altitudes, summer hot, dry climates predominate; as elevation increases, so does precipitation. Winter storms are moisture-laden and release enormous precipitation on the west slope. In winter, snow covers the landscape to about 6,000–8,000 feet. The transition zone of rain to snow is an important determinant of vegetation types, stream dynamics, and human settlement.

The Sierra summits wring water from the winter storms and summer convection systems, leaving the eastern flank progressively drier each mile east (figure 1.4). From moist mountain ecosystems at the Sierran crest, the transition to semiarid desert near Bishop, for example, can occur in less than two horizontal miles. The west shore of Mono Lake, at the base of the Sierran escarpment, receives an average of 12 inches of rain annually, whereas the eastern edge, lying in Great Basin steppe, receives only 6 inches. Strong gradients of aridity also exist from north to south along the Sierran axis as a result of the location of jet stream and subtropical high pressure cells.

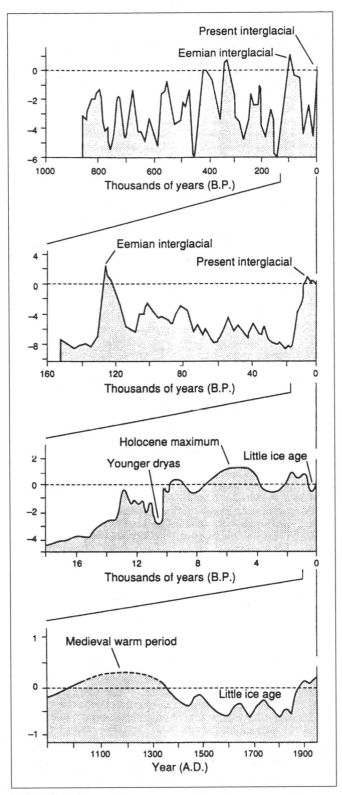

FIGURE 1.3

Global temperatures (relative changes based on oxygen isotopes) at four time scales. (From volume II, chapter 4. Reprinted by permission of the Society for Range Management.)

Climatic and geological forces are the royal architects of Sierra Nevada ecosystems. Water, wildfire, plants, fauna, and humans are highly dependent on regional climate and local weather. Organisms must adjust (migrate, adapt) or die as climate changes. The current patterns of vegetation, water flow and abundance, and animal distribution in the Sierra are determined largely by cumulative effects of past and present climates. Human development in the Sierra has proceeded during a temporary period of relatively wet, warm climate. Patterns of human settlement, perceptions of wildfire, design of water delivery systems, predictions of water availability, future forest and urban planning, and aesthetic expectations about forest condition (size, composition, health of forests) are based largely on conditions of this anomalous climate period. One implication of a longer view of climate is, for instance, that the "droughts" of the mid-1970s and mid-1980s were actually not droughts at all, relative to the century-long dry periods that have been common in recent Sierran climate history.

WATER

Water is an essential and often limiting factor for life. Given strong seasonal mediterranean patterns, high annual variability of climate, natural aridity of the eastern flanks, and the constant thirst of plants, animals, and burgeoning human communities adjacent to the Sierra, water remains a subject of intense competition for all Sierran biota.

Water partitions the Sierra into twenty-four readily discernible river basins or watershed units (figure 1.2). The Sierran crest divides water flow either west to the Pacific Ocean or terminating in the San Joaquin valley, or east into the Great Basin, where the water evaporates. To the west, the major watersheds are defined by the Feather, Yuba, American, Cosumnes, Mokelumne, Stanislaus, Tuolumne, Merced, San Joaquin, Kings, Kaweah, and Kern Rivers; to the east, by the Truckee, Carson, Walker, and Owens Rivers. Streams, creeks, and temporary waters define subwatersheds at increasingly smaller scales within these areas.

Watersheds at each scale are important to creatures that inhabit water. Sierra Nevada waters are home to a diverse aquatic biota, including fishes, amphibians, invertebrates, and plants. To denizens of rivers, the landscape is defined and limited by linear connections; the arterial nature of water systems isolates aquatic populations. Watersheds also isolate aquatic organisms, so that entirely different aquatic biotas may exist from one watershed to another. Rivers and their watersheds extend beyond the geologic edges of the Sierra Nevada to their final destination in ocean, valley, or basin. Fish and other aquatic life have evolved to occupy habitat zones within certain elevations along the rivers, but they do not have sharp or readily defined downstream or upstream boundaries (figure 1.5).

FIGURE 1.4

Mount Tom and the steep eastern escarpment of the Sierra Nevada, with piñon woodlands at the base. (Photo by Deborah L. Elliott-Fisk.)

At middle and low elevations, the Sierra Nevada once supported a diverse fish population, including anadromous species such as chinook salmon. Extensive and abundant populations of frogs and salamanders inhabited Sierran streams, lakes, and meadows. The largest numbers of aquatic species in the Sierra Nevada are the little-known invertebrates. The many lakes of the high Sierra, once mostly fishless, originally supported a diversity of aquatic amphibian and invertebrate species. These groups of aquatic animals have been extremely vulnerable to changes in their habitat, and the story of their composition and distribution is now quite different from that of the past.

PLANTS AND VEGETATION

The Sierra Nevada today is rich in vascular plant diversity, with more than 3,500 native species of plants, making up more than 50% of the plant diversity of California. Hundreds of rare species and species growing only in the Sierra Nevada (endemics) occupy scattered and particular niches of the range. The assemblage of plants growing together in an area creates characteristic vegetation types. Vegetation is a dominant element of ecosystems, for plant diversity, for ecological functions plants engage in (e.g., soil aeration, microclimate alteration), and as habitat and sustenance for other organisms. The architecture of each vegetation type creates habitat suitable for some species and unsuitable for others. The distribution of wildlife is closely associated with the distribution of vegetation, and the same is true for less visible and less familiar forms of life such as fungi, bacteria, and insects.

The major vegetation zones of the Sierra form readily apparent large-scale elevational patterns. Unlike aquatic systems, whose dominant Sierran pattern is defined by east-west watersheds, primary vegetation types of the Sierra form north-south bands along the axis of the Sierra. Major east-west trending watersheds that dissect the Sierra into steep canyons form a secondary pattern of vegetation in the Sierra. Diversity of regional and local plant species as well as vegetation types in the Sierra Nevada are highly influenced by climate,

❋ *Ecosystems*

Ecosystem refers to the collective entity formed by the interaction of organisms (e.g., plants and animals) with each other and with their physical environment (e.g., soil, water, weather) at a particular location. SNEP considers people, when they are present, as part of ecosystems. Ecosystems exist at many, potentially overlapping, scales, from a rotting log to the entire Sierra Nevada; they all have three fundamental attributes. *Components* are the kinds and numbers of organisms (biodiversity of genes, individuals, populations, species, and groups of species) and physical elements (soil, rock, water) that make up the ecosystem—the "pieces." Trees and wildlife are important to Sierran ecosystems but equally important are the myriad less visable or unseen organisms, such as insects, fungi, and bacteria. *Structures* are the spatial distributions of the components—the way the ecosystem "pieces" are arranged at a location and time in the ecosystem. Plant communities, such as the mixed conifer forest, and forest structure, such as old-growth stands, are important examples of ecosystem structure. *Processes* or *functions* refer to the flow or cycling of energy, materials, and nutrients among the components over space and through time. Processes are the work of the ecosystem; they contribute to changes in the components and the structure of the ecosystem. Ecosystems are linked to one another, so that changes in components, structure, and function in one ecosystem may have consequences in contiguous and noncontiguous ecosystems.

elevation (temperatures), and soil type. From an aerial perspective, it is obvious that only part of the Sierran landscape is forested, the rest being meadow, chaparral scrub, woodland, savanna, canyon land, alpine habitat, bare rock, and water. As might be expected, the boundaries of the Sierran floristic province differ from boundaries defined by geology, watersheds, aquatic diversity, or wildlife, especially at the northern and southern edges of the range.

At the lowest elevation on the west side, interfingering with the Central Valley grasslands and chaparrals, are the foothill woodland vegetation types. These woodlands are unique to California, although not to the Sierra (they extend around the Central Valley), and include several deciduous and evergreen oaks as well as foothill pine. Tree cover here ranges from open savannas to lush riverside forests. Of all the Sierran vegetation types, the foothill plant communities have supported the most native biodiversity and highest human populations during the last few centuries. Now these are most at risk of loss by conversion to human settlement.

Intermixed with the foothill woodlands are a large group of dense shrublands called chaparral. Although chaparral veg-

etation looks similar throughout the range, there is great variation in species composition from one location to another. Many factors determine the location of chaparral types, but generally they are restricted to rocky soils with low fertility. The mediterranean climate is an overriding environmental factor in the ecology of Sierran chaparrals, including the climate's promotion of frequent burning in intense wildfire. The boundary between chaparral and forest is dynamic and determined partly by wildfire. Shrublands on the east side of the Sierra Nevada are the Great Basin sagebrush steppe and bitterbrush vegetation types, which begin near the base of the eastern escarpment and extend across the vast expanse of the Great Basin. These arid shrublands have much less species diversity than west-slope chaparrals.

Depending on latitude, a broad conifer zone begins at elevations between 1,000 and 3,000 feet on the west and between 3,000 and 5,000 feet on the east side. Ponderosa pine (mixed with hardwoods) dominates the lower western mon-

FIGURE 1.5

Aquatic and riparian ecosystems in healthy condition provide critical habitat for Sierra plants and animals. (Photo by Jerry F. Franklin.)

FIGURE 1.6

Mixed conifer forest with giant sequoias, Kings Canyon National Park. (Photo by Constance I. Millar.)

tane zones, whereas at lower elevations on the east side, piñon pine and juniper, then Jeffrey and ponderosa pine forests occur. Above these zones on the west side is the commercially important mixed conifer forest type (figure 1.6), typified by varying mixtures of Douglas fir, ponderosa pine, white fir, sugar pine, and incense cedar. On the eastern front, this mixed conifer zone is less diverse, and species mixes vary more from place to place than on the west side.

With increasing elevation , the mixed conifer zone gives way to a fir belt—first white fir, then predominantly red fir. The location of this shift in forest type depends on the transition from rain to snow, which varies with elevation at a particular latitude, shifting uphill farther south in the range. The fir zone is less extensive on the east side; south of Lake Tahoe, only a few pockets exist. Trees become shorter and more scattered with increasing elevation. The subalpine zone is a mixture of vegetation types and distributions, ranging from clusters of dense hemlock or lodgepole pine to open forests of limber pine or western white pine, to sparse, mostly rock-slope types containing whitebark pine, foxtail pine, and western juniper. Above this zone is alpine vegetation adapted to the cold, dry conditions of the highest Sierran elevations; trees

give way to low shrubs and finally cushion-plant communities that grow among rock crevices in a zone of ice and wind.

As one drives or hikes through the Sierra, it is obvious that each vegetation type is in itself a mosaic. Small changes in topography, differences in soil and rock characteristics, and the history of disturbance (fire, storm blowdown, insect and pathogen activity, avalanche) contribute to the complex mixture of patches that characterizes Sierran forests. Plant patterns vary not only from place to place in the Sierra but also over time. This complexity at the local scale makes it difficult to map vegetation, to generalize relationships of structure to function, and to assess forest conditions.

Characteristic structure and function develop in Sierran forests as they age. Under aboriginal conditions, fires and other disturbance events regularly burned entire stands of trees, leaving openings that passed through continuous but distinctive phases as they aged. This succession of a forest through time between major disturbances is important for plants and animals that use different stages as habitat. Different ecological functions develop with successional phase in a forest. From seedling colonists to mature forest stands, forests develop in structural complexity and species composition until they reach a stage known as late successional, or, more popularly, old growth.

We know most about late successional/old-growth attributes—and the relationships of structure to ecological function—in middle-elevation conifer forests, specifically mixed conifer, red fir, and east-side pine. A dominant feature in middle-elevation forests is the spatial variability that develops as a result of succession in Sierran forests. In these and other vegetation types of the Sierra, wildfire, which was a frequent characteristic of presettlement conditions, has been an architect and important ecological agent of forest and stand structure. The vagaries of fire, from low to high intensity, small to large areas, contribute to the great variability that typifies Sierran middle-elevation forests. Each stand passes through its own history, thus developing a distinctive structure. Various events (tree fall, windfall, avalanche, fire hot spot, insect outbreak) create small and large openings in some areas, whereas other areas maintain standing trees (alive and dead) despite disturbance. Patches develop a characteristic structure in their abundances of large, old trees (relicts left after ground fires); multiple age-classes of live trees; mixtures of dominant species; snags and downed woody debris of different sizes and degrees of deterioration; closed crown canopy; and layers of vegetation. Collectively the forests containing these patches are highly heterogeneous. The image evoked popularly by the term *old growth*, i.e., extensive uniform stands of even-aged, old trees, although descriptive of some Pacific Northwest forests, is inappropriate to the complex and heterogeneous Sierran forests.

The forests of the Sierra are part of the river of change in the mountain range. Many of the current vegetation distributions have been in place locally for only a few thousand years. At shorter intervals within that time, changes in individual distribution have occurred. For instance, during the Little Ice Age of the last centuries, tree lines dropped and forest densities and wildfire patterns changed; during the warm centuries of the last millennium, many species grew in different locations from their current sites, wildfires burned in different patterns, and water flows and lake levels were very low. During the glacial-interglacial periods, most vegetation zones shifted altitudinally up and down by as much as 1,600 feet; throughout the millennia before the ice ages, vegetation types of the region were vastly different from anything we see in the Sierra now. Today Sierran forests show the effects of decades of fire suppression, which has changed the character of many forests even in places otherwise minimally influenced by humans, such as the national parks.

ANIMALS

About 400 species of terrestrial vertebrates (including mammals, birds, reptiles, and amphibians) use the Sierra Nevada, although only a fraction are restricted to the range. Animals that live in the Sierra Nevada depend greatly on the distribution and quality of vegetation for their habitat and food needs. Many native Sierran species are adapted to habitats maintained by the precontact fire regime (the regime that prevailed before non-Indian settlement of the area). Although only a handful of species require late successional habitats, many more depend on the presence of large, old trees, snags, and logs in Sierran woodland and forest communities for some part of their life cycle. Late successional and riparian forests are important habitats to wildlife, as are the low-elevation foothill woodland types. In the latter zone especially, conversion of habitat and loss of ecological function have dramatically altered the suite of species that flourished in these communities. A common and important pattern for Sierran birds is their migratory patterns up and down slopes, following seasons. When a specific habitat needed for completion of a critical life stage (e.g., foothills for breeding) is disrupted, species may be put at risk even if they are able to use alternative habitat for other needs.

❄ *Insect Species Found Only in the Sierra*

The following numbers of known endemic terrestrial insect species are found in each of the major river basins in the SNEP study area. (From volume II, chapter 26.)

Eagle Lake	0
Honey Lake	0
Feather	2
Upper Sacramento	0
Yuba	1
Truckee	7
American	0
Carson	2
Cosumnes	0
Mokelumne	4
Walker	2
Stanislaus	0
Calaveras	0
Mono Basin	6
Tuolumne	7
Owens	17
Merced	0
San Joaquin	3
Kings	1
Kaweah	3
Kern	3
Tule	1
Caliente	2
Mojave	0

HUMANS IN THE SIERRA

Humans are an integral part of Sierra Nevada ecosystems, having lived and sustained themselves at various elevations in the region for at least 10,000 years. Indigenous populations were widely distributed throughout the range at the time of European immigration. Archaeological evidence indicates that for more than 3,000 years Native Americans practiced localized land management for utilitarian purposes, including animal hunting, forest burning, seed harvesting, pruning, irrigation, and vegetation thinning. These practices no doubt influenced resource abundance and distribution in areas of early human settlement. On a longer timescale, humans may have played a role in the decline of large vertebrates during prehistoric times. Extinction of a large and diverse megafauna throughout western North America, including the Sierra Nevada, at the end of the last major ice age (around 10,000 years ago) coincided with the arrival of humans in North America. Some scientists link these extinctions to overhunting by humans of animals already stressed by changing environments.

Immigration of non-Indian settlers in the early 1800s began a period of increasingly intense resource use and settlement. By the late 1800s, parts of the Sierra had been transformed as a result of intense interest by these immigrants in Sierran resources. Agriculture, mining, logging, and grazing activities were extensively practiced in many regions of the Sierra. The need to divert water to support resource extraction and settlement led to a major reordering of natural hydrological processes through a vast network of ditches and flumes. In some areas, impacts from early use of the Sierra created rapid and irreversible changes from precontact conditions.

By the early 1920s, a new phase of Sierran history was emerging, in which resource use was more regulated and forest and range protection was emphasized. Suppression of fires became a primary goal of federal, state, and private efforts, controls were imposed on the timing and locations of grazing, and timber harvest was systematized under government and industrial forestry programs. Although trends of use have varied over the last 150 years, increasing population pressure and complex demands on Sierran resources pose serious ecological threats in some regions and severe management challenges elsewhere. Similarly, changing values for natural resources present economic and social challenges to rural communities within the Sierra Nevada.

SOCIAL INSTITUTIONS

The web of institutions laid across the Sierra by successive generations of Americans is central to an understanding of the mountain range and its future management. This web is the eventual target of the current study, in that the project's assessments and strategies must be absorbed, adapted, and implemented not by the biology or geology of the mountain range but rather by the institutions through which human society operates.

Institutions are central elements in the ecology of the Sierra Nevada because they mediate the relationship betwen the labor and desires of people and the Sierran ecosystems those people use. In a biological analogy, institutions—the governmental and nongovernmental organizations, agreements, and regulations—constitute a key part of the life history strategy that the human species currently uses in the Sierra. Institutions are in large measure how people link themselves to other parts of the ecosystem.

Institutions govern not only what people extract from the ecosystem—water, timber, recreation, amenities—but also how they reinvest in the natural capital through actions such as planting trees or restoring habitats. The extent to which institutions and policies "close the loop"—that is, mitigate the environmental impact of human activities—is a critical part of a Sierra Nevada ecosystem assessment.

As institutions regulate the exchanges between people and the ecosystem, they also link people who reside outside the mountain range with the ecosystem within it. Institutions that close the loop by extracting water or reinvesting (for instance, in hatcheries to mitigate for habitat loss) are also closing a loop that passes beyond the Sierra to include urban and agricultural water users in the San Francisco Bay Area, southern California, and the Central Valley. Closing the loop, then, includes identifying and accounting for the values of all stakeholders in the Sierra Nevada, regardless of their locations within or outside the range and understanding how benefits and costs flow among coupled ecosystems.

Although institutions are part of the ecology of the Sierra, nothing ensures that those institutions perceive the entire ecosystem, much less manage it in a sustainable manner. Heretofore, institutions have largely focused on portions of ecosystems. For instance, for streams on the east side of the Sierra, the Lahontan Regional Water Quality Control Board has jurisdiction over the quality of water, the California Water Resources Control Board over the rights to the water, the California Department of Fish and Game over the trout in the water, and the U.S. Forest Service and the state Department of Forestry and Fire Protection over the trees that grow next to the water. Jurisdictions split along geographic as well as resource lines. The U.S. Forest Service and the National Park Service manage the land along the upper reaches of most Sierran rivers, while private landowners, the federal Bureau of Land Management, municipal utilities, and local irrigation districts manage much of the land along the lower reaches. There are no existing mechanisms to ensure that the sum of the management of the parts of the ecosystem adds up to wise management of the whole ecosystem.

Like all other parts of the Sierran ecosystem, the institutional components change over time in response to larger forces.

❋ *Land Ownership and Reserve Allocation in the Sierra Nevada*

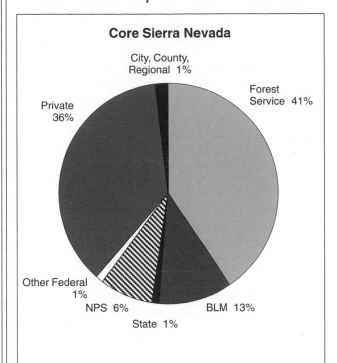

Core Sierra Nevada

City, County, Regional 1%

Forest Service 41%

Private 36%

Other Federal 1%

NPS 6%

State 1%

BLM 13%

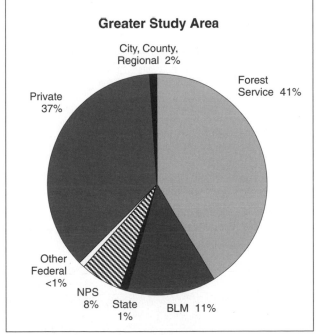

Greater Study Area

City, County, Regional 2%

Forest Service 41%

Private 37%

Other Federal <1%

NPS 8%

State 1%

BLM 11%

FIGURE 1.7

Sierra Nevada ownership, percentage of land within the core Sierra Nevada ecoregion, and percentage within the greater study area. (From volume II, chapter 23.)

The Sierra Nevada core area includes 20,663,930 acres. Of this, 36% is private. About two-thirds of the land area is publicly owned (figure 1.7). Most of that is national forest (U.S. Forest Service). Bureau of Land Management (BLM) is the second largest category of public land. The National Park Service (NPS), the state of California, and local jurisdictions administer smaller pieces within the SNEP study area (table 1.1). Most of the high elevations throughout the Sierra are public (see back cover), as are large proportions of the eastern Sierra. Public lands extend to middle elevations on the west side, with large areas of intermixtures of private and public sections ("checkerboard") in the northern half, which track areas of early railroad crossings of the Sierra Nevada. Much of the large private forest company land derives from acquisitions originating from these early railroad land grants. South of the central western Sierra Nevada, fewer large blocks or intermixtures of private land occur at middle elevations. Below about 3,000 feet in the western Sierra, private lands predominate.

Reserve areas account for 21% of the Sierra Nevada, as indicated in table 1.1.

TABLE 1.1

Areas of designated biological reserves in the SNEP core study area.

Public/Private Ownership	Acres (Subtotal)	Acres (Total)
Private Reserves		31,340
Nature Conservancy reserves	31,340	
State of California		144,675
Ecological reserves	2,090	
State parks and reserves	28,837	
Wildlife areas	113,748	
Federal		4,282,204
Bureau of Land Management		
Areas of Critical Environmental Concern and Wild and Scenic Rivers	208,550	
Wilderness Areas	306,535	
Fish and Wildlife Service	1,129	
National Park Service		
Devils Postpile National Monument	806	
Lassen Volcanic National Park	37,979	
Sequoia and Kings Canyon National Parks	861,077	
Yosemite National Park	746,121	
Forest Service		
Research Natural Areas	45,617	
Special Interest Areas	54,916	
Wild and Scenic Rivers	34,055	
Wilderness Areas	1,985,419	
Total reserve areas		4,458,219

Population growth and development bring more people into the region, increasing not only the demand for services but also the diversity of values and issues influencing management of the range. The creation of markets for values and benefits that heretofore have been allocated by right or administrative arrangement—water is the preeminent example—upsets many existing arrangements and creates the need for different types of institutions. Interagency and intergovernmental cooperation blurs lines of authority and blunts institutional prerogative but may allow movement in arenas currently stymied by gridlock. Grassroots activism creates new institutions, which compete with existing ones for legitimacy and authority. These driving forces interact in different ways in different regions of the Sierra and force the evolution of institutions in the range.

SNEP owes its existence to the desire of Congress to search for policies and institutions that can transcend their "ecosystem component" status to perceive the Sierra Nevada as a set of ecosystems with links to stakeholders within and outside the range, and to manage both extraction and reinvestment to ensure the long-term persistence of the ecosystem and the people who depend upon it.

THE SIERRA NEVADA OF THE FUTURE

The images of the Sierra Nevada—snapshots from the past, words and maps from SNEP, mental images of a mountain range—reveal in sketch the unfolding process that has shaped Sierra Nevada ecosystems. Our view of the Sierra is flawed if we consider today's ecological or social environment to be stable: The old-growth forests we study today developed in a different environment from our current one and are headed into a different future. Many of the forests that we now measure and manage originated under an anomalously wet climate. The water systems we have developed are based on predictions of flow derived from this unusually favorable period. Snapshots of the present may give us misleading pictures of what is needed to support a full range of biotic and human systems in the near and distant future.

If there is natural environmental change, does this give license for humans to act however they like in ecosystems? If ecosystems are always changing, why should it matter if we retain the diversity and function of any specific time and place? It matters because both the *rate* and the *direction* of change in natural systems are extremely important to ecosystem sustainability. Plants and animals, and the ecosystems they compose, evolve and adapt to the gradual pace of most environmental change, that is, they produce the successors who are able to survive and prosper. Humans may make conscious decisions to alter the rate and directions of ecosystem change. The important consideration is that we make these decisions with knowledge of potential consequences. As we consider limits to change and tease out the practical meaning of sustainability, we are best prepared when we understand the context of change in the Sierra Nevada.

CHAPTER 2

People and Resource Use

Recent Population Growth Population doubled in the Sierra Nevada between 1970 and 1990; 40% of the population growth occurred in the Sierra portion of just three counties: Nevada, Placer, and El Dorado.

Population Forecasts Official projections forecast that the 1990 Sierran population of 650,000 will triple by 2040.

Impacts from Population Growth Population growth and its accompanying effects are causing significant impacts on resources.

Biotic Vulnerability The oak woodland communities of the western Sierra Nevada foothills are the most vulnerable of the widespread vegetation types as a result of greater access by humans and of their continuing potential for urban development.

Local Mitigation Some rapidly growing counties that SNEP examined have not collected information sufficient to adequately monitor and forecast impacts of development on biological and social resources. In addition, the current project-level approach to planning does not account for changes in regional or Sierra-wide conditions or address the need for larger-scale monitoring and improvement.

Jobs The number of jobs has more than doubled in the Sierra Nevada since 1970, but the relative proportion of commodity-producing and service-producing jobs has stayed constant.

Personal Income Income earned by commuters, interest, dividends, and transfer payments to retired and other households now constitute more than half the total personal income in the Sierra Nevada.

Ecosystem-Based Revenues Water is the most valuable commodity, followed by timber, livestock, and other agricultural products, based on gross revenues. The Sierra Nevada ecosystem produces approximately $2.2 billion worth of commodities and services annually, based on estimates of direct resource values (not the total revenue produced by resource-dependent activities).

Regional Patterns of Economic Activity The flow of economic values from the Sierra Nevada provides an empirical basis for assessing how different levels of government, producers and consumers, and employers and employees could be involved in new approaches to ecosystem management.

Community Dependence Communities in the Sierra Nevada are dependent on the ecosystem for a combination of direct and indirect natural resource benefits, including noneconomic benefits associated with aesthetic and sense-of-place values. Few economies are dependent exclusively on resource-extractive activities (timber, mining, grazing).

Timber-Based Employment Timber industry employment may decline from present levels due to trends of increasing labor productivity within the region and a shift in remanufacturing facilities out of the region.

Timber Harvests on National Forests National forest timber harvests have averaged 650 million board feet from 1950 through 1994; the highest level was just over 1 billion board feet in 1988, and the lowest was 227 million board feet in 1994.

Community Well-Being One hundred eighty communities were identified in the Sierra: twenty-eight ranked low and thirty-one ranked high in a measure of well-being that includes community capacity and socioeconomic status.

Regional Well-Being Six distinct socioeconomic regions were delineated by transportation corridors, commuting patterns, economies, community identification, and administrative boundaries.

Concentration of Low Socioeconomic Status Sierra residents living in poverty are concentrated in the larger cities and communities.

SETTLEMENT IN THE SIERRA

The Sierra Nevada is highly heterogeneous in terms of human settlement. Some parts of it are remote and inaccessible, while others are within easy commuting distance of rapidly growing metropolitan regions. Adjacent to the region's western boundary lies the Central Valley, where there are at least six rapidly growing urban centers, each with a 1990 population greater than 100,000. In contrast, the northern and eastern boundaries abut the sparsely populated high desert of the Great Basin. These areas are often isolated for months every year as winter snows either close or constrain travel on the mountain passes linking these rural areas to the rest of California. There are thirty-two counties (twenty-seven in California and five in Nevada) with all or part of their territory within the SNEP study region, but only twenty-two (eighteen in California and four in Nevada) of these counties include portions of the SNEP core area. Only ten counties (all in California) lie entirely within the boundaries of the region (figure 2.1).

Within 100 miles of the western foothills lie major metropolitan centers such as Sacramento, Fresno, Bakersfield, San

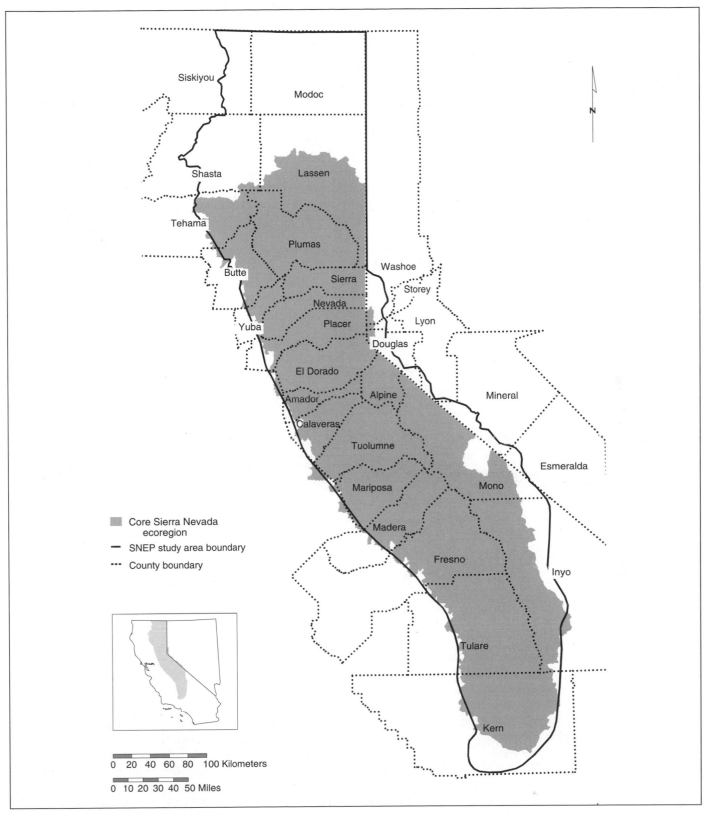

FIGURE 2.1

Sierra Nevada counties in California and Nevada. (From volume II, chapter 11.)

❋ *Deforestation in the Mid-1800s*

As towns and settlements grew during the post–gold rush years, circa 1850–80, the forests of the Mother Lode country were extensively changed. What we see there today is the result of human action that accelerated about 150 years ago. Native forests of mixed conifers were cut for housing and mine construction, and the lower edge of the mixed conifer belt shifted uphill. Exotics were planted in the towns. Seeds from the remaining pines fostered regeneration of pines on open sites (figure 2.2). Black oaks resprouted from stumps (foreground).

FIGURE 2.2

Nevada, California, 1856. Drawn from nature and on stone by Kuchel and Dresel. Lithographed by Britton and Rey and reproduced by their successors, A. Carlisle & Co., by Lithotone, for John Howell, San Francisco, 1935. (Courtesy of The Family of Joseph and Hilda Marinelli.)

Francisco, and Los Angeles. Major urban centers near the eastern flank of the Sierra are Reno and Carson City, both near Lake Tahoe. Interstate 80 and U.S. Highway 50 connect the Reno, Carson City, and Greater Lake Tahoe Basin regions to the Sacramento metropolitan area and the rest of northern California. This complex road network links the Sierra Nevada to social and economic activity throughout California and the world. It allows recreational visitors to access the wonders of the Sierra Nevada and provides avenues for the export of natural resources extracted in the range. The transportation network is therefore a primary determinant of the pattern of human settlement in the Sierra Nevada. It has determined the number of residents in the Sierra Nevada and their location over time. It also determines and reflects the relationship between humans and the resources of the Sierra Nevada.

Human beings have lived in and utilized the natural resources of the Sierra Nevada for millennia. Over the last ten thousand years and until the early part of the nineteenth century, Native Americans were sustained in the Sierra Nevada by hunting and fishing, gathering, tool quarrying, and trade.

Population estimates for the Native Americans vary considerably, but in late prehistoric times (ca. A.D. 1300–1800), close to 100,000 from roughly thirteen tribes inhabited the region. Native American population densities were similar to current settlement patterns, highest below 4,000 feet on the west side of the range. Warfare, starvation, and the devastating epidemics of the 1830s dramatically reduced populations of native people.

Only four ships dropped anchor in San Francisco Bay in 1848, the same year that James Marshall discovered gold at Sutter's Mill near Coloma and the South Fork of the American River. The next year brought nearly seven hundred ships through the Golden Gate. Most of their passengers disembarked in the ports of northern California and promptly set out for the gold fields of the Sierra Nevada foothills. The region has been intensely inhabited ever since, and the patterns of settlement reflect the geography of both natural and human resources. The pattern of towns, roads, waterways, and related infrastructure established by the forty-niners continues to constitute the framework within which a new wave of migration has swept over the Sierra Nevada during the past three decades.

Settlement patterns and resource utilization have historically reflected the export value of Sierra Nevada resources as commodities. Mining of Mother Lode gold deposits resulted in extensive settlement and intensive ecosystem change along a foothill belt just below the mixed conifer zone. In some areas settlement and ecosystem change extended into the ponderosa pine–black oak type, while other areas had concentrated activity only in the foothill grassland below. The new residents placed significant demands on nearby resources for timber, water, and agricultural production. Early mining activity led to significant timber harvesting and water diversions in higher-elevation areas that laid down the skeletal framework for today's hydrologic system. New demands were placed on higher-elevation resources by the Comstock Lode of Nevada and the building of the Central Pacific Railroad.

An estimated 150,000–175,000 people moved into the Sierra Nevada from 1848 to 1860, with up to one-third being foreign-born. These new residents further displaced the Native Californians, reducing their already diminished population by 75% between 1852 (the peak year of gold production in California) and 1860. Only 4,919 Native Americans were counted in the 1860 census. Chinese residents increased dramatically during this period, however, from around 6% of the total population (9,005) in 1852 to 18% (26,161 residents) by 1860. These census figures probably understate the peak numbers of Chinese residents considerably, because thousands of Chinese laborers helped to construct the Central Pacific Railroad across the Sierra Nevada during the 1860s (but were not necessarily present or accounted for in the census figures for 1860 or 1870).

Following a slight post-gold-rush decline, the population of the Sierra Nevada continued to grow, albeit slowly over the next century, not quite doubling from 150,000 residents in 1860 to around 250,000–275,000 residents by 1960. The ethnic composition of these residents became considerably less diverse, however, as Chinese residents dropped precipitously as a fraction of the population from about 12% in 1880 (20,642 residents) to less than 1% (3,347 residents) by 1920. Since then, the Sierra Nevada population has been overwhelmingly white. This pattern has persisted despite increasing ethnic and racial heterogeneity in the rest of California's population during the same period. In 1990, the Sierra Nevada was 92% white, compared with 69% for the state of California as a whole.

Construction of Interstate 80 and U.S. 50 have increased accessibility and changed patterns of resource utilization in Nevada, Placer, and El Dorado Counties. This area has become the focal point for the rapid population growth that more than doubled the Sierra population from about 300,000 people in 1970 to around 650,000 in 1990 (plate 2.1). More than one-third of the current Sierran population lives in this area. Figure 2.3 shows 1990 census population totals for six Sierra

regions. These regions differ from hydrologic and other geographic regions and are based on transportation corridors, commute patterns, economies, community identification, and other information collected from local resident experts.

Current human settlement is not equally distributed across the Sierra, nor is it equally distributed across regions, a pattern that has significant implications for future land conversion and ecosystem impacts. Almost 70% of the total Sierra population is located in the west-side foothill zone. About two-fifths of all Sierra Nevada residents live on a total of roughly 89 square miles at an average housing density of at least 640 units per square mile (1 acre per unit). This land area constitutes less than 0.3% of the 32,000 total square miles of the Sierra Nevada. Approximately three-fifths of the residents live on about 298 square miles with at least 160 units per square mile (4 acres per unit) on a land area that constitutes just less than 1% of the total Sierran land base. Four-fifths of all residents live on about 1,471 square miles with at least 20 units per square mile (32 acres per unit). These residents occupy 5.4% of the total Sierran land base, or nearly 14% of all private land (including industrial timberlands). Up to 10% of the entire Sierra Nevada (3,905 square miles) may have been affected by human settlement in 1990, however, at an average density of at least 1 housing unit per 128 acres.

New residents are increasingly drawn by the amenity values of Sierra Nevada resources. Retirees, commuters, and ex-urban migrants are all coming to the Sierra Nevada at the same time that employment is declining in the traditional resource extraction industries, changing the social, economic, and ecological fabric of the area. The Sierra Nevada now has a very different age structure and ethnicity than the rest of California. There are more older residents and fewer in their twenties, as high school graduates leave the area for employment and school opportunities elsewhere. The new migrants are in

FIGURE 2.3

Sierra Nevada population in 1990 by region. (From volume II, chapter 13.)

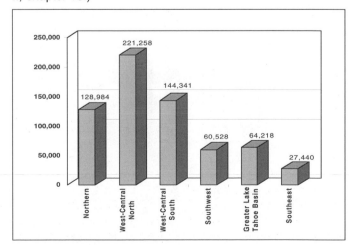

general more educated and wealthier than existing residents. The new residents are also decreasingly dependent on resource extraction and increasingly bring outside sources of income into the region, altering the nature of the relationship between residents and resources.

Our analysis of future population projections suggests that numerous communities are likely to go through a similar transformation over the next fifty years (plate 2.2). Rapid population growth in California's metropolitan areas is forecast to increase the size of many Central Valley cities, which are within commuting range of many western Sierra Nevada foothill areas. The more isolated northern Sierra and eastern Sierra are forecast to have much slower growth, largely because they are beyond the reach of metropolitan commuting. These more distant areas are therefore likely to remain less economically or socially diversified, making them more likely to be affected by changes in land and resource management policy that directly affect resource extraction or recreation and tourism.

The entire Sierra Nevada is forecast to grow to somewhere between 1.5 million and 2.4 million residents by the year 2040, with the most likely forecast 1.8–2.0 million people (figure 2.4). Most of that growth will not be associated with the traditional resource extraction industries that dominated the social, economic, and ecological geography of the Sierra Nevada for its first century following the gold rush. This growth will have a profound effect on both the characteristics of Sierra Nevada residents and their relationship to its resources. The total land area converted to human settlement to accommodate 1990–

Development in the Sierra foothills: Glenbrook Basin between Grass Valley and Nevada City in Nevada County. (Photo by Timothy P. Duane.)

2040 growth will depend upon the spatial pattern and average density of settlement, which will in turn depend upon the complex interaction of public policy, infrastructure, and land economics. The large expanse of federal land in the Sierra Nevada will limit this growth in some areas while concentrating it in others.

RESOURCE USE: CHANGING NEEDS THROUGH TIME

The complex history of resource utilization in the Sierra Nevada can be followed through the use patterns of six different resources over the past 150 years:

- gold and other minerals
- grazing and agriculture
- timber harvests
- native fish
- water diversions
- recreational and residential development

The latter half of the nineteenth century was marked by intense boom-and-bust patterns. The first half of the twentieth century was marked by strong federal protection policies and reduced but still significant levels of private resource utilization. Resource utilization in the past 50 years added new patterns of water and residential development to the more local patterns of resource uses that characterized the preceding century. Since the 1960s, all resource utilization on both public and private land has been guided by new environmental

FIGURE 2.4

Distribution of Sierra Nevada population projected for 2040. (From volume II, chapter 11.)

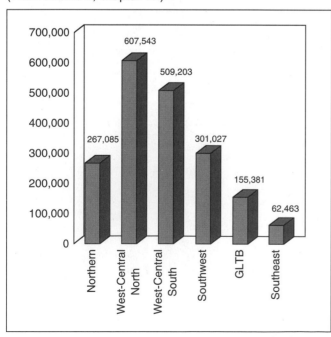

regulations. Figure 2.5 summarizes the patterns of resource utilization at three points during the past 150 years. Utilization of any single resource has never been constant or sustainable for the whole period but the Sierra Nevada as a whole has constantly produced large quantities of valuable resources. Since the 1884 *Sawyer* decision to limit hydraulic gold mining because of environmental damage, resource utilization has been governed to protect broad social interests.

Resource utilization in the Sierra Nevada has always been closely intertwined with the markets and institutions of urban California. For resources other than gold and other minerals, linkages to urban markets often had more influence on utilization patterns than the availability of the natural resources themselves. After the destructive clearings of the foothills during the first years of the gold rush, timber harvests in the higher-altitude and less accessible regions were limited by the relatively small size of California markets and cheaper imports from Oregon. The decline of hydraulic gold mining after 1884 was the result of court injunctions stemming from the damage done downstream by hydraulic mining debris. The capture of Owens Valley water to promote urban growth in Los Angeles rather than a federally financed reclamation project is the most well known example of the value of a resource in a distant urban area dominating its potential value within the Sierra Nevada.

Opening the Sierra Nevada: 1848–1900

The discovery of gold at John Sutter's mill in 1848 began a series of boom-and-bust cycles of resource utilization. During the 1850s, the Sierra Nevada produced nearly half the world's gold output and spurred an enormous migration to California. By 1860, the 25,000 gold miners had collected the easily accessible placer gold deposits, and many miners left

FIGURE 2.5

Resource utility indices in the Sierra Nevada for three periods: 1880s, 1950s, and 1985–95. (From volume III, chapter 23.)

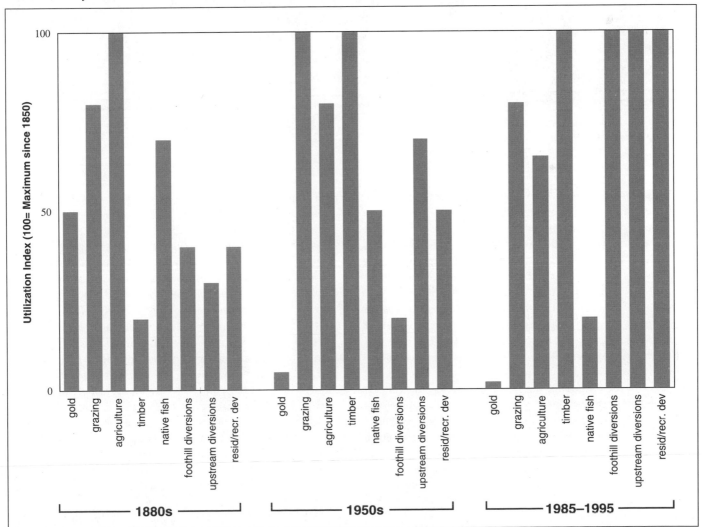

Hydraulic mining, Malakoff Diggins State Historic Park, North Bloomfield, Nevada County, Humbug Creek, tributary to the South Yuba River. (Photo by Timothy P. Duane.)

or shifted to other resource-related work. Twenty years of hydraulic mining begun in the 1850s created an enormous amount of sediment and altered the river systems for decades. Large areas of the foothills were cleared and converted to farms and grazing lands to supply the growing population of California and Nevada. More land in the Sierra Nevada was under cultivation in 1860 than in any year since.

Thousands of acres of forest were cut each year to provide timber for mining structures and houses. The completion of the trans-Sierra railroad in the 1860s allowed timber to be sold to the growing Central Valley, and even San Francisco, in addition to local mines and towns. Timber harvests for the Sierra Nevada region during the late 1800s averaged over 500 million board feet, with most coming from the western foothill region. By 1880, over 1.5 million acres of pine forests had been cut or burned in the western foothills. By the late 1800s, the foothill landscape was a mix of cutover forests, grasslands, burned areas, and agricultural fields. In the higher elevations, difficult access and lower prices for species other than the pines limited timber harvesting and the associated fires that affected the lower forests.

Cattle grazing increased fivefold in the first decade of the gold rush and stayed at these high levels for the next century. Sheep proved to be more effective harvesters of the higher-elevation meadows. By 1870, sheep ate more grass than did cattle in the Sierra Nevada and probably caused considerably more ecological damage than cattle. It is widely acknowledged that the essentially unregulated grazing led to ecological damage still visible across much of the Sierra Nevada.

One of the most enduring legacies of the 1800s is the physical and institutional impact of water diversions in the mining camps and the surrounding farms. The need to divert water to make it useful for the mining communities led to the "first in time, first in right" miner's code that eventually became enshrined in California water law. Water diversions through ditches or wooden flumes crisscrossed the Sierra Nevada to create financial wealth by reordering hydrologic processes. Even after the restrictions on hydraulic mining in 1884, the ditches continued to be used for irrigation and power production for many widely dispersed but relatively small operations.

More than 300 communities grew up in the Sierra Nevada

to house all the resource-based workers as well as the many people who provided services, nearly 50% more than the number of communities in the region today. The recreation industry got off to an early start with the creation of state parks in Yosemite Valley and at Calaveras Big Trees in the 1860s. In the 1880s the California legislature created a special commission to protect Lake Tahoe for tourism. By the end of the 1800s, three national parks had been established, and a veritable army of tourist guide writers extolled the Sierra Nevada for tourism and recreation.

Conflicting interests laid the institutional groundwork for the strong local desire for governmental regulation of resource use. The 1884 court decision to limit hydraulic mining because of the damage it caused downstream cities and agriculture broke with water law based on "first in time, first in right" and validated broader state constraints on resource utilization. The creation of the State Board of Forestry in 1885 was designed to address problems of poor regeneration of cutover forests, large fires, and grazing-related erosion. Federal forest reserves and national parks were created in the 1890s with strong support from urban Californians. In all three cases, what were considered to be the excesses of resource utilization led to a strengthened governmental role in resource management.

Continued Commodity Use and the Expansion of Conservation: 1900–1950

Resource utilization during the first half of this century was marked by new concerns for conservation and reduced levels of commodity extraction. The most destructive practices of the nineteenth century were brought under control through expansion of federal control over new national forests and national parks. Overgrazing of mountain meadows in the newly created national forests and parks was largely curtailed. Gold production declined because few new sources could be developed without serious downstream impacts. The depression years reduced private extraction of timber and dampened agricultural output temporarily. Federal employment policies in response to the depression led to increased federal support for water development, road building, and recreational facilities projects.

The control of Owens Valley water supplies by Los Angeles stopped a proposed federal reclamation project on the east side that probably would have allowed the valley to become a major agricultural area. Small irrigation projects throughout the Sierra Nevada replaced dry-land farming as the major source of agricultural production (figure 2.6). Agriculture was the major source of employment and livelihood across the Sierra Nevada throughout most of this period. The total number of irrigated acres in the Sierra Nevada in 1922 was the same as it was in 1994.

Large salmon runs, especially on the San Joaquin River, supported a major inland fisheries industry. Throughout the period, major changes in the water systems of the Sierra Ne-

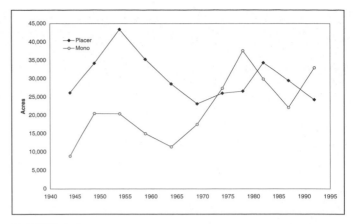

FIGURE 2.6

Irrigated acres in Placer and Mono Counties, 1944–92. In the foothill counties the expansion of irrigation works has been going on for the last half century, although the number of acres under irrigation declined temporarily in the late 1950s. Orchard crops have been grown on foothill farms since gold rush days yet have increased in importance. (From volume II, chapter 17.)

vada were being planned by engineers who surveyed the Sierra Nevada for sites to generate hydroelectric power and provide water for the growing metropolitan areas around San Francisco and Los Angeles. By 1950, approximately half of the current high-elevation reservoir capacity had been constructed by municipal water authorities, power companies, and a few irrigation districts, thereby all but eliminating the anadromous fisheries.

During the first half of the twentieth century, the Forest Service was given responsibility for millions of acres of forests that had not been privatized before the 1890s. It provided fire protection, policing against poor resource utilization, and expansion of the road infrastructure for future use. Harvest levels went up and down as market demand changed but never achieved very high levels because of relatively high costs and low demand during the depression. Old-growth timber on private land constituted more than 90% of the harvest for most of the period. The second-growth forests that followed the heavy cutting and fires of the gold rush era were growing with relatively little management, and the sawmill industry was dominated by hundreds of small sawmills processing locally harvested timber.

The Modern Era: 1950–1995

The 1950s marked the beginning of a major shift in resource utilization in California. A rapidly expanding urban population increased to new highs the demand for wood, water, hydroelectric power, and recreational opportunities. Considerable new investment flowed into the Sierra Nevada to develop resources not previously considered financially feasible. Timber harvests surged in the early 1950s and re-

FIGURE 2.7

Timber harvest from federal
and private lands in the Sierra
Nevada, 1948–93. (From
volume III, chapter 23.)

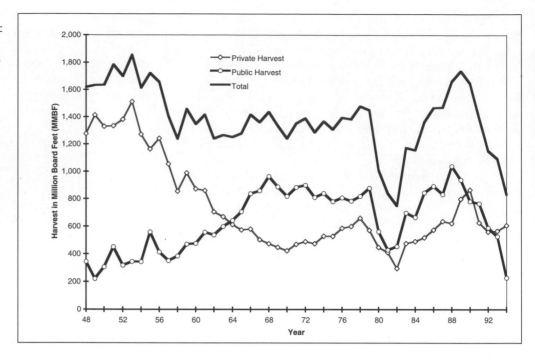

mained consistent until the recession of the early 1980s (figure 2.7). Private harvests declined because the old-growth volume in accessible forests declined and the second-growth forests were not yet mature. The Forest Service increased harvests from federal lands and created a fairly constant total harvest for decades.

Industrial forestry marked by large-scale operations and long-term investment in timber production was on the ascendancy. The nonindustrial share of harvest dropped from 74% to 40% during the 1950s as the Forest Service share went from 20% to 35% and the timber industry share jumped from 8% to 24% of total output.

Recreational use of the Sierra Nevada also increased rapidly as most major trans-Sierra roads were completed during the 1950s and Interstate 80 was completed in the 1960s (figure 2.8). The development of many downhill ski resorts allowed year-round recreation throughout the Sierra Nevada.

The Lake Tahoe region and Yosemite National Park remained the prime destinations. The physical impact of developed recreation led conservation groups such as the Sierra Club to begin to question National Park Service and U. S. Forest Service policies in the 1950s. By the early 1970s, urban growth in the Lake Tahoe Basin would eventually instigate the largest cooperative program in the Sierra Nevada between federal, state, and local governments to reduce the impacts on the lake's ecosystem.

Water Diversions

The 1950s also marked the beginning of the modern dam building era. New dam building technology and ever-increasing demands for water and power led to the development of what would become the Sierra Nevada's most valuable resource—water. Water diversions create enormous economic wealth as well as alter many of the natural hydrologic and ecological processes within the Sierra Nevada. Though most of the early wood flumes and hydraulic mining operations of the nineteenth century are gone, an enormous network of newer concrete dams now covers nearly every major river basin in the Sierra Nevada. The capacity of upstream reservoirs was doubled, and enormous multipurpose reservoirs were developed at the base of almost all major rivers as they left the Sierra Nevada and entered the Central Valley. Eighty percent of the present reservoir capacity in the Sierra Nevada was completed after 1950. There are currently 490 medium to

A powerhouse in the Southern California Edison Big Creek system, Sierra National Forest. (Photo by Richard Kattelmann.)

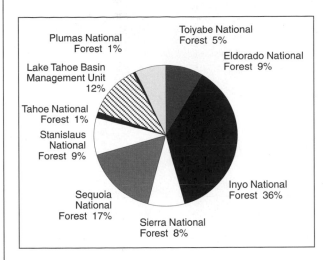

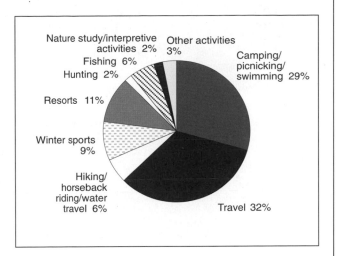

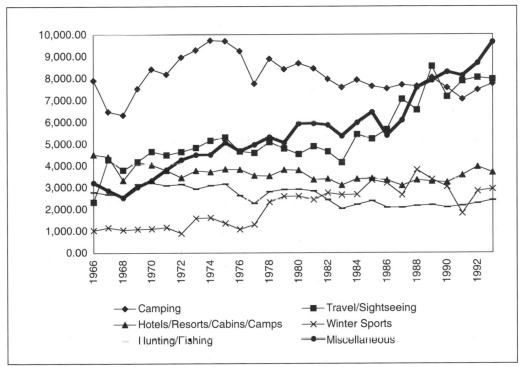

FIGURE 2.8

Recreation in Sierra Nevada national forests. *Top left:* Distribution of annual wilderness use in recreation visitor days. *Top right:* Distribution of types of recreation activities (as percentage of annual recreation visitor days), 1987–93. *Bottom:* Trends in various recreation activities (in recreation visitor days), 1966–93. (From volume II, chapter 19.)

large dams in the Sierra Nevada, more than 120 hydroelectric plants, and thousands of smaller water diversions (figure 2.9; see chapter 8).

Cumulative Major Reservoir Capacity in the Sierra Nevada

Excluding the hard-to-quantify "public good" value of flood control and reservoir-based recreation, the hydroelectric gen-erating, irrigation, and urban use values of water are far greater than the combined value of all other commodities produced in the Sierra Nevada. Since 1980 there has been very little increase in the number of reservoirs in the Sierra Nevada (figure 2.10). Increased concern about the ecological impacts of diversions as well as the social decisions about who should bear the financial burdens of plans to reduce, or at least stop the growth of, these impacts requires a greater

FIGURE 2.9

Location of dams
greater than 25 feet in
height or 50 acre feet
in volume on streams
in the SNEP study
area. (From volume II,
chapter 35.)

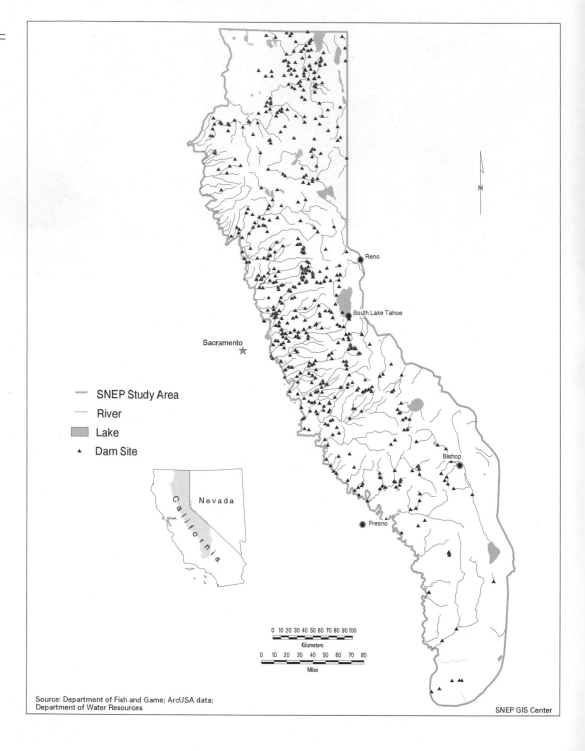

Source: Department of Fish and Game; ArcUSA data;
Department of Water Resources

SNEP GIS Center

understanding of how diversions, economic benefits, and ecological impacts are linked.

The rivers of the northern Sierra Nevada have been extensively diverted in both the upstream and the foothill stretches. The central rivers draining the western side have been moderately diverted upstream and heavily diverted in the foothills (only one small river is allowed to flow into the Central Valley without a major dam and reservoir). The southernmost rivers have been moderately diverted in both the upstream and the foothill stretches.

The dominant purpose of the dams varies by location. Two-thirds of foothill reservoir capacity is managed to provide irrigation water to the Central Valley. Conversely, two-thirds of upstream reservoirs are managed to provide municipal water supplies and hydroelectric power. This difference suggests that efforts to reduce the negative ecological impacts of up-

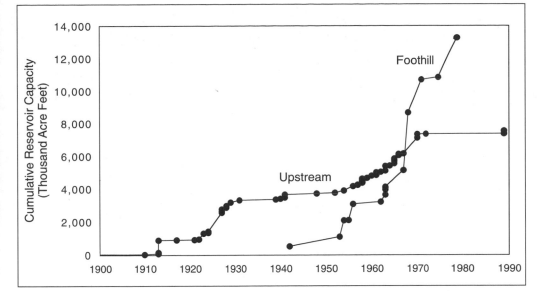

FIGURE 2.10

Cumulative capacity of reservoirs at the date when the reservoir was installed, 1910–89. Reservoirs in the foothills are shown separately from those upstream due to differences in pattern of capacities. (From volume III, chapter 23.)

stream diversions will need participation by quite different institutions from those involved in similar issues downstream.

Current Status and Future Directions

Resource utilization is permitted across most of the land and water resources in the Sierra Nevada. In contrast to largely agricultural or urban landscapes such as the Central Valley or the Los Angeles Basin, the prevailing land cover types of the Sierra Nevada are managed forests, rangeland, and alpine ecosystems that sustain many if not most elements of native biodiversity while also supporting activities based on natural resources. The history of the Sierra Nevada and recent ecological assessments suggest that Sierran biodiversity could be maintained by ecologically sound management of lands designated for renewable resource extraction, in combination with a moderate system of areas specifically reserved for native biodiversity.

Table 2.1 summarizes the economic value of different resource uses as well as the financial reinvestment and local employment associated with them. The economic value of the basic resource is much less than the total revenue of the sectors that use the resources because the total revenue is based on other inputs in addition to the basic commodities and services. Employment figures, however, are based on full revenues of each sector and are not tied only to the basic commodity or service. The key conclusion is that different patterns of resource utilization will lead to relatively large economic and employment changes. The degree to which these different sectors are complementary or competing can be assessed only at scales smaller than the whole Sierra Nevada region.

The relative importance of the major resources in terms of employment, resource values, and reinvestments varies con-

siderably. The benefits of water use accruing outside the Sierra Nevada region account for more than half the total value of basic goods and services but provide limited employment or funds for reinvestment. The historic allocation of water rights benefits those who made the large investments in the dams, canals, and power plants that impact many of the rivers and streams of the Sierra Nevada.

Most of the value of timber stumpage, forage, and other agricultural output comes from private rather than public lands in the Sierra Nevada. Federal revenue sharing of timber receipts is the largest single source of reinvestment funds, but it is partially canceled out by the effective subsidy provided through low grazing fees on public lands.

Conservative estimates of the ecosystem value or "rent" for the large recreation and tourism industry as well as new construction are estimated at 10% of total revenue for the two sectors. The remaining 90% of the actual revenues are assigned to services over and above the estimated ecosystem value or "rent." Taxes on overnight visitors and property constitute a significant source of funds to county governments.

The 1990 census–based estimates of employment overestimate the impact of many seasonal jobs in the recreation and construction industries. After correcting for seasonality and wage differentials, commodity-related employment and service-related employment each constitute a little more than 10% of the total employment for the Sierra Nevada as a whole. In terms of reinvestments, the commodity and service sectors each provided around $20 million per year over the past decade. Each region within the Sierra Nevada exhibits a different mix of sectors in terms of relative size and trends over time.

Management practices for many forms of resource utilization have been altered over the past few decades to specifically improve the complementarity between the resource

TABLE 2.1

Estimated annual resource values and reinvestment for major ecosystem commodities and services. (From volume III, chapter 23.)

Ecosystem Commodities and Services	Resource Value (Millions of Dollars)	Percentage of Sierra Resources	Economic Sectors Benefiting	Direct Reinvestment (Millions of Dollars)
Downstream irrigation water	450[a]	20	Central Valley agriculture	[g]
Downstream municipal water	290[a]	13	Metropolitan areas	[g]
Hydroelectric power	610[a]	27	All users of electricity	[h]
Water total		**61**		
Private recreation and tourism	140[b]	6	Overall recreation and tourist sector	10
Public recreation in parks and forests	225[c]	10	Users of public recreation facilities (45 million visitor days per year)	[i]
New residential ecosystem values	110[d]	5	Total residential sectors within Sierra Nevada	10
Recreation/residential total		**21**		
Public timber	150[e]	7	Timber industry	23
Private timber	170[e]	8	Timber industry	3
Timber total		**14**		
Public grazing	8[f]	<1	Livestock industry	−7[j]
Private grazing	16[f]	1	Livestock industry	<1
Private pasture	8[f]	<1	Livestock industry	<1
Other irrigated agriculture	50[f]	2	Local agricultural processing, wineries, etc.	<1
Agriculture total		**4**		
Overall total	**2,227**	**100**		**39**

[a]Derived value of water rights.
[b]10% of 1995 total revenue estimate.
[c]$5 per day for estimated 45 million annual visitor days.
[d]10% of annual new construction value.
[e]California State Board of Equalization, 1985–94.
[f]County agricultural commissioners, 1985, 1994.
[g]Water rights are not taxed as property, hence return no value to area of origin.
[h]Hydroelectric power plants are taxed as commercial property but the assessments are very low compared with revenue generated.
[i]Public recreation in national forests, national parks, state parks, and other facilities is funded primarily from general funds rather than user fees.
[j]Public grazing fees are far below those charged by private or other public landowners.

extraction and ecological conditions. Management of forests under many new guidelines will require modified silvicultural approaches (figure 2.11). For instance, the focus may be on density management of stands to reduce the potential for insect epidemics, to reduce fuel, to maintain a diverse species composition, and to stimulate growth of larger trees. This general approach can be used in both general purpose forestlands and areas managed for late successional structure. Carefully thought out and implemented, site-specific prescriptions may be needed on all harvested lands. These prescriptions may employ both prescribed fire and mechanical removal of wood. Regeneration may occur by natural and artificial means to maintain species composition and restock stands after fire or timber harvest. The purpose of management may be to reduce fire and insect potential on general-purpose timberlands, while maintaining stands that produce both wood and wildlife habitat. In areas emphasizing biodiversity and forest structure, the focus may be on reducing fire and insects, while providing the characteristics and habitats of old forests; wood production may be a by-product.

Alterations in schedules of water release from dams, closer management of grazing animals in meadows and riparian areas, and new silvicultural techniques to preserve specific forest ecosystem characteristics reduce the conflict between resource utilization and the protection of native biodiversity. Monitoring of individual sites and the larger landscape may be required to determine the net impacts of these new approaches to resource utilization in the Sierra Nevada.

REGIONAL ECONOMIES
Income, Jobs, and the Growth of Local Economies

Over the past twenty years the economy of the Sierra Nevada region, like the population, has more than doubled. The natural and cultural environment of the Sierra Nevada has attracted new business owners, employees, and retirees to the region. From 1978 to 1993 alone, 7,500 new small businesses were started in the twelve-county area all or mainly within the SNEP core region. During the last twenty years, the major commodity-based sectors—agriculture, timber, and min-

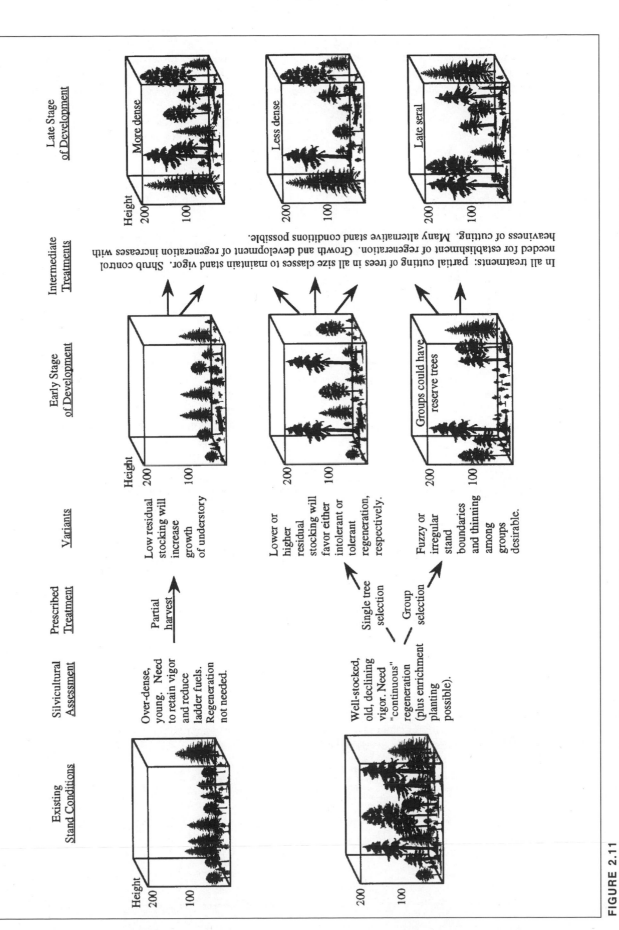

FIGURE 2.11

Schematic diagram showing how different silvicultural treatments in mixed conifer stands can lead to different structural conditions. Initial stands are uneven-aged forests. (From volume II, chapter 15.)

ing—experienced little or no growth in employment. On a rangewide basis, recreation and tourism provide more jobs and roughly the same total amount of wages as all the commodity-based sectors combined. Individual workers in the recreation and tourism sectors, however, earn lower hourly wages and work fewer hours per week on average than most commodity production workers.

The major demographic trends of in-migration of new residents employed in new businesses and retirees bringing transfer incomes have had a much greater impact on the economy than the large commodity and recreation-based industries of the region. Similarly, the economic stimulus from new businesses, commuters, and retirees is now far greater than that provided by all the commodity and recreation-based employment in the region. One of the major implications of this trend is that the economic character of the region is less influenced by the major resource industries and agencies and is becoming more similar to the diverse economy and society of California as a whole.

Patterns of demographic and economic change vary considerably across the range. By 1992, personal income levels in the Sierra portions of the counties of Nevada, Placer, and El Dorado, where 40% of the recent population growth in the Sierra took place, were on a par with the rest of the state. Personal income levels in the rest of the region have remained at 80% of state average for the past twenty years. Although all regions are now less dependent on the historically important agricultural, mining, and timber sectors, only the more metropolitan counties experienced large changes in economic status. The experience of the west-central north region may be repeated in other parts of the Sierra Nevada if they follow similar demographic trends over the next few decades.

Personal Income

In 1972, locally earned wages made up nearly 70% of all personal income in the region. Wages earned by commuters working outside of the region, interest and dividends, and

government transfer payments such as social security made up the rest of personal income. By 1992, local wages constituted less than half of all personal income. Income earned by commuters, interest, dividends, and transfer payments to retired and other households now constitute more than half the total personal income in the Sierra Nevada. A significant implication of this change is that the regional economies are now less influenced by fluctuations in local employment in the cyclical commodity, construction, and tourism sectors. Differences in employment patterns still define the unique aspects of local economies but do not drive them as they did before the 1980s.

Regional Economies by Ecological Regions

Specific linkages between the economy and the ecosystem vary across the range and are most apparent at regional levels. To illustrate the regional differences, we analyzed the entire Sierra using two different types of regions: one based on socioeconomic characteristics and the other on major biophysical characteristics. The six economic regions are based on socioeconomic characteristics, following county boundaries and influence zones of major metropolitan economies. The broad-scale ecosystem boundaries follow a simple west foothill, conifer, and east-side breakdown. The population living in the foothill zone was estimated by allocating the 180 census block–based community aggregations (described later) where most people lived below the 3,000-foot elevation line that approximates the boundary between foothill and conifer ecosystems. Table 2.2 shows the population by ecological region. The east-side region includes the Greater Lake Tahoe Basin (GLTB) west of Donner Pass but does not include the small communities in Sierra, Plumas, and Lassen Counties that are topographically east of the Sierra Nevada crest and are more similar to communities on the west side of the crest. The population within each economic region is not spread evenly across the major vegetation zones.

TABLE 2.2

Regional population by ecological and socioeconomic regions. Population sums are approximate and are based on a simple classification that does not split large community aggregations. (From volume III, chapter 23.)

Socioeconomic Regions	Ecological Regions			Total	Percentage of Total
	West-Foothill	Conifer	East-Side		
Northern	84,000	44,000		128,000	20
West-Central South	192,000	28,000		222,000	34
West-Central North	98,000	30,000		128,000	20
San Joaquin	68,000	9,000		77,000	12
Greater LakeTahoe Basin			63,000	63,000	10
Southeast			28,000	28,000	4
Total	443,000	112,000	91,000	646,000	
Percentage of total	68	17	14	99	

TABLE 2.3

Major employment sectors (all numbers are percentages). (From volume III, chapter 23.)

	Local Services	Non-timber Manufacturing	Construction	Timber	Agriculture and Mining	Travel	Public Administration	Total
Northern	61	7	9	4	6	5	8	100
West-Central North	61	9	12	3	3	5	7	100
West-Central South	57	9	11	3	6	7	8	100[a]
San Joaquin	58	0	10	9	7	6	9	100[a]
Greater Lake Tahoe Basin	51	4	9	0	2	31	4	100[a]
Southeast	59	3	10	0	8	13	7	100
Foothills	59	8	12	3	6	5	7	100
Conifer Belt	56	2	9	8	8	8	9	100
Tahoe and East Side	53	3	11	0	6	21	6	100
Sierra-wide total	59	6	11	4	5	8	7	100

[a]Total does not equal 100 due to rounding.

Jobs and Wages

Employment patterns provide the simplest and clearest illustration of the linkages between the Sierra Nevada ecosystem and the local economies of the households, communities, and counties in the Sierra Nevada. Table 2.3 summarizes employment patterns for the different regions. Across all regions, most employment is in providing local services in sectors such as health, education, retail, wholesale, finance, real estate, and public utilities. Most of these jobs exist because other residents are bringing new income into the economy by selling goods or services outside the region, receiving income from interest and dividends, or receiving government transfer payments. The amount of income generated by retirees is primarily determined by the demographic makeup of the different regions. Income earned by selling goods or services outside the region is closely related to jobs associated with natural ecosystem products. The six nonlocal service sectors show the relative importance of the different sectors. Most construction and non-timber manufacturing employment is related to development of a relatively small area on the western fringe of the Sierra Nevada. The travel-related employment covers only 70% of total recreation and tourism employment because restaurant employment is combined with other local service employment when census-based categories are used. Employment in agriculture and mining on private land or long-term public leases is significant throughout the Sierra Nevada and is slightly larger than timber-related employment overall. Finally, the significant level in federal and state employment is dominated by jobs in resource agencies as well as the expanding number and capacity of prisons in the region.

With the exception of the travel-dependent economies in the Greater Lake Tahoe Basin and the southeast region, most of the regional economies have considerable diversity in employment. Patterns of timber dependency are not visible in any region even though they are noticeable in the ten remaining mill towns and in other communities where sawmills have shut down over the past twenty years. The population of the heavily forested areas of Plumas, Sierra, and Lassen Coun-

ties is diluted in our statistics by the much larger foothill population in the northern region. Labor mobility via commuting (the average travel time to work for every region is around 25 minutes) and permanent relocation make it difficult to define community-level economic patterns that will be stable for more than a few years.

Although basic wages contribute less than a third of the total personal income entering local economies, the sources

❊ Social and Economic Analysis

Sociologists and economists in SNEP used different analytical techniques and different approaches with the wide range of existing and new data available on individuals, households, communities, and larger regions within the Sierra Nevada. Complementary and sometimes contradictory conclusions are presented depending on disciplinary orientation and on which patterns are highlighted or which scales are used in analysis. For example, the socioeconomic assessment, based on the 1990 census data of 180 communities, was evaluated at the level of an individual community, a county, and several counties. The economist's approach aggregated the data to examine regionwide and temporal patterns, whereas the community sociologist explored patterns of relationships—some qualitative—at the level of the community. Personal income was a primary assessment measure in the economic approach; the measure of community capacity was used as part of the sociological assessment of community well-being.

Although it sometimes makes integration more difficult, use of diverse approaches and debate about their differences lead to a richer analysis and to identification of human and institutional issues operating at different scales.

of these wages strongly influence the character of local economies because they are more variable than income from capital assets (interest, dividends, and rent) or government transfer payments such as social security. When corrections are made for wage differentials in different sectors and wages are aggregated into similar groupings, the regional variation becomes apparent (table 2.4). Basic wages were grouped into four different categories depending on the relative dependence of wages on different uses of the ecosystem. Two categories are directly related to the ecosystem: jobs and wages related to commodity production (timber, agriculture, and mining) and those related to services (recreation and tourism). The other two categories (residents and regional) have little dependence on the ecosystem. The resident category includes wages earned by resident workers in construction and high-wage services such as financial and health services. The regional category includes wages from basic jobs that exist in any regional economy, such as manufacturing not related to local raw materials and government employment not related to resources. These latter two categories provide wage stimulus that comes from residents who choose to live in the Sierra but could live elsewhere. They enjoy the social and environmental amenities of the Sierra, hence have an indirect link to the ecosystem. But they receive most of their personal income from sources other than local jobs. The basic proportion of these jobs was estimated with the standard location quotient methodology commonly used in regional economics. Employment in government and construction is divided among the different sectors according to local economic activities. Only in the Greater Lake Tahoe Basin does a single sector (services, 59%) provide more than half of all wage stimulus. Some of the commodity sector basic wage stimulus for the San Joaquin region may be associated with agriculture in the Central Valley rather than the Sierra Nevada. Sierrawide, the wage stimulus from jobs not dependent on the ecosystem accounted for 58% of the total.

Growth Trends

Over the past twenty years the economy of the Sierra Nevada has diversified and grown. Small businesses provide more than half the local jobs and are spread across all sectors of the economy. Manufacturing employment has remained a stable portion of regional employment because of the growth of non-timber manufacturing on the western edge of the region. Employment directly related to ecosystem-dependent commodities and services has grown principally because of the expansion of private sector recreation and capital-intensive fruit, grape, and vegetable agriculture and related value-added activities such as wineries.

Unemployment and Income Maintenance Programs as Measures of Poor Economic Conditions

Household income levels in most regions of the Sierra Nevada are lower than those of California as a whole. In addition to the large fraction of retired households, other major factors reducing income levels are seasonal unemployment and households with children but no wage earner. Figure 2.12 shows the monthly unemployment rate for four regions. Unemployment rates are higher in many counties in the Sierra Nevada than the rates for California as a whole. Nearly all of the difference is a direct result of seasonal unemployment during the nonsummer months. During the summer months, there is little "extra" unemployment compared with the state as a whole. Seasonality of many jobs related to agriculture, forestry, and recreation is characteristic of all but the more metropolitan-oriented labor markets in the region. Long-term reductions in overall unemployment in the region have always been driven by greater integration with the more robust metropolitan economies of the Central Valley.

The largest income-maintenance programs are the family

TABLE 2.4

Percentage of basic wage stimulus of nonlocal employment sectors. (From volume III, chapter 23.)

	Ecosystem Dependent		Not Ecosystem Dependent		
	Commodity	Services	Residents	Regional	Total
Socioeconomic Regions					
Northern	27	16	27	30	100
Central North	16	11	33	39	100[a]
Central South	26	17	23	34	100
San Joaquin	42	16	29	13	100
Greater Lake Tahoe Basin	5	59	23	13	100
Southeast	19	38	23	19	100[a]
Sierra-wide total	22	20	28	30	100
Ecological Regions					
Foothill	22	13	30	36	100
Conifer	37	17	28	18	100
Southeast and Greater Lake Tahoe Basin	9	52	24	16	100[a]

[a]Total does not equal 100 due to rounding.

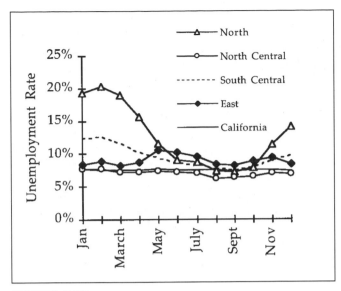

FIGURE 2.12

Monthly unemployment rates for four Sierra Nevada regions, 1990–95 average. (From volume III, chapter 23.)

group and unemployed parent programs within Aid to Families with Dependent Children (AFDC). Over the past twenty years, the ratio of AFDC cases to total population has always been below the state average for the ten counties fully within the Sierra Nevada. The large Central Valley counties that are also represented in the SNEP region (Butte, Yuba, Madera, Fresno, Tulare, and Kern) have been above the state average for most of the past two decades. Although AFDC cases are not an exact measure of poverty, the regional difference does suggest that poverty may be more serious in the lower foothills than in the higher-elevation areas of the SNEP region.

Conclusion: Regional Economy

The economic health of the Sierra Nevada depends on a diversified employment base that grows as fast as population, population growth rates that do not outstrip the ability to be served by local social (e.g., schools, health services) and physical (e.g., roads, water supply, sewage) infrastructure, and levels of resource stewardship that provide both direct and indirect benefits to a wide range of residents and business enterprises. Although personal income levels in areas of the Sierra Nevada not closely linked to major metropolitan areas are not as high as those for the state as a whole, economic and demographic diversification has generally reduced the historical problems associated with local economies dependent on only one or two industries.

COMMUNITY WELL-BEING IN THE SIERRA

Consistent with the changing settlement pattern and resource use in the Sierra, our assessment of well-being is based on a broadened understanding of the relationship of Sierra Nevada residents to resources. Our assessment of community well-being in the Sierra is unique because it focused on communities rather than county-level data. The measure of well-being is composed of two elements: (1) measures of community capacity drawn from the knowledge of local experts and (2) measures of socioeconomic status.

Communities

The SNEP social assessment is based on an improved understanding of communities and an expanded definition of human dependence on the Sierra Nevada ecosystem. Communities located in or near forests have long been called resource-dependent communities. Well-being of these communities has historically been discussed in terms of "community stability," and viewed as a function of a steady flow of timber products to ensure stable employment in the timber industry. This idea of community well-being is based on an antiquated view of forest communities, particularly for many Sierran communities today. As illustrated in the earlier discussion about major employment sectors, the well-being of a majority of Sierran communities is dependent on far more than the flow of timber products and jobs in the wood products industry. Even communities historically reliant on the wood products industry are generally less dependent on it than they were a decade ago. This decreased dependence is due to a combination of factors, including increased concentration of the industry, declining labor demands associated with mill modernization, the movement of wood processing facilities closer to urban consumers and away from forest areas, and declining timber harvest levels. In addition, other sectors of the economy, particularly those sectors linked to recreation, tourism, and recent in-migration of retirees and others, have grown and therefore further reduced the relative impact of the timber industry. The timber industry is but one strand of the tapestry of well-being in Sierra Nevada communities.

Ecosystem dependence today may occur with no apparent economic relationship to the ecosystem. Many residents choose to live in Sierran communities because of the aesthetics, the symbolism, and even the perceived sacredness of the natural landscape. The Sierran landscape in this vein is highly valued, albeit noneconomically, and is a vital part of a human sense of place and community.

The focus on communities for well-being assessment represents a significant improvement over studies of well-being that have relied on county-level data. County data are too general for the purposes of assessing well-being at the community level because differences between individual communities are often obscured through averaging. Well-being for a single community may be very different from well-being for the parent county. For example, well-being in the community of Graeagle is higher than the average level of well-being in Plumas County, whereas the well-being in Kings Beach in the Lake Tahoe area is considerably lower than the Placer County average. In addition, county measures for foothill counties such as Kern, Fresno, Yuba, and Placer include large Central Valley populations that are not part of the Sierra.

Community Capacity Component

We invited local experts, knowledgeable about community issues, local institutions, and resources, to workshops to help assess well-being. The experts consisted of planners, community development professionals, current and former county supervisors, education administrators, business people, health and human service providers, and long-term residents with diverse backgrounds and experiences. These experts focused on community capacity assessment but also offered valuable insights into local socioeconomic measures and determining boundaries of regions and community aggregates.

Community capacity is a dynamic and multidimensional measure of the collective ability of residents to create and take advantage of opportunities and adapt to a variety of circumstances. The measure represents both a state or dimension of well-being and the dynamic ability of community residents to improve well-being. High capacity suggests a higher level of well-being for a given economic status than low capacity and also reflects a high ability of local residents to improve well-being. Experts assessed three primary components of capacity: *physical capital*, which includes physical elements and resources in a community such as sewer systems, housing stock, schools, and open space; *human capital*, which includes the skills, education, experiences, and general abilities of residents; and *social capital*, which includes the ability and willingness of residents to work together for community goals. A low-capacity community is one in which residents generally do not work well together, do not have or use existing resources effectively, and adapt poorly, if at all, to change. Low capacity, then, reflects a reduced ability to improve local well-being, including socioeconomic status.

Socioeconomic Component

Well-being was assessed in part using a socioeconomic scale consisting of five separate measures. The socioeconomic scale, developed from 1990 census data, includes measures of home ownership, education, poverty, unemployment, and homes with children receiving public assistance income. Higher levels of home ownership and education, and lower levels of poverty, unemployment, and homes with children receiving public assistance are presumed to indicate higher socioeconomic status.

The socioeconomic scale and the measure of capacity reflect different dimensions of well-being and together offer a comprehensive picture of the state of well-being of communities. It is important to point out that the combination of high capacity and high socioeconomic status does not mean that all residents of a community aggregate enjoy a high level of well-being. Similarly, low socioeconomic status and low capacity do not mean that all residents experience low well-being. Just as some families enjoy a higher level of well-being than others in the same community, some groups—ethnic, occupational, or other—may collectively have considerably lower well-being. Some of these distributional effects were identified in the capacity workshops, yet they remain beyond the resolution of much of the SNEP well-being assessment.

What We Found

180 Community Aggregations

A total of 180 community aggregations in the six regions were identified in the Sierra Nevada core area. The community aggregations are based on Bureau of the Census block group boundaries, input from county planners, and information collected in workshops with local experts. In many community aggregations a majority of the population is associated with a single community. In others, residents are linked through common service centers, community service districts, or school systems.

Well-Being in Community Aggregations

Sixteen percent of all community aggregations—comprising 18.5% of the total Sierra population—have the lowest level of well-being. These communities have medium-low to very low capacity and medium-low to very low socioeconomic status. Of these communities, 39% are located in the northern Sierra, 25% in the west-central south, and 14% in the southern Sierra, with the remaining scattered throughout the other regions. A number of these low well-being communities are formerly resource-dependent communities that, for a variety of reasons, have lost resource-based industries and jobs. The residents of these communities have, on average, low socioeconomic status and also lack the resources at a community level to take advantage of opportunities that might improve socioeconomic conditions. The low capacity in these communities is important to recognize because it suggests that these communities are unlikely to improve without substantial intervention strategies.

Seventeen percent of all aggregates, which include 15.5% of the Sierra population, have the highest level of well-being. Of these communities, 55% are in the Sacramento commuter counties of Nevada, El Dorado, and Placer. The remaining high well-being aggregates are scattered throughout the Sierra. All of the high well-being community aggregations have a high or very high socioeconomic status. Capacity scores range from medium-low to very high. Low capacity associated with high socioeconomic status is unlikely to reduce well-

The Sierra Nevada offers a wealth of recreational opportunities. Every year, millions of people visit, enjoy, and impact this national treasure. (Photo by Dwight M. Collins.)

being as much as low capacity associated with lower levels of socioeconomic status because residents of aggregations with high socioeconomic status can, and in fact do, buy their way out of situations that other communities must work internally to overcome. In some of the high socioeconomic status communities, predominantly retiree-dominated aggregates, residents buy services such as fire protection, security, and recreation programs, whereas other communities might rely on volunteer activities, the county, or the state for provision of such services. Nonetheless, among the high socioeconomic status aggregates, high capacity reflects a higher level of well-being than aggregates with high socioeconomic status and medium to low capacity.

The remaining community aggregations have moderate to moderately high well-being and can be further subdivided into three groups with varying combinations of socioeconomic status and community capacity. One group has low socioeconomic status and medium community capacity (12% of all the aggregations). Another has medium socioeconomic status and low community capacity (20% of the aggregates). The largest group of aggregates (35%) had medium capacity and medium socioeconomic status.

Well-Being in the Sierra Regions

The northern Sierra region has the lowest average socioeconomic status and capacity scores of any region. Compared to the other five regions, it has the largest proportion of people in poverty and the highest level of poverty intensity, the lowest average education level, the highest level of unemployment by a considerable margin, and the highest rate of children in families receiving public assistance. Three-quarters of all aggregations in the Sierra with very low socioeconomic status are located in this region. In contrast to these low measures of well-being, the northern Sierra has a few of the highest socioeconomic status communities in the Sierra. Lake Almanor West and Graeagle are two such examples. They are small aggregations with many high-value second homes and well-to-do retirees.

The west-central north region has the highest average socioeconomic status and the second highest average capacity score. Aggregations in this region are characterized by bedroom communities with relatively homogeneous populations of out-of-county commuters and retirees. The region has a number of commuter-dominated aggregations like El Dorado

Hills, one of the wealthiest in the Sierra, yet also has aggregations like Georgetown and Camino, locales once largely dependent on resource extraction that have in recent years grown considerably more diversified. The region also has pockets of extreme poverty within some of the aggregations. Grass Valley, Nevada City, and Placerville aggregations have relatively high poverty levels but also have high community capacities due to strong business communities within them.

The average socioeconomic status and capacity scores for the west-central south region are virtually the same as the average scores for the entire Sierra. It is important to point out that the west-central south region discussed here differs slightly from the west-central south region discussed in the "Regional Economics" section. Madera County is included in this region rather than in the San Joaquin region, as a result of expert input collected at well-being assessment workshops. The five counties of this region are linked by Highway 49, which runs north and south along the Sierra foothills and terminates in Oakhurst in Madera County. Community aggregations in this region are collectively some of the most diverse in the Sierra. There are communities, such as North Fork, historically dependent on resource extraction, and growing retiree and commuter community aggregations, including Jackson and Sutter Creek/Amador City/Volcano. There are also aggregations that have a varying mixture of retirees and economies dominated by recreation and agriculture. The southern three counties are also linked by their identification with and economic relationship to Yosemite National Park.

Community aggregations of the Greater Lake Tahoe Basin (GLTB) display a strikingly unequal distribution of wealth in this region dominated by tourism, recreation, and service economies. Slightly more than 40% of the permanent basin population resides in community aggregations with low or very low socioeconomic status, while 47% live in aggregations with medium-high to very high socioeconomic status. A vivid example is the Kings Beach aggregation, with extremely high poverty and surrounded by the much higher capacity and well-to-do aggregations of North Tahoe and Incline/Crystal Bay/Brockway. Low socioeconomic status in the GLTB is strongly influenced by low-paying seasonal jobs in the recreation, tourist, and casino industries.

The San Joaquin region discussed here differs from the San Joaquin region described previously; it excludes Madera County, which is included in the west-central south region. This region has the second lowest capacity score and a socioeconomic score that equals the average for the entire Sierra region. Despite an average socioeconomic status, there is significant poverty in the region. This region has a poverty level second only to the northern Sierra region. The Tule Indian Reservation aggregation has a low socioeconomic status, and Native Americans are almost half the population. Many of the aggregations in the southwest region were at one time economically dependent on the timber industry. Ranching and other agricultural activities remain culturally if not economically important in a number of aggregations. Local economies,

however, are increasingly oriented to tourism, recreation, and retirement living. And as in many community aggregations to the north, a growing number of Fresno, Visalia, Bakersfield, and other Central Valley workers are settling in the Sierra foothills in aggregations like Lower Foothills/Millerton Lake. These new commuter residents are bringing with them both increased wealth and impacts to local communities. These changes challenge long-standing ranching and agricultural lifestyles, though conflicts are not necessarily inevitable.

The average socioeconomic status and capacity scores for the southeast region are the same as the average scores for the entire Sierra. The economies of the region are primarily based on recreation and tourism, and there is a high proportion of workers in the government and service sectors. As in the Greater Lake Tahoe Basin region, there are sharp contrasts in aggregations: the Greater Lone Pine and Antelope Valley (Walker, Coleville, Topaz) have low socioeconomic status, while Lee Vining/Mono Basin and Long Valley/Wheeler Crest/Paradise aggregations have medium-high and high socioeconomic status, respectively. This region is characterized by a land ownership pattern dominated by public agencies, primarily the Los Angeles Department of Water and Power, the Forest Service, and the Bureau of Land Management. As a result, land available for development is limited and landholding decisions generally are beyond the reach of local residents. At the same time, however, current land managers are retaining much land in open space and in a natural condition that is widely valued and upon which the region's tourist economy is established.

Conclusion: Social Well-Being

Measures of socioeconomic status and community capacity in the Sierra Nevada community aggregations reflect relatively independent components of well-being, and they measure different dimensions of it. The five-factor socioeconomic scale offers a useful though static perspective on socioeconomic status, while the measure of capacity provides a current and important complementary perspective on overall well-being. Low socioeconomic scores are found in areas where high percentages of individuals and families within community aggregations may lack sufficient socioeconomic resources to maintain a reasonable standard of living and hence experience lower well-being. Capacity provides an indication of the ability of local communities to foster an environment in which local residents can identify and address their needs and goals. Low capacity scores indicate a reduced ability to effectively address the needs of local residents and take advantage of local development opportunities that might benefit them. Low capacity therefore reflects not only lower well-being but also a reduced ability (and likelihood) by residents of aggregations to improve local well-being, including socioeconomic status. Community capacity scores are positively associated with the socioeconomic scale, but this correlation is weak. The independence of these two measures appears to be due mostly to the critical role of social capital, which proved to be a primary determinant of community capacity.

Community capacity varies widely across the Sierra Nevada. The three components of community capacity (physical, human, and social capital) sometimes appear to be in conflict with one another. That is, where human capital is perceived as high or increasing, social capital may be low or in decline. This is particularly true in aggregations in which well-educated retirees or professionals move into an area and do not work on community issues cooperatively with one another or with residents who have lived there longer. Community history was identified as playing a role in community capacity. There are a number of community aggregations, particularly in the San Joaquin region, to which medium-high or high capacity was related to a long history and continued presence of multiple old families. In some cases, community capacity was negatively affected by divergent values of populations of different ages. Conflicts between retirees and younger families with children were noted in a number of aggregations. Retirees often demand services but resist changes that may be necessary to provide them, and retirees are often reluctant to pay for schools and other services that appear to benefit only families with children. These clashes appear to be strongest in some of the affluent, gated communities, where community capacity is negatively affected by internal strife and lack of cooperation between these two groups. In a few community aggregates, however, the knowledge, experiences, and willingness of retirees to help the community were particularly noted as positively contributing to capacity. Other volunteerism-based community services are negatively affected by populations aging in place, particularly in areas where youth leave communities and in bedroom communities with a large percentage of commuters.

MANAGEMENT SCENARIOS AND STRATEGIES

We begin this section with a scenario of future population growth and distribution in the Sierra. This analysis shows that if growth and development continue as they have to date, significant impacts to Sierra Nevada resources and a reduction of social and economic well-being are likely. We conclude the section with a strategy that outlines a general approach to improving community well-being by directly linking ecosystem management activities to Sierra Nevada communities.

Future Population Growth and Settlement

The Sierra Nevada is likely to undergo significant land conversion through continuing population growth over the next half century. The total land area converted to human settlement to accommodate 1990–2040 growth will depend upon the spatial pattern and average density of settlement, which will in turn depend upon the complex interaction of public policy, infrastructure, and land economics. Strict development controls, significant expansion of water and sewer systems and higher land prices would be likely to lead to a more intensive pattern of development with less land conversion than would occur otherwise. Continuing the existing patterns of development would consume more land than could be achieved under these conditions.

Current population growth and economic activity in the Sierra Nevada are increasingly dominated by the amenity values of resources and the environment for commuters, retirees, and people working in the recreation and tourism sectors. The impacts of future growth will therefore affect the social and economic well-being of the Sierra Nevada as well as its ecosystems. Public policies designed to manage growth will need to encourage patterns of development that reduce the impacts of human settlement.

Land conversion due to human settlement can have a wide range of indirect effects on ecological structure and function. The most important of these in the Sierra Nevada is associated with impacts on the fire regime in both settled areas and adjacent wildlands. Human settlement affects the structure and level of fuel load, viability of presuppression fuel-management strategies, ignition risk, availability of suppression resources, and the manner in which suppression efforts are allocated and deployed (e.g., to protect structures rather than wildlands). Each of these will in turn affect the future risk and characteristics of fire in the Sierra Nevada. Vegetation management in the "urban forest" of areas converted to human settlement can either decrease or increase fuels in the urban-wildland intermix zone. Without additional research on the relationship between alternative patterns of human settlement and specific ecological impacts, it is difficult to forecast ecological implications of continuing existing patterns of development and using a range of alternative growth management policy mechanisms for mitigating those impacts.

General relationships can still be inferred, however, based on theoretical and empirical research to date. In particular, land conversion causes at least five direct effects on vegetation and wildlife:

1. Reduced total habitat area through direct habitat conversion

2. Reduced habitat patch size and increased habitat fragmentation

3. Isolation of habitat patches by roads, structures, and fences

4. Harassment of wildlife by domestic dogs and cats

5. Biological pollution from genes of non-native plant species

In addition to these direct effects upon vegetative composition, structure, and function (which in turn affect wildlife habitat and wildlife viability), land conversion for human settlement has several direct effects on hydrologic regimes that could be important:

6. Increased impervious surface and increased peak runoff

7. Increased heavy metal and oil runoff from impervious surfaces

8. Increased risk of ground-water and/or surface water contamination through septic effluent disposal

9. Decreased ground-water flow to surface water system due to ground-water pumping

10. Modified surface water flow due to irrigation, septic system effluent disposal, and treated wastewater discharges

Scenarios

Without assuming any linkages to specific policies or market conditions, six alternative distributions of future population by housing density class were considered. These were based upon GIS analysis of the distribution of population by housing density class under the following: (1) 1990 Sierra Nevada census blocks; (2) 1990 Nevada County census blocks; (3) 1990 El Dorado County census blocks; (4) Nevada County General Plan; (5) El Dorado County General Plan Project Description; and (6) El Dorado County General Plan Alternative (figure 2.13). The three General Plan distributions were based on the planimetric estimates of area designated for "buildout" at specific density classes in the General Plan land-use maps but did not account for the greater development in some density classes that is likely to take place due to existing parcelization. They therefore overstate the degree of future concentration.

Four alternative future growth projections from 1990 to 2040 were considered for each of the forty-six county census divisions (CCDs) in the analysis: (1) based on each CCD's 1970–90 share of overall county growth; (2) based on each CCD's 1970–80 share of overall county growth; (3) based on each CCD's 1980–90 share of overall county growth; and (4) a lower projection at two-thirds the first described projection, which was the approximate absolute growth rate historically from 1970 to 1990 for the entire Sierra Nevada. Combined with the six alternative population distributions by density class, these four alternative population projections for 1990–2040 result in twenty-four possible land-conversion estimates for each of the forty-six CCDs in our analysis for the year 2040. The resulting 1,104 cells of land-conversion estimates are a bit overwhelming for presentation, however, and many of the population distributions by housing density class are similar to one another. Therefore, the set was simplified to four scenarios:

A. Low population growth with compact human settlement patterns (Low-Compact)

B. High population growth with compact human settlement patterns (High-Compact)

C. Low population growth with sprawling human settlement patterns (Low-Sprawl)

D. High population growth with sprawling human settlement patterns (High-Sprawl)

The most "compact" population distribution was the Nevada County General Plan, in which 71.3% of the population is accommodated in the highest housing density class (640+ dwelling units per square mile). Note that this is a significantly higher fraction of the population than there was in this class in 1990, when Nevada County's distribution was not significantly different from that for the entire Sierra Nevada. The "compact" distribution assumed in the Nevada County General Plan still consumes roughly a quarter-acre per person in the highest housing density class in an average of roughly two dwelling units per acre. This "compact" pattern is therefore considerably less dense than most suburban subdivision densities in metropolitan areas. This pattern likely reflects a bimodal distribution within this density class, where there are clusters of parcels close to one acre in size (with on-site domestic well water and on-site wastewater disposal through septic systems) and around one-quarter acre in size (with public water and sewer). Unfortunately, it was not feasible to disaggregate housing density below this level for the analysis. Doubling the average density for this class (through an infrastructure-directed development strategy) could reduce the land conversion estimates for the "compact" scenarios by 50% in the highest-density class. It would have little effect, however, on the total land area converted by human settlement at any of the lower thresholds for human settlement. As noted in the more detailed assessment, the Nevada County General Plan also underestimates the amount of land that is likely to be developed at lower densities due to existing parcelization. The quarter-acre-per-person estimate for the highest housing density class is therefore a reasonable basis for estimating the land-conversion effects of "compact" human settlement patterns across the entire Sierra Nevada.

The most dispersed ("sprawl") population distribution was the 1990 Sierra Nevada census block distribution, in which 39.5% of the population resided in the highest housing density class. We therefore assumed continuation of this existing distribution across all CCDs in the Sierra Nevada for our "sprawl" scenarios of human settlement. This assumption allowed us to estimate the total land area required in each CCD to accommodate 1990 to 2040 population growth if existing patterns of human settlement were to continue. Land tenure relationships constrain the potential to expand the land area converted to lower housing density classes, however, so the lower housing density classes generally increase their average densities within their density ranges rather than expand in area (e.g., land in the class with ten to twenty dwelling units per square mile might move from twelve dwelling units

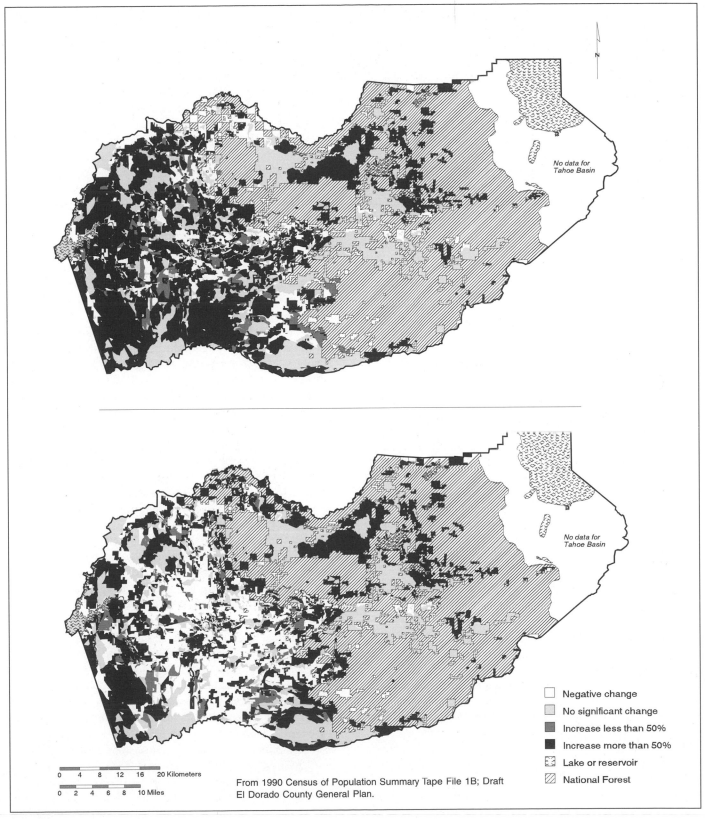

Negative change

No significant change

Increase less than 50%

Increase more than 50%

Lake or reservoir

National Forest

No data for
Tahoe Basin

No data for
Tahoe Basin

0 4 8 12 16 20 Kilometers

0 2 4 6 8 10 Miles

From 1990 Census of Population Summary Tape File 1B; Draft
El Dorado County General Plan.

FIGURE 2.13

Projected change in relative housing density, El Dorado County, from 1990 to buildout, based on General Plan alternatives.
Top: Projection based on primary project model. *Bottom:* Projection based on alternative project model. (From volume II, chapter 11.)

to eighteen per square mile). This analysis therefore estimated land converted to human settlement only above the density threshold of twenty dwelling units per square mile (32 acres per dwelling unit).

Implications

Based upon these four scenarios, the range of additional land conversion required to accommodate population growth from 1990 to 2040 (beyond the land area already converted for human settlement in 1990) is estimated to be:

- 106 to 579 square miles at an average density of at least 640 units per square mile

- 299 to 875 square miles at an average density of at least 160 units per square mile

- 480 to 1,655 square miles at an average density of at least 80 units per square mile

- 477 to 2,957 square miles at an average density of at least 40 units per square mile

- 134 to 5,105 square miles at an average density of at least 20 units per square mile

The Low-Compact scenario (A) always represented the lower bound of our range and the High-Sprawl scenario (D) always represented the higher bound of our range, with the exception of the 640+ dwelling units per square mile threshold. For this one exception, these two extreme scenarios resulted in approximately the same land area conversion, while the Low-Sprawl (C) scenario resulted in the least land conversion and the High-Compact (B) scenario resulted in the most land conversion. This result primarily reflects the fact that the "compact" scenarios concentrate 71.3% of the total population into the highest housing density class. The "compact" scenarios therefore show more land area converted to human settlement in the highest housing density class, but they still show less land area converted to human settlement in all of the other housing density classes. This is made clear at all of the other density thresholds.

The social, economic, and ecological ramifications of future development will depend upon specific spatial patterns of human settlement in relation to existing communities, infrastructure services, vegetation and habitat types, and watershed boundaries. As discussed earlier, our understanding of those relationships is still poor at this time. It is therefore impossible for us to characterize the specific impacts that population growth and human settlement will have in the Sierra Nevada. The range of impacts could be quite significant, however, if existing development patterns continue. Continuing the existing pattern of "sprawl" development with a high-growth scenario could result in human settlement on nearly half the private land in the Sierra Nevada (6,846 square miles) at an average density of at least one housing unit per

32 acres. A low-growth scenario with the existing pattern of "sprawl" development would reduce that figure by 44%, to just 3,817 square miles. This is still more than twice as much land area as the 1,741 square miles affected by human settlement at that density in 1990.

Even modified settlement patterns are forecast to result in significant land conversion from 1990 to 2040, suggesting that the scale of population growth alone could lead to significant impacts. A high-growth scenario with a more "compact" form of settlement would still result in nearly a doubling of land converted to human settlement, from 1,741 square miles to 3,363 square miles at an average density of at least one housing unit per 32 acres. A low-growth scenario with a more "compact" form of settlement, on the other hand, could nearly be accommodated within the land area already converted to human settlement at an average density of at least one housing unit per 32 acres in 1990. Through infill and carefully targeted density transfers, the low population forecast for 1990–2040 would require only 1,875 square miles (only 8% more than in 1990). Both the scale and pattern of human settlement will therefore affect—and must therefore be considered by—local, state, and federal land and resource management agencies with responsibility for the health and sustainability of Sierra Nevada ecosystems.

These estimates of land conversion associated with human settlement from 1990 to 2040 are not uniform throughout the Sierra Nevada. They reflect the distribution of population forecast by the Department of Finance (DOF) for each county and the allocation of that population by our allocation models to each of the CCDs in our analysis. In general, the land most likely to be converted to human settlement is primarily in the western foothills and within commuting distance of rapidly growing cities in the Central Valley. Some specific vegetation (Holland) types and Wildlife Habitat Relationships Model (WHR) types are therefore more threatened by human settlement than others, reflecting the nonrandom spatial distribution of growth, private ownership, and vegetation.

The ultimate environmental effects of General Plan buildout will depend upon the spatial patterns of development and the infrastructure used to provide services to that development. Both these characteristics are in part a function of local land-use planning and policies, which are central to the General Plan process. Detailed assessment of that process was completed for the recently adopted Nevada County General Plan and El Dorado County General Plan. These two counties have experienced very rapid growth over the past thirty years and have committed significant resources to updating their plans over the past five years. Despite their efforts, however, the environmental impact reports for the two General Plan updates (together with independent analysis described in volume II, chapter 11) show that future development will result in significant environmental impacts and significant shortfalls in infrastructure investments to mitigate those impacts. The existing institutional mechanisms for mitigating the anticipated impacts of future development in the Sierra Nevada appear to be inadequate. Significant changes in local land-use and infrastructure investment policies are therefore likely to be necessary to achieve the lower-impact scenarios associated with the more compact form of development described earlier. Without those significant changes, the existing patterns of development are likely to continue to dominate and to result in at least a doubling of the total land area affected by development at an average density of at least one unit per 32 acres.

Strategy: Improving Community Well-Being through Ecosystem Management

A fundamental SNEP charge is to maintain the health and sustainability of Sierra Nevada ecosystems while meeting human needs. Another way to view this charge is to maintain the health and sustainability of Sierra Nevada ecosystems that *include* human communities. Healthy ecosystems contribute to healthy communities, and healthy communities are better able and more likely to maintain healthy ecosystems than unhealthy communities. Health of communities is discussed here as well-being.

Ecosystem management activities may be pursued in many different ways, but the most effective ecosystem management will maintain a healthy and sustainable ecosystem *and* improve community capacity and well-being. Building this reciprocal relationship is a first step toward genuinely integrating humans with natural ecosystems, as well as strengthening communities, which, in turn, will lead to better ecosystem management and protection.

Low well-being in the Sierra is the result of many factors, some of which have played out decades ago in resource boom-and-bust cycles and others that have little to do with management of the ecosystem. Nevertheless, well-being of community residents can be improved by management of the Sierra Nevada resources that is tailored to meet both ecosystem objectives and community well-being objectives, including the well-being in communities that have few jobs in traditional resource sectors.

Goal and Approach

This strategy follows a general approach that links ecosystem management activities to Sierra Nevada communities to improve community well-being. Ecosystem management activities are specific to community capacity because use of these activities for improving local well-being is partly dependent on community capacity. What works in a community with high or medium capacity may not be successful in a community with low or very-low capacity. Improving community capacity, one dimension of well-being, is a goal as well. Lower capacity communities are less able to respond to assistance or intervention and improve well-being. Low capacity and low socioeconomic status communities often require intensive and long-term assistance to improve well-being beyond ecosystem

management. Community and economic development projects of any sort must address underlying reasons for low capacity if they are to be successful at improving long-term well-being.

In the short term, ecosystem management activities are most likely to improve well-being in communities with moderate levels of well-being already. Hence, communities with low socioeconomic status and moderate to high levels of capacity should receive very high priority for expansion of ecosystem management activities that contribute to well-being. These communities have not yet lost the resiliency they need to take advantage of opportunities that will raise their low socioeconomic status as well as capacity. Understanding the local conditions, including community capacity, can lead to development of more effective ecosystem management activities.

Components of Ecosystem Management

Ecosystem management involves various activities. It is useful to outline these activities to make clear the nexus between ecosystem management and communities and how management might be structured to improve community well-being. For example, with three levels of community capacity (high, medium, and low) and eight broad categories of ecosystem management activities (research, planning, survey and assessment, monitoring, maintenance and restoration, recreation and tourism, commodity extraction/processing/production/use, which includes primary and secondary production processes, and reserves) there are twenty-four combinations depending on capacity and a single activity for a community. Any ecosystem activity will need to be modified to fit the particular circumstances and the context of the community. Diverse communities such as those in the Sierra require diverse approaches to improving well-being. No single approach is complete or adequate. Several examples of the relationship between capacity and ecosystem activities are offered in the next section.

These ecosystem management categories are incomplete; they are offered to show a range of ecosystem activities and to help broaden how we think ecosystem management can contribute to community well-being. The category of monitoring includes biological and ecological as well as social and economic monitoring. Maintenance and restoration activities apply to watersheds, forests, and roads, and include activities such as general erosion control, watershed restoration, stand density management, building of fuel breaks and other fuels maintenance, fish and other wildlife habitat improvement, and mining reclamation. Commodity extraction/processing/production/use includes activities associated with wood products, special forest products, forage, water and minerals, and other commodity resources. The category of recreation and tourism encompasses dispersed and nondispersed recreation and activities associated with destination resorts and tourism services more generally. The category of reserves may be viewed as less an activity than a land-management classification, but it is listed here because traditional reserves (e.g., wilderness) and nontraditional reserves, such as those managed for biodiversity or for the protection of unique cultural areas, involve different management activities that can and do contribute to community well-being.

Examples of Linking Ecosystem Management Activities with Community Capacity

A few examples are offered to describe how ecosystem management activities linked to community capacity can be tailored to improve community well-being. In virtually all categories of ecosystem management, successful linkage will require a change in investment patterns in resources. Natural resources have historically been used with inadequate reinvestment or underinvestment in the resource base, by both public and private entities. This ongoing process is further exacerbated by recent cuts in federal land-management budgets. New funding mechanisms that tie resource use to reinvestment in the sustainability of the resource base must be developed, or it will be difficult to ensure sustainable ecosystem management activities, much less tie them thoughtfully to concerns for community well-being.

The ecosystem management activities that fall into the categories of research, planning, survey and assessment, and monitoring have generally been the province of government agencies, private landowners, managers and scientists. Increasingly, there are local watershed- and community-based groups that want to become involved with these activities. Local collaborative and consensus-based groups can make significant contributions to ecosystem research, planning, survey and assessment, and monitoring and in the process improve community capacity and local well-being. Medium and high capacity communities are far more likely to independently spawn and support watershed- and community-based groups than low capacity communities are. Because all of these activities require significant training, the capacity to train workers will prove vital in being able to complete the work itself. Low capacity communities are more likely to lack training facilities and resources, hence will have a harder time participating in these types of ecosystem management activities.

Watershed maintenance and restoration is a combination of equipment-intensive and labor-intensive activities. High capacity communities will benefit most from watershed reinvestment strategies. Low capacity communities are likely to require training to be conducted by agencies without charge and a consortium of rural development partners such as Vocational Training, Job Training Development, and local economic development organizations in maintenance and restoration training activities. Access to capital for operating expenses and equipment in low capacity communities will be problematic because financing is impossible without secured contracting experience. Contractors will generally have to start with labor-intensive activities and then pool resources through business incubator frameworks to develop toward equipment-intensive ecosystem work. Multiyear and multitask stewardship contracting in a watershed designed to favor local contractors and workers can be used to increase local community access to ecosystem work. Increased watershed maintenance and restoration activities are likely to offer opportunities to develop "ecosystem worker" training programs that can enhance access of local workers to watershed rehabilitation projects and other forest health projects. These are just a few activities associated with watershed improvement that can lead to improved local well-being. Other maintenance and restoration activities include wildlife habitat enhancement, fuels treatment, timber stand improvement, and other forest health work.

In the commodity extraction/processing/production/use category, ways of improving local well-being would include managing nearby areas with significant resource degradation or ecological or cultural sensitivity using "community management." These local communities could develop partnerships with local land managers to develop joint-management agreements. Forest commodity harvest and production activities can be bundled with ecosystem health initiatives using a community management or stewardship framework. This structure would help link commodity harvest and production to payment for ecosystem service and maintenance work. High capacity communities are more likely than low capacity communities to participate in community management, but increasing local access to forest products generally can assist low capacity communities. Other ways of making the link between forest commodity use and local communities include using an approach in which a product stream from stewardship lands is made available locally for processing and secondary manufacturing development; offering price incentives to processing facilities that demonstrate more worker years per million tons processed in low well-being areas; and developing incentives and seeking ways of providing capital for the creation and expansion of local firms for value-added work.

Special forest products are harvested on public land by permit, not high bid. Some areas of a forest can be limited to use by traditional forest product harvesters with "special use" permits under which they would be responsible for care and sustainable management of the resource and harvest. This permit process would provide access to products and would create broad management responsibilities. An objective of this approach is to build incentives and responsibility for forest health and to focus attention on the condition of the land rather than on a single product.

Ecosystem reserves are conceived here as broader in purpose than wilderness and parks and include areas that are managed for biodiversity and cultural objectives. While management is directed to ensure the maintenance or sustainability of cultural or natural resources in these areas, other human activities may be allowed. For example, in an area identified as important for maintaining Sierra Nevada biodiversity, some human settlement can be allowed so long as it does not conflict with and is consistent with long-term biodiversity objectives. Settlement in such a reserve must be approached conservatively, and human impacts must be continually monitored and reassessed. Rather than reserving areas for exclusive use and trading off human use against reserve values, this approach to reserves explicitly acknowledges the connection between humans and their natural environment and makes sustainable ecosystem management and protection of biodiversity part of the living experience.

Implications

Ecosystem management can and should be designed where possible to contribute to community well-being. Resource management that includes the objectives of improving human well-being does not require a trade-off with ecosystem health and sustainability objectives. In fact, building this linkage can result in community self-interest ensuring resource stewardship and sustainable resource management, including protection of biodiversity. Without deliberate restructuring of the relationship between ecosystem management and local communities, it is unlikely such a relationship will develop on a meaningful scale. Because the success of ecosystem management is largely dependent on who takes responsibility for it and carries it out, linking it to local communities that benefit from it can build powerful local incentives and improve the likelihood that it is done well.

CHAPTER 3

Institutions

Institutional Incapacities Many Sierran ecosystem declines are due to institutional incapacities to capture and use resources from Sierran beneficiaries for investment that sustains the health and productivity of the ecosystems from which benefits derive.

Sources of Institutional Incapacities Institutional incapacities arise from four primary sources: (1) fragmented control of ecosystems among different jurisdictions, authorities, and ownerships, (2) absence of exchange mechanisms among these entities to sustain rates of investment and cooperative actions that reflect ecosystem values, (3) detachment between those who control ecosystems and communities that depend upon and care for them, and (4) inflexibility in response to rapid changes in population, economy, and public interests.

Regionalism The souces of institutional capacity and of potentials to improve upon capacity differ among the regions of the Sierra, which vary greatly in their institutional as well as ecological, demographic, and economic characteristics.

ASSESSMENT

The Sierra Nevada is embedded in a wide range of human interests extending throughout the region and beyond. Public and private institutions relating to natural resource use and environmental quality have evolved in part to serve those interests and in part to safeguard the Sierra Nevada itself. Institutions include governmental jurisdictions and public agencies as well as market and community structures. Timber, water, wildlife, and minerals—resources traditionally associated with the Sierra—are consumed by people outside the Sierra, principally in urban or agricultural areas of California. The amenity values of the Sierra drive a real estate market that increasingly draws on the wealth of exurbanite commuters or retirees. Recreational and spiritual values of the Sierra draw people from around the world. Although these values generate employment and income within the Sierra, a vast proportion of these benefits accrue to parties and interests outside the region. Several important social forces drive change in Sierran institutions, and problems emerge as they respond. Collaboration, market capitalization of the cost of ecosystem maintenance, activism, and legal rules contribute to the search for solutions to these problems.

Institutional Setting

The institutional context of the Sierra is a story of mechanisms that express social preferences. Institutional arrangements attempt to "close the loop," or tighten the connection between the ecological systems of the Sierra and the multiple stakeholders of the region. Institutions govern both the means by which benefits flow to beneficiaries and the manner by which these beneficiaries absorb the cost of, and reinvest in, the ecological systems that support them. Reinvestment, broadly defined, includes a range of initiatives whose aim is to ensure the continued integrity and function of Sierra Nevada ecosystems. Reinvestment may include mitigation of environmental impacts or rehabilitation of prior environmental degradation. Market institutions used elsewhere to close the loop between consumers and resources are generally underdeveloped or missing in the Sierra Nevada, leaving government institutions as the principal means by which preferences are expressed and reinvestment promoted.

Government entities, rather than market mechanisms, manifest preferences and direct reinvestment in the Sierra Nevada. Over the years, an institutional landscape has evolved that is diverse, complicated, and fragmented (figure 3.1). Institutions differ by purpose, authority, and jurisdiction. A large part of the Sierra Nevada is administered by federal agencies, and public agencies have responsibility for two-thirds of the land in the region (see chapter 1).

The institutional arrangements in the Lake Tahoe Basin, where there are more than seventy different federal, state, and local government entities, epitomize the complexity present in the larger region. Across the Sierra, each institution responds to, and implements, a different array of policies. The picture that emerges is one of byzantine complexity in which institutions involving every layer of government focus on a single component or process of Sierran ecosystems. In other sectors of the economy, markets perform that function; public institutions struggle together to articulate the definition of public and private good for the Sierra.

Timber harvest and replanting on private land and state land is regulated by the Forest Practice Rules promulgated by the State Board of Forestry and enforced by the California Department of Forestry and Fire Protection (CDF); various stewardship programs funded by CDF, the U.S. Forest Service's State and Private Forestry program, and the Natural Resource Conservation Service subsidize reinvestment. Congress, through laws and policy direction (e.g, National Forest Management Act, the National Environmental Policy Act, and other environmental laws), establishes the framework for the way national forests are managed. The Forest Service, guided by these laws and policy, determines timber

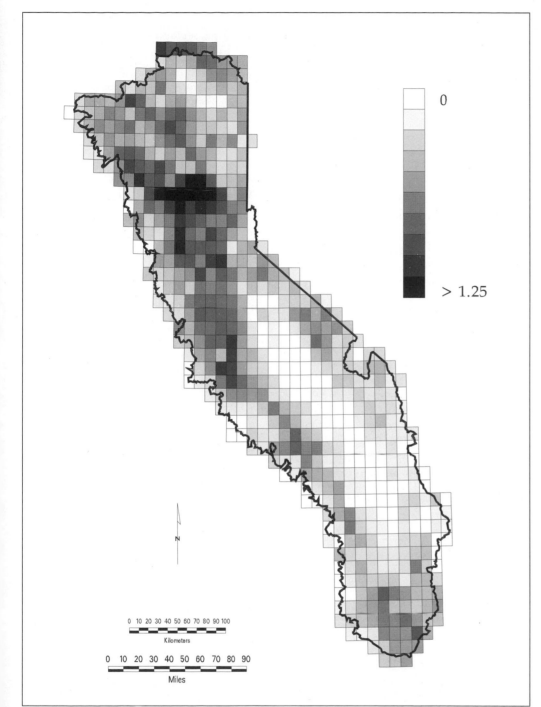

FIGURE 3.1

Public/private interface, relative densities of fragmentation. Units are kilometers of boundary between public and private land per square kilometer.

harvest levels but attainment of these levels is dependent upon congressional appropriations.

Development of private land is regulated directly through General Plans developed by county governments as well as through legislation at the state level, particularly the Subdivision Map Act and the California Environmental Quality Act (CEQA). Certain areas, such as the Lake Tahoe Basin, have even more complex arrangements involving adjoining states, local governments and authorities, and the federal government. The extension of the road network by county and state

transportation agencies influences land development indirectly.

Wildlife and plant species are managed by the California Department of Fish and Game. Funds for reinvestment in wildlife, wildlife habitat, or native plants come from hunting and fishing permits, special government funds earmarked for game species (e.g., Hill Bill, AB 1580), and, on national forest lands, from timber harvest receipts (Knutson-Vandenberg [K-V] funds). When species or their habitats become sufficiently rare as a result of a number of factors, including pressures related to human activity, they fall under the jurisdiction of the state and federal endangered species acts. At this threshold, a new web of regulatory authority is invoked to prevent harm to a species or its habitat. Depending on the habitat requirements of the specific species, government intervention may affect a wide range of activities in an attempt to preserve or restore certain ecosystem attributes.

Existing institutional arrangements related to water include the State Water Resources Control Board, which confers rights to water and is therefore required to articulate the public trust in in-stream flows. Additionally, the U.S. Bureau of Reclamation and the Army Corps of Engineers are responsible for administration of certain reservoirs, dams, and other facilities. The overall structure also includes water purveyors (local irrigation districts, municipal water districts, state and federal irrigation projects), which convey water to users. Users are frequently located in areas quite distant from the Sierra. Public and private utilities and federal regulatory agencies together effect water diversions, in some cases only temporary, in order to produce hydroelectric power. The quality of the water that flows through the vast natural and human plumbing of the Sierra is overseen by several regional water quality control boards and affected by a wide range of activities—road building, timber harvest, mining, grazing—each of which engages its own special web of authorities.

Public and private institutions express the priorities of human society. As social needs change, public expectations of these institutions also change. Accordingly, institutions respond by attempting to change their outlook, function, and methods. In the case of private markets, competitive pressures lead to voluntary changes in private behavior. In public institutions, where competition is generally absent, large-scale population shifts, new social demands, and grassroots activism are the most powerful forces of change. Institutions now dominant may find their positions eroding as other institutions wax powerful and new institutions arise.

Promoting ecosystem sustainability is not a priority common to all of the region's resource-related institutions. Sustainability and ecological health are viewed by many public and private institutions as compatible with their other institutional priorities, but to some degree, sustainability is a goal added on top of more established organizational functions. Consequently, these institutions rarely perceive the implications of their actions for the larger ecosystem or effectively review the cumulative effects of actions across a region. Undesired environmental impacts may not be addressed by either public or private institutions, leaving these problems, such as the mitigation of impacts or restoration of impaired environmental resources, to be solved in the future.

Drivers of Change

Several forces influence present and future ecosystem conditions in the Sierra Nevada.

Human Settlement and Development Scales and Patterns

Expanding urban, exurban, commercial, and recreational development directly and indirectly affect ecosystem status and health and cause institutional change. Population growth and development bring more people into the region, increasing not only the demand for services but also the diversity of values and issues influencing the management of the range.

Absence of Market Capitalization of Resource Use and Environmental Risk

Outside of markets in selected natural resources, such as timber, that emerge as commodities, markets for ecosystem resources have been relatively undeveloped and have drawn capital investment in the natural systems from which they arise. Several factors have contributed to this situation. First, many attributes of the ecosystem are simply not valued in a manner that motivates investment. Second, restrictions on exchange prevent value formation for aspects of the ecosystem that generate economic benefit. Third, localities lack the capacity to capture economic surpluses they generate and to then invest these surpluses for ecosystem health and social well-being. Fourth, the creation of markets for values and benefits that heretofore had been allocated by right or administrative arrangement—water is the preeminent example—upsets many existing arrangements and creates the need for different types of institutions.

Governmental Coordination

Current institutional arrangements provide a weak basis for ecosystem management. Jurisdictions and ownerships do not conform to ecosystems, and overlapping jurisdictions do not deliver public programs efficiently. Appropriations to some major federal agencies have supported production of timber and other commodities, while supplying substantially smaller amounts for administration of nonconsumptive uses. Interagency and intergovernmental cooperation may overcome these structural problems, which in many arenas led to gridlock. Although intergovernmental coordination blurs lines of authority and blunts institutional prerogatives, this trade-off may be necessary to pursue ecological approaches to management and to maximize the effectiveness of agency expenditures.

Grassroots Activism and Sustained Participation in Regional Environmental Affairs

Individuals with extensive knowledge about the Sierra Nevada who reside within the region and elsewhere are important sources of knowledge and energy. Grassroots and local activism creates new avenues of influence that compete with current institutions for legitimacy and authority. Local activism and involvement provide:

- Information and perceptions about the environmental conditions of the Sierra

- Monitoring of resource-related activities on public and private land

- Oversight of the conduct by public officials and agencies

- Influence on the direction of management

These driving forces interact in different ways throughout the Sierra region, so much so that subregions within the Sierra are readily apparent and may form the basis for institutional interventions.

Approaches Taken by Government Agencies

Public institutions and agencies involved in conservation and resource management have neither anticipated nor responded well to change. As a result, legislative bodies and outside groups have employed legal and legislative means to attempt to move agencies—with mixed success. Changing agency direction does not ensure, however, that ecosystem sustainability will be achieved. Many public agencies and institutions were organized to manage individual resources or geographical areas or to promote natural resource development. Effective as they are for many purposes, existing agency structures may not be entirely compatible with the concept of ecosystem sustainability or with ecological approaches to management.

Recent initiatives of the U.S. Forest Service and other federal and state agencies to address ecosystem concerns suggest that several aspects of ecosystem management, including the conservation of biodiversity and the control of cumulative environmental impacts, create particular institutional difficulties. These newer missions run afoul of the functional approaches to conservation and management utilized by agencies.

First, current institutional arrangements do not deal with environmental systems or parts of systems very well. Agency missions focus on particular areas defined by political geography rather than by landscapes or whole systems. Alternatively, they are empowered to administer particular attributes, with lesser authority to control what happens in the rest of the ecosystem in which they are embedded. For instance, a county General Plan regulates land use along a stream, the state water board regulates the final disposition of water within the stream, and a federal commission regulates the utility that determines the flow regime that carries water to its final user.

Second, agency planning methods differ enormously and consequently vary greatly in their ability to express the public interest. County land-use plans rely on county boards and commissions, as well as contracted outreach to discover the public interest, while federal land management agencies rely heavily on internal technical expertise, with Congress as integrator of public opinion. Given the divergence in mecha-

nisms to discover the public interest in adjacent parcels of land that frequently differ not at all ecologically, it is not surprising that policies and project-level decisions seldom generate consensus.

Third, agencies and supporting arrangements do not capture surplus revenue or generate new capital. The role that lands play now in the Sierra Nevada often differs substantially from the role they played at the time the State Board of Forestry, U.S. Forest Service, and other critical institutions were created. As a result, the institutions may treat an area as if its principal role were the production of timber when in fact its major benefits are now watershed protection for power production and recreation. Without a means to tap all the benefits conveyed, agencies perpetuate a serious market imperfection and rely on budgets and other funding unrelated to ecosystem issues.

Fourth, as agencies fail to meet public expectations, the public questions their mission. This crisis of legitimacy and the loss of agency prerogatives render management even more difficult. Whereas in the private sector competitors would step in to meet the market's needs, the monopoly or oligarchy of resources agencies offers reform rather than substitution. And reform is frequently a slow and painful process, often requiring changes in law.

Fifth, government agencies continue to rely on relatively narrow technical expertise. Implementing effective ecosystem management, however, requires a broader range of expertise and information. Moreover, managing processes that elaborate the public interest requires management and political skills to complement technical expertise. Despite this need, county, state, and federal governments are only beginning to combine their expertise to address resource issues in a context that reflects the true political dimensions of the endeavor.

Finally, almost all public institutions simply avoid dealing with population growth and its effects on the resources, lands, and ecosystems for which they are responsible. Despite the profound influence that population growth, new human settlement, and development have had on ecosystems in the region, agencies lack authority or competence to respond effectively to these pressures.

If public agencies are to respond effectively to public wishes, scientific guidance, and legal imperatives for more ecologically sensitive approaches to resource management, then gaps in agency or institutional capacity must be addressed. The following examples illustrate how the problems just discussed impair the efforts of agencies to address current concerns.

Attacks on the U.S. Forest Service and Its Mission

Implementation of the National Forest Management Act (NFMA) of 1976 and other policies pertaining to natural resource management (e.g., Endangered Species Act) has been largely unsuccessful in overcoming polarization of opinion on natural resource policy. NFMA mandated extensive planning and monitoring to promote conservation of forest resources and to resolve forest management controversies. Demand for increased public timber supplies, however, conflicted with other demands for increased recreation and wilderness preservation. Thus, in the absence of a clear mandate for management of the national forests that reduced conflict, controversy and conflict have grown. The more recent shift to ecosystem management attempts to deal with a constantly growing set of legal demands arising from controversy.

The requirements and standards in these resource management policies provided much of the force impelling state and federal managers and regulators toward sustainability. Without them, agency managers would lose much of their support for many activities critical to ensuring ecosystem sustainability. Yet the stringent legal requirements are insufficient by themselves to ensure that agencies will be able to implement sustainable management practices. Statutory mandates do not solve problems, nor do they necessarily imply a method to resolve problems in an equitable or efficient manner. Despite successive planning efforts that may ensure better ecosystem conservation, the ability of the Forest Service to implement a plan for land management that complies with current mandates and provides for conservation of biological diversity, fuels management, and a range of other forest functions is still subject to question by many scientists, by resource professionals, and by the public.

Agency Expertise

Resolution of many environmental matters facing decision makers, however, requires consideration of social, economic, and demographic trends that are frequently beyond the authority or the capability of the Forest Service and other resource institutions. Public policies and legal requirements impel the Forest Service and other federal and state agencies and other resource institutions to rely on technical expertise to resolve resource conflicts and respond to opposition to public programs. Over the past two decades, agencies have more effectively utilized a broader spectrum of ecological expertise and incorporated new kinds of scientific information in their planning, but they have neglected to use the planning process to develop political constituencies. Agencies therefore increasingly appear either unresponsive to contemporary demands to consider and retain ecological integrity as a part of all management actions or incapable of accomplishing traditional agency objectives while also ensuring ecosystem protection.

Funding for the Forest Service

Implementing an ecosystem management strategy requires funding sufficient to support budgetary requirements of new programs for land and resource management. Existing budgets of the U.S. Forest Service, the Bureau of Land Management, and other resource management agencies must themselves be placed in perspective as the product of a venerable and implicit congressional compromise. Historically, agency appropriations have been designed to support production of timber and other commodities; substantially smaller amounts were supplied for administration of nonconsumptive uses, forest-level research, and monitoring. This arrangement was designed to support multiple use of forest resources, including production of timber and other commodities, while respecting the role of the national forests in conserving natural landscapes and ecosystems. The diminishing emphasis on revenue-producing functions has led to lower overall revenue from resource activity on federal lands. Reductions in appropriations and funding from Forest Service timber programs have significantly reduced staffing levels of resource professionals within the Forest Service and other agencies. Strengthened commitments by federal natural resource agencies to improve scientific assessments of the condition of public lands and natural resources require added funds for research and monitoring and greater deployment of experts in the field. Activities associated with ecosystem restoration, including fuels management, require funding for activities that do not result in direct returns to the U.S. Treasury.

Increased funding sufficient to support these activities cannot be assured. As a result of shifting legislative priorities and deficit reduction, budget proposals supporting ecosystem management items are exceptionally vulnerable to attack and attrition during legislative debates. For this reason, approval for a fund supporting ecosystem management priorities such as monitoring, research, and adaptive management may be difficult to secure. Budget requests must compete against other deserving programs and projects.

County General Plans

County General Plans and associated environmental impact reports integrate information critical to the conservation of ecosystems and the management of natural resources. Studies within General Plans assessing the rate of conversion of undeveloped land to urban and suburban development are an important source of information about areas of potential future impacts. Similarly, open-space elements contained within plans have an enormous potential to foster conservation of important areas and resources. With respect to the future of undeveloped areas, General Plans frequently appear to be ratifiers of change rather than strategic plans for the conservation of biological diversity. In particular, General Plan projections for future buildout and the environmental impacts associated with buildout often fail to account for the effect of already approved subdivision of larger parcels and of shortfalls in infrastructure investment under current fiscal arrangements. The environmental impacts of future development are therefore likely to be significantly greater than estimated in the environmental impact report (EIR) of General Plans under CEQA. Moreover, mitigation measures to address identified impacts are often not developed due to so-called overriding considerations. Many of today's most difficult and intractable environmental and fiscal problems associated with development reflect decisions made two to three decades ago, and today's policy choices will constrain future decision makers' options two to three decades hence. Existing coordination among open space, infrastructure, and land-use planning agencies seems very limited, and many policy actions by these agencies appear to be in direct conflict with one another.

Existing Market Mechanisms

Only a few of the resources generated in the Sierra—timber and land, in particular—pass through a market and are therefore controlled by institutional arrangements that may provide opportunities for reinvestment without government intervention. Even these resources, however, have complex webs of government authority regulating the market. For example, numerous authorities impinge on the land market in the Sierra. Reinvestment in this case means the mitigation of land development effects such that the range of values inherent in undeveloped land is at least maintained, if not enhanced. Such mitigation is governed almost entirely by nonmarket mechanisms involving compliance with the California Environmental Quality Act (CEQA) and the various development permit requirements of state and local government.

The market plays little or no role with respect to the other resources of the Sierra, including water. The value generated by the water that flows down the Sierra exceeds that of nearly all other resources, with the possible exception of recreation (including gambling). Reinvestment in the aquatic ecosystems of the Sierra is conspicuous in its absence. In only a few cases (the Feather River, Lake Tahoe, and to a lesser degree, the Mokelumne River) have the institutions involved generated reinvestment of time, energy, and resources in the maintenance or restoration of aquatic ecosystems. In other examples, reinvestment in wildlife, wildlife habitat, or native plants comes from hunting and fishing permits, from special government funds earmarked for game species, and, on national forest lands, from timber harvest receipts.

NEW FORCES FOR CHANGE

The traditional (progressive and technocratic) models for public administration have not responded adequately to the range of ecological, social, political, and economic aspects of resource management. The primary reason for this failure to respond seems to be the dominance of centralized policy and administration. Individuals and public and private interests are frustrated by these failures and have developed pragmatic solutions to centralized institutional failures. Observation of incipient efforts indicates a move away from centralized administration of policy and its implementation, with a cautious nod to local and regional collaborative strategies. The following section briefly discusses several examples, illustrating both the promise of these approaches and the problems facing resource management and conservation agencies.

Attempts at Interagency Collaboration

Fire Protection

Interagency collaboration for fire fighting in California and other western states has grown steadily since the early 1970s, when severe fires in southern California led the California Department of Forestry and Fire Protection (CDF), the U.S. Forest Service, and other fire control agencies to discuss formal cooperation. The aim was to more effectively marshal forces to fight severe wildfires, thereby reducing losses to private property owners and to the public. Project Firescope brought together agencies with fire protection responsibilities in southern California and included fire research, development, and application funded by the Forest Service. It required collaboration among cities, counties, the state, and federal agencies.

The project vastly improved the coordinated response of multiple agencies to wildfires. Several mutual aid agreements were concluded to further the idea of interagency cooperation. Agencies now automatically respond to wildfires as parts of a larger integrated force. Exchange of personnel and equipment from one agency to another, for example, is standard procedure, as is reimbursement from one agency to another for service and assistance rendered. As a result, there is now a relatively well coordinated multiagency fire protection system to control severe wildfires. This model has spread worldwide as an effective way to integrate emergency response.

The agencies could undertake cooperation of this kind for implementation of ecologically sensitive resource management as well, but they have not. Interagency initiatives to promote fuels management, for example, have been extremely limited. Where cooperation has occurred, it has tended to focus on assistance to private landowners. Scant federal-state collaboration has occurred regarding either federal or state land. Interagency fire protection appears to be a special case. As a result of a nearly universal perception that fighting fire had paramount importance, institutions were able to make enormous innovations quickly and to collobarate successfully. The example set by fire-fighting agencies demonstrates, however, that a cooperative approach can be successful.

Protecting Forest Values on Private Lands

Driven largely by interagency controversy, California state agencies have developed a reasonably effective approach for ensuring sustained management of privately held forests. Although the authority to regulate various environmental goods produced on forest lands is distributed among several state and federal agencies, these agencies have attempted over the years to coordinate their enforcement programs through the state's administration of the California Forest Practices Program.

Forest practices on private and state lands in the Sierra and throughout California are administered under the California Forest Practices Act of 1973. Under this law, the California State Board of Forestry adopted rules and regulations that implement the intent of the act and other state and federal laws. To gain the approval of the California Department of Forestry and Fire Protection (CDF), landowners are required to submit a timber harvesting plan specifying the harvesting and reforestation activities they expect to pursue. Provisions to protect soil and land productivity, water quality, wildlife habitat, endangered species, historical and archaeological sites, and aesthetics are included in the harvesting plan.

The timber harvest planning review process was originally deemed to be independent of the California Environmental Quality Act. However as a result of a 1970s lawsuit, the review process was brought under the state's far-reaching environmental quality program. Subsequent executive, legislative, and administrative action made the review process a "certified program." As such, the fundamental principles and requirements of state environmental law are administered through the CDF-led program. Foremost are the requirements that the potential environmental impacts of timber management be disclosed and that all feasible mitigations be applied to reduce or avoid significant adverse effects. Where adverse effects cannot be avoided, a statement of overriding concerns must be provided.

When critical wildlife, plant, or habitat resources are thought to occur on a timber management site, consultation is required between the individual or entity submitting the plans and the California Department of Fish and Game (CDFG). In the case of federally listed species, the U.S. Fish and Wildlife Service also can become involved in plan review. Required consultation consists of a review by a CDFG biologist of species locations and potential project hazards. The biologist can consult with species experts and the project proponent to develop project mitigations and alternatives. The CDFG must then issue findings and permits as necessary to protect a species or habitat area. No project can be approved that would jeopardize a species.

Water quality protection also is handled through the timber planning review process. Negotiations between the Board of Forestry and the State Water Resources Control Board began in 1977 to identify nonpoint pollution sources related to silviculture on private forest lands and to determine whether the Board of Forestry's forest practice rules met the standards of protection required under federal and state water quality laws. After years of negotiation, the Board rules are provisionally certified as being in compliance with the federal Clean Water Act.

Environmental and landowner groups, and the general public, regularly express concern about the effectiveness of the private forest regulatory program. In a review of the application of best management practices, adequacy of protec-

tion could not be fully evaluated because practices were not applied in many cases. Nevertheless, the state has managed to construct a coordinated approach for addressing sustainable management of its private forests in a way that helps to minimize administrative and compliance costs and to reinforce the view that forest lands produce important environmental and social values beyond timber.

Other Examples

Concern over the viability of the California spotted owl led to an unprecedented cooperative effort involving state and federal agencies in research aimed at the development of a strategy to protect the owl and its habitat. Cooperation collapsed, however, when the U.S. Forest Service, in response to legal mandates, independently implemented new policy for national forest lands. This incident demonstrates both the opportunities and the limitations inherent in interagency cooperation as it exists under current legal and administrative arrangements.

Seeking to facilitate intergovernmental multiagency planning and cooperative management to conserve biological diversity, the state of California, federal agencies, and others signed California's Memorandum of Understanding on Biological Diversity. Led by the state Resources Agency, the federal Bureau of Land Management, and the U.S. Forest Service, an array of local, state, and federal organizations and agencies has agreed to cooperate to ensure better conservation of the state's various biological resources and habitats. Many citizens, resource professionals, local groups, and others involved in natural resource issues contend that existing agency structures are incapable of or, at best, inefficient in promoting and implementing ecologically sound resource management agendas. The agreement sought to rectify this deficiency by overcoming stumbling blocks of jurisdictional differences and bureaucratic inertia. The California Biodiversity Council, formed as a result of the agreement, is facilitating the sharing of information among public organizations and other partners to develop more effective approaches to conservation.

Agencies, through actions like those just described, are beginning to deal with complete environmental systems. Recent management efforts on the national forests and in other parts of the Sierra attempt to incorporate deeper understanding of the role played by ecological disturbance in maintaining and sustaining the Sierra landscape. Within agencies, at least, managers are drawing on broader sets of scientific and technical expertise. Agencies also recognize that cooperation with one another is essential, although legal mandates make it difficult for agencies to truly share responsibility and management authority.

Market Solutions and Capital Reinvestment

Insufficient funding limits many conservation objectives, even though the Sierra generates great wealth. Another perspective suggests that there is insufficient agency capacity to capture the economic value that does exist for purposes of promoting reinvestment in Sierra Nevada ecosystems and their resources. The absence of mechanisms to tap economic values for reinvestment causes underinvestment and even disinvestment in ecosystems, and it distorts the priorities of the investments that do occur. The search for other methods to finance environmental improvements has led to an effort to recover from the beneficiaries the costs of maintaining the benefits provided by the environment.

Reinvestment in the resources and ecosystems of the Sierra Nevada depends on the creation or modification of the institutional framework. Institutions in certain subregions are already being altered to permit and encourage greater reinvestment in environmental resources. In the Lake Tahoe Basin, for example, the loop between overall environmental quality and those who benefit is nearly closed. Public and private priorities have channeled hundreds of millions of dollars and years of human effort into reinvestment in the restoration of the basin's environment. In the Feather River basin a Coordinated Resource Management program joins together a water supply to the State Water Project, an abundant forest and timber resource, relatively slow population growth, and resource-dependent communities. Closing the loop in that environment implies institutional arrangements quite different from those in the Sierra foothills around Sacramento, where a very different mixture— amenity values, fire control, high population growth, and economic diversification—define the environment.

Reinvestment in these systems faces several obstacles. The first of these is the simple inability to value certain resources or ecosystem attributes. It is difficult, for example, to obtain agreement on the value of an intact ecosystem in the Sierra Nevada. A second difficulty arises due to restrictions on exchange and markets, even where it is possible to place a value on resource attributes. An illustration may be seen in the opposition to suggestions that campground and other recreational fees be increased to better reflect the cost of providing those services. A third obstacle is the absence of effective cooperative responses to environmental and resource-related problems. Even where the diagnosis of environmental impacts is clear and methods to address environmental impacts are known, legal, institutional, and financial barriers may thwart the implementation of effective coordinated responses. A final, related problem is the inability to ensure that capture of the value accruing from a variety of natural resources and ecosystems will lead to reinvestment in the areas where these ecosystems and resources are located. The surplus value in resources such as water and hydroelectric power chiefly accrue to downstream users who are out of the area of origin. Mechanisms for reinvestment in the watersheds that support these areas are emerging, but their full potential has yet to be explored.

Local Community Involvement

Citizens and local interests in the Sierra Nevada have a central role to play in the formation, adaptation, and implementation of natural resource conservation measures. Resource agencies, no matter how professional, are not equipped to address local ecological and socioeconomic concerns, even where a landscape is wholly under the jurisdiction of one agency. In light of the local variability in landscapes and economies, designing an approach to implementing environmental policies can benefit from the input of those with local knowledge. Local and regional "place-based groups" and others are organizing in the Sierra to address these issues at the regional and subregional levels. Perhaps as never before, landholders, agencies, and other players are coming together to plan the implementation of environmental policy and to discuss its implications at the local level.

Local and regional groups, both those with established roles and unofficial groups, have rapidly proliferated, and recently they have begun to figure prominently in discussions about resource policy. Some of the better known and more diverse examples include the Applegate Partnership in Oregon, the Klamath Bioregional Group, and in the Sierra, the Feather River CRM and the Quincy Library Group. The impetus for the formation of many watershed or ecosystem planning efforts has been the failure of more traditional agency planning or regulation to achieve intended goals. Consequently, agency personnel often regard these groups as adversaries or competitors of public agencies, but a local place-based approach can speed implementation of ecosystem policies by addressing whole environmental and regional economic issues and by suggesting imaginative methods to reallocate existing capital to pragmatic solutions. Observation of incipient watershed and ecosystem planning groups in California and elsewhere suggests that industrial concerns and other commodity interests, environmental groups, and rural communities all participate in these efforts.

Local groups, although often able to draw on considerable talent and expertise, will not displace agencies, nor will they succeed in developing workable resource management or conservation programs in every case. Several factors bear on the enormous potential in this approach for innovative program development and problem solving. First, because they do not possess the formality of public agencies, these groups bring fresh approaches to contemporary problems. Generally, however, a local group cannot replace the depth of knowledge, expertise, and research capabilities of public agencies. Additionally, local groups may not entirely reflect local perspectives, nor does the creation of a place-based group ensure protection of the nation's broader interest in public lands and ecosystem integrity. Increasingly, however, this type of community involvement appears as a complement to centralized agency planning and to project-level decision making.

Law as a Force for Bargaining and Innovation

Existing legal arrangements contribute significantly to progress toward sustainability. Although the SNEP assessment illuminates certain difficulties with existing laws and public programs and their administration, the existence of large legal "hammers" imposed by state or federal authorities, designed to ensure representation for the interests of nonlocal parties, compels some parties to come to the table. These laws also specify the power and authority of all public and private/individual and corporate players in any collaborative relationship. Nevertheless, these two elements—the relationship of agency mandates to resource or environmental issues, and the relationship of the agency to the public—largely determine the context for policy implementation and establish the structure for environmental planning and management. The SNEP assessment has not systematically addressed the functional relationship between those variables and the success of "collaborative planning"; thus it is premature to make strong claims about what kind of local or regional coordination will work. Surely there is no value in emphasizing a particular new institutional form just because it is different from the poorly functioning system we currently have in place. There is no assurance that the alternative will be any better.

STRATEGIES

Sierran institutions do not yet invest the money and effort that are needed to sustain the health and productivity of the ecosystem against the tremendous withdrawals of the benefits it affords. It is increasingly important to attain institutions that overcome pervasive tendencies to separate the beneficiaries, owners, and stewards of ecosystems; to fragment ecosystems among often-competitive authorities and interests; and to resist adaptation to intensified pressures on ecosystem capacities.

Goals

The SNEP assessment suggests five goals for institutional reform to sustain and restore the ecosystems of the Sierra Nevada. Develop institutions that:

1. Return resources from beneficiaries of the Sierra to those who will improve the ecosystem qualities from which benefits flow.

2. Strengthen cooperation among federal, state, and local governments and agencies whose authorities and resources converge, overlap, or interact in the ecosystem, and strengthen cooperation between the public and private sectors.

3. Increase community involvement in the protection and management of Sierran ecosystems.

4. Provide legal, regulatory, and financial support to advance such reforms beyond current levels of ad hoc spontaneity.

5. Take advantage of characteristic aspects of Sierra Nevada regions to leverage progress on issues of regional and rangewide scale.

Examples in the Sierra suggest how these goals can be achieved for some problems and how these examples of success might be extended to other problems. They also show how different regional conditions within the Sierra may affect the appropriate combinations of strategic possibilities in different places.

Potential Solutions

Goal 1. Investing Shares of Ecosystem Benefits in Sustained Ecosystem Health and Productivity

Institutionalized strategies of timber-based reinvestment such as yield taxes or "K-V" funds have not been extended to other values the Sierra provides in abundance.

Despite the vast financial basis of the migration of settlers and recreationists to the Sierra, there are virtually no institutions through which the values thus generated can be captured and invested in sustaining the very qualities that attract people to settle, stay, and play. Possibilities for changing these situations include fair-market recreation fees, and subdivision and land transfer taxes, that flow into funds and banks designed specifically for ecosystem reinvestments. Other examples of strategies are described in chapter 8—requiring that water users outside the Sierra pay taxes to support management in source areas—and in chapter 4—recovering funds during fuel reduction treatments.

Goal 2. Developing Multijurisdictional Coordination

Over five decades, the federal, state, and local governments of California have developed a remarkable system of coordination for fire protection throughout the Sierra and elsewhere in the state. Such coordination seems necessary, appropriate, and attainable for other aspects of the Sierra ecosystem. For example, riparian systems and aquatic regimes cross federal, state, and local jurisdictions throughout the Sierra, to the extent that no one jurisdiction alone can undertake the actions necessary to sustain or restore the quality of these deteriorated systems. Multijurisdictional coordination, such as cooperative riparian zones or watershed agreements and councils, is essential if maintenance and restoration of the Sierra's depleted riparian and aquatic systems are to be achieved. These are described more in chapter 8. The Tahoe case demonstrates what is possible when circumstances are particularly ready and able to support the necessary cooperation.

Other candidates for multijurisdictional coordination include wildlife habitat regimes and timbersheds. Species complexes are difficult to preserve, for example, if efforts to do so occur on but one side of a jurisdictional fence crossing a habitat system. Sierra timber stocking and age structures are also difficult to sustain when shifts in relative federal or state harvest restrictiveness transfer price pressures for harvest between private and public lands. California's Biodiversity Council has made an important initial stride toward the kinds of complementary endeavors that are needed.

Goal 3. Involving Communities in Ecosystem Stewardship

In recent years, community efforts in the northern and southern Sierra have demonstrated the great knowledge, capacity, and care that residents are prepared to bring to the large problems of ecosystem management. Whether or not the specifics can be generalized, the basic lesson has general value: residents of the Sierra will bring unique resources to the enhancement of ecosystem health and productivity if allowed the opportunity to do so. Resident communities can serve broad public purposes if recognized as having special interests and capacities. The lesson seems to have particular possibilities in problems of riparian restoration and watershed, habitat protection, and recreation development. Community task forces that have been successful in initiating local restoration, monitoring projects, and doing environmental education may serve as models for communities elsewhere.

Goal 4. Making Legal, Regulatory, and Financial Reforms

The small number of specific examples of success indicate the institutional resistance to more general applications of their principles. Specialized and spontaneous endeavors take immense energy and commitment within a framework of institutions that does not facilitate them. Legal, regulatory, and financial reforms will be necessary if the fundamental problems of underinvestment in ecosystem viability, weak coordination among jurisdictions, and isolation of resident communities from ecosystem management are to be overcome on more than an ad hoc basis.

Goal 5. Developing Regional Strategies

Although the solutions mentioned apply Sierra-wide, priority combinations are likely to vary by region because of diverse circumstances. The assessments demonstrated the importance of, for example, differences among regions in population density, ecosystem potential, economic base, wealth and its distribution, and jurisdictional mixes as well as physical and ecological aspects. Such factors create differences that affect regions' particular needs and capacities to encourage reinvestment, coordination, and community involvement. The following sections are illustrative.

Feather River Basin: Develop Cooperative Water and Timber Regimes. The economy of the lightly populated Feather River basin depends upon the export of timber and water. Institutional possibilities in this region seem to be of two primary kinds. One would focus on transferring shares of downstream water benefits to upstream watershed maintenance. It might require a mechanism that brings the State Water Project and its water contractors, Pacific Gas and Electric Company and its customers, the timber industry, and the U.S. Forest Service into an arrangement whose aim is to ensure finance and cooperation to sustain the timber-and-water system of resource management and the natural functions that underpin this system.

The second possibility would focus on integrating local communities in multijurisdictional management of the region's timberlands. The Quincy Library Group has demonstrated the value of local voices, talents, and resources in guiding national forest management. Broader possibilities arise when attention turns to the problem of sustaining the regional timber economy as a whole. Contemporary versions of "cooperative sustained yield units," for example, "cooperative ecosystem management units," may offer a useful direction, with the state playing a more central role than in the earlier versions of such public-private-local partnerships.

Tahoe Basin: Diversify Purposes of Jurisdictional Integration. In the Tahoe Basin to the south and east, the relationship between the stakeholders and the land is explicit. There is no place in the Sierra where beneficiaries pay a greater share of the upkeep, enhancement, and restoration of the natural system. Jurisdictions, finances, policies, and programs have been integrated through a number of public agencies, including the University of California, the Tahoe Regional Planning Agency (TRPA), the state Water Resources Control Board, the U.S. Forest Service, the California Tahoe Conservancy, the Nevada State Lands Division, and, significantly, local government. The presence and clarity of Lake Tahoe, the access provided by two major highways, and the historic pattern of public and private land have fostered a developed recreational economy, with regional and national stakeholders who recognize the importance of environmental quality to business in the basin. The unique definition of the mission, the depth of institutional capability, and the wealth of the stakeholders have goaded institutional innovation across many levels of government, leading to considerable investment in ecological restoration and, increasingly, in management of surrounding wildland ecosystems. There is real potential in exploring the Tahoe case to identify possibilities that may work in situations that are less well endowed or that, like the Highway 80 and 50 corridors, are evolving into conditions such as prevailed in Tahoe when the TRPA first was conceived.

Gold Country: Strengthen Local Governments. To the north and east of Sacramento, the Gold Country region and its communities have been dramatically transformed from a resource-

❄ *The Feather River Coordinated Resource Management (CRM) Group*

Fierce polarization around natural resource use and management, a growing recognition that continued battles would only further local anguish and lead to continued loss of local control, and recognition of the need to develop local economic opportunities through local watershed restoration projects all led to the development of the Feather River Coordinated Resource Management (CRM) Group. Begun in 1985, the Feather River CRM Group, which encourages local initiative and participation in resource management on public and private land in the headwaters of the State Water Project, is the longest running CRM group and one of the most successful in the state of California.

The birth of the Feather River CRM took place in 1985 when, following local initiative, twelve federal, state, regional, and local entities signed a Memorandum of Understanding (MOU) with the objectives of optimizing beneficial uses of water; emphasizing education and prevention over regulation; and resolving participants'

concerns through proactive involvement in a consensus-based planning process. After several erosion control project successes, the groups cooperating under the MOU decided to become an official Coordinated Resource Management Planning (CRMP) Group. As Mike Kossow, one of original organizers of the group, stated, "We were a CRMP but just didn't know it yet." The decision to become a CRMP group was in part to foster better coordination among resource management agencies and in part to gain increased access to federal programs and grants for work on public and private land. Although CRMP formation led to a new institutional structure for the group, members did not hesitate to modify this structure to meet their specific needs and values. The commitment of the group to maintaining a results-focused process and an emphasis on projects and not just planning, led the group to drop the *P* (for planning) in the CRMP name and call itself the Feather River CRM. The remediation of

Restoration in Hoskins Creek, Plumas County. (Photo courtesy of Plumas Corporation.)

cumulative watershed damage remained a primary objective of the group.

The Feather River CRM has achieved considerable success by developing a process that reflects the particular ecological, institutional, and social contexts of the CRM area and links a range of ecological, institutional, and social goals. The coordinator of the CRM, Leah Wills, is personally and professionally committed to a vision of economic and ecological sustainability, a vision that has been embraced by most if not all CRM members. This joining together around common goals has reduced tensions and increased cooperation both between public agencies and landowners and between agencies themselves. The process has also stimulated personnel at different agencies to undertake cooperative projects. One observer of the Feather River CRM noted that the group represents an important evolutionary phase of bringing communities together around sustainable development, and in a way that is not theoretical but concrete and grounded. In roughly ten years of operation, the Feather River CRM has initiated thirty-eight watershed restoration projects on 4,100 acres, rehabilitated 14.5 stream miles, and contributed $4 million dollars to the local economy, mostly through creation of local jobs.

The ability of a wide range of individuals representing varied (and often historically conflicting) institutions to come together around a common goal has been deemed the most important success of the CRM. A fundamental quality of the Feather River CRM process has been that members have been able to subjugate their individual differences to the larger mutual goal of a healthy community in a healthy watershed. By demonstrating the real benefits of cooperation, the CRM has created a local atmosphere of increased trust that catalyzes additional community-building activities and allows other consensus-based groups, such as the Quincy Library Group, to grow and flourish.

dependent to a development-driven economy by the enormous influx of new residents. The qualities of the landscape now form a principal component of property values and social motivation. Local activism mobilizes intense energies around issues of private land development (county oak ordinances, General Plans), public land use (timber versus recreation versus wildlife habitat), and the management of the rivers (flood control versus power production, and water supply versus recreation). Fire is a growing concern, both as a threat and as a scarce or distorted ecological process. Councils of government and economic diversification are rapidly supplanting Coordinated Resource Management Plans (CRMPs) among landowners, which continue to be important in the Feather and other water-focused regions, as the principal means by which governments interact with economic activity and other private behavior.

Closing the loop between residents and beneficiaries in this region means building tighter connections, at many scales and between many groups and jurisdictions, in a context where traditional community identities are diminishing and common visions of the land and its future are eroding. This seems most likely to occur through a strategy of strengthening local governments and their relations with private capital.

Mother Lode: Strengthen Local-State-Federal Cooperation. South of the Gold Country, the Mother Lode displays demographic and economic characteristics akin to those of the "new gold rush" counties in 1970. Particular areas retain their industrial, timber, or water emphasis, for example, the Mokelumne and Tuolumne river basins and ranching and mining in the foothills. Continuing urbanization along the Highway 99 corridor will create metropolitan areas similar to Sacramento and Fresno, and highway improvements will translate urban growth in the valley into suburban or exurban development in the foothills. Consequently, while closing the loop in this region will certainly involve local governments, with their control over land use, it must also involve state agencies, with control over water and private forest land, and federal agencies, with control over public land and irrigation development. Perhaps most critical among these governmental partners are state and local agencies that control development in the adjacent valleys and those that review and approve transportation improvements for the region.

San Joaquin: Modify and Tax External Influences to Protect and Restore. Farther south, another part of the western slope of the Sierra extends from Madera County south to the Tehachapis. These counties, unlike counties farther north, have economic and political centers located in the agriculture of the San Joaquin valley and in agencies and representatives in Washington, D.C. This region contains three national parks, many wilderness areas, and other recreational sites. On the basis of land allocation alone, recreational use of the land appears paramount. Budget and management decisions are subject to congressional discretion. The important flows are imports into the Sierra from the Central Valley: that is, recreation-seekers and air pollution. Ozone and other pollutants generated by activities in the Central Valley threaten forest integrity and lessen the recreational value of the region. Closing the loop in this region means changes in the movements and activities of people so as to reduce or respond effectively to undesired ecological impacts in the southern Sierra.

East Side: Create Development Nodes and Capture Their Value for Ecosystem Investments. Finally, the eastern side of the Sierra Nevada is in transition to being primarily an amenity-

❄ Coalition for Unified Recreation in the Eastern Sierra (CURES)

Created in 1992, the Coalition for Unified Recreation in the Eastern Sierra is an informal partnership of recreation providers, chambers of commerce, local businesses, the environmental community, and federal, state, and local governments. As its mission, "CURES is dedicated to preserving the Eastern Sierra's natural, cultural, and economic resources and enriching the experiences of visitors and residents."

Members of CURES spent one year working on a description of a collective vision for the future state of recreation in the eastern Sierra, taking into consideration divergent viewpoints involved in the coalition. The vision statement is used as a tool for prioritizing and strategizing the projects that CURES undertakes.

Since defining a future vision, CURES task groups have developed the following projects:

- Annual compilation of interpretive activities and special events and activities available for visitors at all the visitor contact points in the eastern Sierra.

- Production of a regional recreation opportunities map/ brochure that is translated into Spanish, French, and German.

- Tourism enhancement projects such as "Good Host" seminars for business owners, a computer link to the Yosemite Area Transportation Information system, and market research.

- Development of a 200-mile scenic byway on Highway 395, considered one of the crown jewels of California. The byway will feature twenty-eight interpretive stops and visitor information kiosks. Information will be provided on recreation opportunities and the services that are provided in twelve different communities. The geologic, ecological, and cultural resources of the area—including Mono Lake, Bodie State Historic Park, the Ancient Bristlecone Pine Forest, and Mount Whitney—will be interpreted.

Through their collaborative efforts, CURES members are leveraging dollars, avoiding duplication of effort, and providing high-quality recreation to visitors and residents of the area. In line with achieving their vision, their efforts are working toward a regionally sustainable economy that is linked to the sustainability of the natural environment of the eastern Sierra.

Nancy Upham, Public Affairs, U.S. Forest Service, Bishop
Andrea Lawrence, Supervisor, Mono County, Mammoth Lakes
Ralph McMullen, Director, Mammoth Lakes Visitors Bureau

dependent economy. While export of water and power has long been a key activity, both dispersed and developed recreation are major industries. The region, containing both wilderness areas and Mammoth and June Mountain ski resorts, straddles the setting of the dispersed recreation of the southwestern slope of the Sierra and that of the developed recreation of the Tahoe Basin. Investment in transportation and urban cultural amenities may determine both the development trajectory of the region and the nature of the institutional mechanisms that arise to bind the southern California recreational users to the management of the region's predominantly public land. In contrast, the loop between urban water users, not just in Los Angeles but also in western Nevada, and riparian and lake-based beneficial uses within the region has been established over time as a result of legal action and judicial decisions. There may well be no surplus or slack left in water supply in this area. Unless the loop can be expanded to include alternative suppliers of water, legal action may remain the primary recourse for balancing water supply and obligations to protect the public trust. In the recreation-based eastern Sierra, recreation user fees may become an especially effective way to close the loop.

Implications

Institutional reforms need to draw their direction from local circumstances and the perceptions of external threats and opportunities. Thus, different places contain different possible responses to the disparities they face between the ecosystem benefits they provide and the shares of benefits they receive to sustain them. Our regional illustrations are intended more to provoke innovation than to prescribe particular approaches.

But it is also true that innovations can be easy or hard, successful or not, depending upon whether the institutional context in which they are tried is sympathetic or resistant. Various of these contextual issues are Sierra-wide: institutional conditions that make quite difficult the formation of links between benefits and ecosystem sources; among different governmental jurisdictions, agencies, and private sector groups; and between those who control Sierran ecosystems and those who live in them. The regional illustrations indicate the diversity of institutional opportunities. The Sierra-wide picture argues as well for sharp attention to the general difficulties confronting investment, cooperation, and community involvement for the sustainability and restoration of Sierran ecosystems.

CHAPTER 4

Fire and Fuels

Ecological Functions of Fire   Fire is a natural evolutionary force that has influenced Sierran ecosystems for millennia, influencing biodiversity, plant reproduction, vegetation development, insect outbreak and disease cycles, wildlife habitat relationships, soil functions and nutrient cycling, gene flow, selection, and, ultimately, sustainability.

Effects of Climate   Climatic variation plays an important role in influencing fire patterns and severity; fires have been most extensive in periods of dry years.

Presettlement Fire Regimes   In most lower-elevation oak woodland and conifer forest types of the Sierra Nevada, presettlement fires were frequent, collectively covered large areas, burned for months at a time, and, although primarily low to moderate in intensity, exhibited complex patterns of severity.

Effects of Suppression   Fire suppression in concert with changing land-use practices has dramatically changed the fire regimes of the Sierra Nevada and thereby altered ecological structures and functions in Sierran plant communities.

Fuel Conditions   Live and dead fuels in today's conifer forests are more abundant and continuous than in the past.

Effects of Logging   Timber harvest, through its effects on forest structure, local microclimate, and fuel accumulation, has increased fire severity more than any other recent human activity.

Fire Size Trends   The commonly expected consequence of decades of fire suppression—that large, infrequent fires are becoming larger and small, frequent fires smaller—is generally not confirmed by records for twentieth-century Sierran forests.

Fire Surrogates   Although silvicultural treatments can mimic the effects of fire on structural patterns of woody vegetation, virtually no data exist on the ability to mimic ecological functions of natural fire.

Urban-Wildlands Intermix   Projected trends in urban settlement— homes intermixed with flammable wildlands—place an increasing number of homes and people at high risk of loss from wildfire unless hazards are mitigated.

ASSESSMENT

Fire represents both one of the greatest threats and one of the strongest allies in efforts to protect and sustain human and natural resources in the Sierra Nevada. Residents and visitors alike are well aware of the threats posed by summer wildfires. A growing density of homes and other structures coupled with the increased amount and continuity of fuels resulting from twentieth-century fire suppression have heightened concern about threats to life and property, as well as the health and long-term sustainability of forests, watersheds, and other natural resources. Yet fire has been an integral part of the Sierra Nevada for millennia, influencing the characteristics of ecosystems and landscapes. Today, state, federal, and local agencies put enormous resources into efforts to reduce fire occurrence while at the same time advocating the need to use fire to promote healthy ecosystems. The challenge we face is how to restore some aspects of a more natural fire regime while at the same time minimizing the threat wildfire poses to human and natural resources and values.

The Nature and Ecological Role of Presettlement Fire

> *The most potent factor in shaping the forest of the region has been, and still is, fire.*
> —John Leiberg, 1902

Fire has long been a natural component of Sierra Nevada ecosystems. For thousands of years preceding Euro-American settlement, fires burned frequently—typically multiple times each century—in most Sierran vegetation types. The hot, dry summer mediterranean climate provided suitable weather conditions and dry fuels for burning. Lightning provided a ready ignition source, supplemented by Native Americans, who used fire for a variety of purposes. Fires could spread until weather conditions or fuels, or both, were no longer suitable.

Fire-scar records in tree rings have shown variable fire-return intervals in presettlement times. Median values are consistently less than twenty (and as low as four) years for the foothill, ponderosa pine, and mixed conifer zones of the Sierra Nevada (table 4.1). Only one study—in high-elevation red fir—found a median fire-return interval greater than thirty years. Using total area and our best understanding of the range of fire-return intervals for each of the major vegetation types, and a simplified assumption that, for each type, total area divided by fire-return interval equals area burned annually, we see that it was not uncommon for hundreds of thousands of acres to be burned in the Sierra Nevada in a given

❋ Fire—Alternative Views

All SNEP scientists agree that fire has played a significant if not dominant role in shaping the vegetation pattern; the departure of views begins with the relative certainty of fire frequency and spatial intensity in presettlement times. There is too little compelling evidence and incomplete rangewide research to conclude a precise pattern of fire frequency or severity in presettlement times. There were very probably areas that burned frequently (less than ten-year intervals), but some areas within the same vegetation type probably escaped burning for much longer periods and built up sufficient fuel loads to burn with high intensity if ignition occurred under favorable burning conditions. This point of difference in views centers on the belief that there were probably many variations in the return frequencies and fire intensity patterns that contributed to the mosaic of vegetation patterns on the landscape today.

A second major point of difference relates to the relative "openness" of forests before the disturbances caused by settlers. The alternative view concludes, from the same evidence, that forest conditions were not largely "open or parklike," in the words of John Muir; rather, there was a mix of dark, dense, or thick forests in unknown comparative quantities. Select early accounts support an open, parklike forest, but there were many similar accounts that describe forest conditions as dark or dense or thick. J. Goldsborough Bruff, a forty-niner who traveled the western slopes of the Feather River drainage between 1849 and 1851, kept a detailed diary. He clearly distinguished between open and dense forest conditions and recorded the dense condition six times more often than the open. Many other accounts of early explorers (e.g., John C. Frémont, Peter Decker, William Brewer) identify dark or impenetrable forest; the presettlement forest was far from a continuum of open, parklike stands. From these records it seems clear that Sierran forests were a mix of different degrees of openness and an unknown proportion in dark, dense, nearly impenetrable vegetative cover with variations from north to south and foothill to crest.

A third point of departure has to do with the frequency of stand-terminating fires in presettlement times. One group concludes that such events were rare or uncommon. The alternative view is that stand-threatening fires were probably more frequent. They were heavily dependent upon combinations of prolonged drought, an accumulation of dead material resulting from natural causes (e.g., insect mortality, windthrow, snow breakage), and severe fire weather conditions of low humidity and dry east winds coupled with multiple ignitions, possibly from lightning associated with rainless thunderstorms. Such fires were noted during the last half of the nineteenth century by newspaper accounts, official reports (John Leiberg, U.S. Geological Survey, 1902), and diaries; most were apparently caused by settlers, stockmen, or miners. Fuel loads were obviously sufficient at that time, thus strongly suggesting that similar conditions existed in earlier times with unknown frequencies.

year. Yet fire frequency, intensity, and severity varied through time and across the landscape in response to variations in climate, number of lightning ignitions, topography, vegetation, and human cultural practices.

TABLE 4.1

Historic fire-return intervals compared with twentieth-century patterns. Historical data are extracted from various sources (volume II, chapter 38) and are the average median return intervals for each forest type. Recent fire data are fire rotations based on area burned during the twentieth century. (From volume II, chapter 41.)

Forest Type	Fire-Return Period (Years)	
	Twentieth Century	Pre-1900
Red fir	1,644	26
Mixed confier–fir	644	12
Mixed conifer–pine	185	15
Ponderosa pine	192	11
Blue oak	78	8

Presettlement fire strongly influenced the structure, composition, and dynamics of most Sierra Nevada ecosystems. Many species and most communities show clear evidence of adaptation to recurrent fire, further demonstrating that fire has long been a regular and frequent occurrence. This is particularly true in the chaparral and mixed conifer communities, where many plant species take advantage of or depend on fire for their reproduction or as a means of competing with other biota.

The variable nature of presettlement fire helped create diverse landscapes and variable forest conditions. In many areas frequent surface fires are thought to have minimized fuel accumulation, keeping understories relatively free of trees and other vegetation that could form fuel ladders to carry fire into the main canopy. The effects of frequent surface fires would largely explain the reports and photographs of those early observers who described Sierran forests as typically "open and parklike." However, such descriptions must be tempered by other early observations emphasizing dense, impenetrable stands of brush and young trees.

Several lines of evidence indicate that most presettlement

fires were dominated by areas of low to moderate severity, with high-severity portions (fire sufficiently intense to kill most large trees) most often restricted to localized areas, often a fraction of an acre to several acres—or occasionally several hundred acres—in size. Predominately high-severity fires larger than a few thousand acres almost certainly occurred but were probably less common than they are today. This picture of presettlement fire is supported by our understanding of fuel dynamics as well as information derived from forest age structure analysis, written accounts of early fires, and observations of modern fires.

Periodic fires performed a number of ecological functions. Fire damaged or killed some plants, setting the stage for regeneration and vegetation succession. Many plants evolved fire-adapted traits, such as thick bark, and fire-stimulated flowering, sprouting, seed release, and/or germination. Fire influenced many processes in the soil and forest floor, including the organisms therein, by consuming organic matter and by inducing thermal and chemical changes. And it affected the dynamics of biomass accumulation and nutrient cycling and generated vegetation mosaics at a variety of spatial scales.

Native Americans adapted to this natural role of fire and controlled it to some extent for their own benefit. They are known to have used fire to clear brush from around their dwellings and to enhance habitat for game species. There is reason to believe that in local areas their activities added to the background lightning-induced fire frequency.

Effects of Human Activities Beginning in the Mid-1800s

Euro-American influence on fire in the Sierra Nevada began before the mid-1800s. By this time many Native American populations had been decimated by disease and genocide,

and their traditional use of fire had been greatly reduced. The rapid influx of settlers into California following the discovery of gold, however, initiated more profound changes in the role of fire in Sierra Nevada ecosystems. Logging was undertaken initially to supply the mines and later to support the growing population of the new state. Timber volumes harvested in the Sierra Nevada continued to increase into the twentieth century, reaching a peak in the 1970s and 1980s. Typically, loggers harvested fire-resistant species and large trees, and these were replaced by greater numbers of much more fire-susceptible smaller trees. This pattern of biomass removal contrasted markedly with that of presettlement surface fires, which tended to kill (and later consume) small trees and leave many large trees to survive. Large quantities of debris left after logging led to severe fires, establishing vegetation patterns still evident today. A new pattern of ignitions, characterized in part by careless and indiscriminate burning, was introduced by miners, sheepherders, settlers, and loggers. In other areas there is evidence that heavy grazing by millions of sheep in the late 1800s may have effectively altered fuel conditions to reduce the influence or extent of fires.

The Role and Consequences of Fire Suppression

Suppression of wildland fires had been established as state and federal policy by early in the twentieth century. Following a series of disastrous fires in 1910 and a period of trial and debate about the merits of "light burning" as a management tool in forests and rangelands, intentional broadcast burning was repudiated and aggressive fire control became firmly entrenched. Only in recent decades have the benefits of prescribed fire become widely apparent.

Combined with the loss of ignitions by Native Americans,

❊ *Careless and Indiscriminate Fire Use*

We note here a report in 1888 to the California Board of Forestry (H. S. Davidson): "A half century following the Gold Rush was a period of the careless and indiscriminate use of fire consuming each year thousands of acres of fine timber, endangering and often destroying the property of settlers, menacing the homes of all those who live in timbered regions, the forest fire, year after year continues its ruinous course, unrestrained by the law, and unheeded by the majority of the people. Anyone traveling through the Sierras cannot fail to notice the large number of charred and half burned stumps of large trees, often twenty feet high, whose tops have fallen when the trunks were half consumed, and were themselves wholly or partially consumed upon the ground. These fires often assume such proportions that the atmosphere at a distance of 50 miles from the scene of the conflagration will assume that hazy appearance caused by dense smoke." Burning by sheep-

men became so common from the 1870s through 1900 that the newspapers often printed stories about smoky fall days. In 1889 C. M. Dabney of Fresno, in a plea for control of sheep grazing and sheepherder fires, claimed, "There seems to be a combination of sheepmen . . . who pay no taxes, have no homes, defy our laws, and who say they do not understand English, to burn these magnificent forests as they go along." P. Y. Lewis, who herded sheep in the upper Mokelumne River drainage in 1876–77 asserted: "We started setting fires and continued setting them until we reached the foothills. We burned everything that would burn." And John Muir noted, "The entire forest belt is thus swept and devastated from one extremity of the range to the other" by sheepherder-set fires. This period of fire damage led to the first state laws prohibiting the setting of fires, either willingly or negligently, and a similar federal policy.

fire suppression resulted in significant reductions in area burned by wildfires during the twentieth century. For example, by comparing average annual acreage estimated to have burned during the presettlement period (based on fire history data) with twentieth-century fire-return intervals (table 4.1), we find that the annual area burned during this century has been reduced to approximately 10%, 3%, and 2% of presettlement values for the blue oak, mixed conifer, and red fir forest types, respectively.

The virtual exclusion of widespread low- to moderate-severity fire has affected the structure and composition of most Sierra Nevada vegetation, especially in low- to middle-elevation forests. Conifer stands generally have become denser, mainly in small and medium size classes of shade-tolerant and fire-sensitive tree species. Vertical fuels have become more continuous, contributing to more spatially homogeneous forests (figure 4.1). Selective cutting of large overstory trees and the relatively warm and moist climate that has characterized much of the twentieth century may have reinforced these trends by producing conditions favorable to the establishment of tree seedlings and other plant species. Coupled with fire suppression, these conditions permitted the extensive development of dense, young forests. As a result, stands in many areas have experienced increased mortality recently from the cumulative effects of competition (primarily for water and light), drought, insects, disease, and, in some cases, air pollution. The increased density of young trees together with increased fuels from fire suppression and tree mortality have created conditions favorable to more intense and severe fires. Moreover, severe fires are more likely to be large because they are more difficult to suppress, although data on large fires in the Sierra indicate that current fire sizes vary greatly among national forests. While we cannot be sure whether more absolute area has burned in severe fires in the twentieth century than in pre-contact times, it is clear that within those areas that do burn, a greater proportion of fire is high-severity than in the past.

Several lines of evidence suggest that quantities of live and dead fuels have increased over the course of the twentieth century, although data from the early part of the century are not available to test this assertion directly. Over the same period suppression technology has improved, but in recent years available fire-fighting resources have declined. The net effect on a number of fire attributes has remained remarkably constant.

Trends in Fire Size

Total area burned in the Sierra shows no overall trend during the twentieth century, in contrast to the marked reduction in burned area from the presettlement era to the twentieth century. This stability contrasts with striking declines in area burned during the first half of the century and increases in area burned after about 1970 that have been documented for other areas in the western United States. Other patterns also have remained stable, including (1) the relationship between

FIGURE 4.1

Development of vertical fuels through ingrowth of white fir in a stand of mixed conifer as a result of fire suppression. (Photo by Constance I. Millar.)

fire occurrence and elevation (i.e., more area burns at lower elevations); (2) the relationship between climate and annual area burned (i.e., more area burns in warmer, drier years); and (3) average fire sizes for most national forests in the Sierra Nevada.

In other significant respects, however, fire characteristics have changed. Although human-caused fires have exceeded lightning fires in number and total area throughout this century (figure 4.2), the proportion of total area burned by lightning-caused fires and the average size of lightning fires have increased in recent decades, particularly in the late 1980s and early 1990s. A likely explanation stems from the fact that, unlike human ignitions, many lightning ignitions occur simultaneously during thunderstorms, stretching available fire-fighting resources so thin that not all fires receive adequate initial attack. The increase in total area and average size of lightning fires in recent decades may reflect, in part, a reduction in overall suppression resources. At least as important may be general increases in wildfire hazard (fuel quantities),

The catastrophic Cleveland wildfire of 1992 near Highway 50 partially on the Eldorado National Forest. (Photos by Douglas Leisz.)

which tend to increase difficulty of control and exacerbate limitations in fire-fighting resources. Expanded human settlement in the urban-wildland intermix has also complicated fire suppression by focusing resources on protection of structures.

An evaluation of fire-occurrence risk based on U.S. Forest Service records of twentieth-century fires identified an elevation pattern, with the highest risk in the foothill and lower mixed conifer zone (figure 4.3 and plates 4.1 and 4.2). Maps documenting fuel loads on national forest lands in the Sierra reflect another estimate of risk (plate 4.3).

Prescribed Fire

Prescribed fire has proven an effective tool to reduce fuel loads and fire hazards while restoring a process important for maintaining ecosystem functions. However, practical and political considerations may limit future expansion of this approach. Although prescribed fire is useful in restoring and maintaining natural fire regimes in parks and wilderness areas, it remains to be seen whether the logistical, economic, and social constraints on widespread deployment of prescribed fire for fuel hazard reduction can be overcome. In some places, mechanical fuel reduction, often in conjunction with prescribed fire, can also be of use in reducing fuels and fire hazards.

Challenges for Fire Management

Human activities during the past 150 years have caused a number of fire-related changes in the Sierra Nevada. Fires occur less frequently and collectively cover much less area than they did in the presettlement era. Widespread low- to moderate-severity wildfires have been virtually eliminated because these are the fires that are suppressed most easily. As a result, the ecological functions performed by such fires (e.g., nutrient mineralization, soil sterilization, and understory thinning) have been largely lost, with some known and many

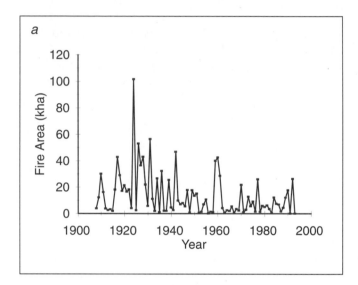

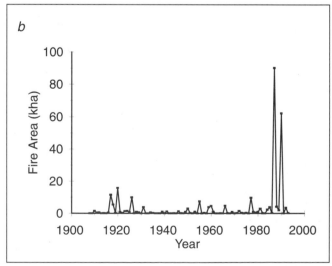

FIGURE 4.2

Acres burned by fires in the Sierra Nevada, 1908–92. *Top (a):* Human-caused fires. *Bottom (b):* Lightning-caused fires. (From volume II, chapter 41.)

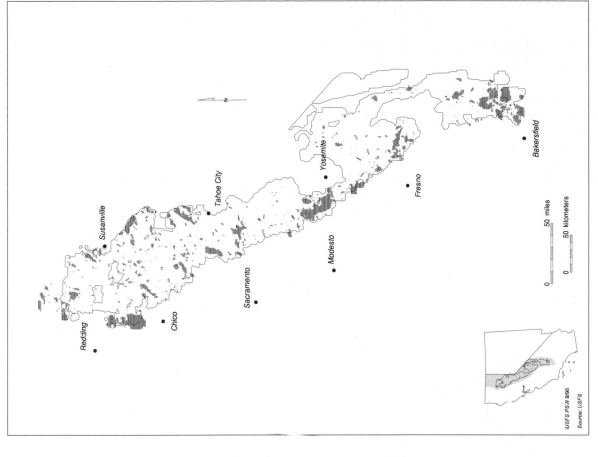

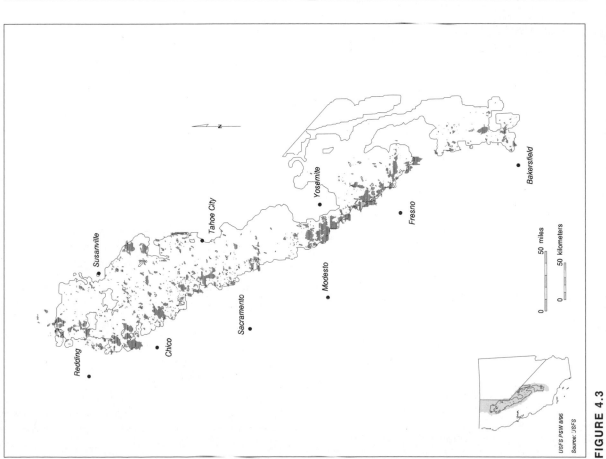

FIGURE 4.3

Fires on and around USFS national forest lands within the SNEP core area. *Left:* Fires from 1900 to 1939. *Right:* Fires from 1940 to 1993. (From volume II, chapter 41.)

A ponderosa pine–Douglas fir stand treated with prescribed fire in 1979 and burned in 1987 during the Elk Complex wildfire. By 1992, when this photo was taken, grass and herbaceous vegetation covered the ground among trees of different ages. (Photo by Carl N. Skinner.)

the Sierra Nevada: (1) too much high-severity fire and the potential for much more of the same; (2) too little low- to moderate-severity fire, with a variety of ecological changes attributable at least in part to this deficiency; and (3) a large number of homes and other structures at risk due to both existing and continued rural development in areas with extreme fire hazards that are not reduced to acceptable levels. Clearly, these are not just "fire problems." They influence virtually all resources and values in the Sierra Nevada and cut across all of SNEP's subject areas. These three problems can be translated into three closely related and complementary broad goals for fire management in the Sierra Nevada: (1) reduce substantially the area and average size of acres burned by large, high-severity wildfires; (2) restore more of the ecosystem functions of frequent low- to moderate-severity fire; and (3) encourage a more rational approach for the intermix of homes and wildland vegetation with high fire-risk hazard. Making significant progress toward these goals will require long-term vision, commitment, and cooperation across a broad spectrum of land-management agencies and other entities. The problems were created over a long time, and they certainly cannot be solved rapidly.

STRATEGIES

There are many possible approaches and strategies for addressing issues relating to the management of fire and hazardous fuels in the Sierra Nevada. We have addressed only a few of these in our illustrations.

Goals

1. Substantially reduce the potential for large high-severity wildfires in the Sierra Nevada in both wildlands and the wildland-urban intermix.

2. Restore historic ecosystem functions of frequent low- and moderate-severity fire.

3. Help communities understand and eliminate unacceptable fire hazards and risks that threaten the safety of people and homes in the wildland-urban intermix.

4. Aid counties, other local governments, and fire districts in attaining and maintaining fire-safe fuel conditions concurrent with all new development or in redirecting development to areas of lower fire hazard.

Possible Solutions

Reducing the potential for large, high-severity fires while at the same time increasing the area burned and the ecosystem effects produced by low- and moderate-intensity fires would

unknown consequences. Furthermore, largely because of fire suppression, fuels—both live and dead—have increased in quantity and continuity, thereby increasing the probability of large, high-severity wildfires. In fact, the fires that do occur are likely to be large and more uniformly severe; these are the fires not readily suppressed. It is these high-severity fires that most conflict with human values and thus pose the greatest concerns about life, property, and natural resource values. The propensity for the rapidly increasing population of the Sierra Nevada to build in flammable areas without mitigating fire hazards and risks has increasingly placed homes and other valuable property at risk of loss to severe wildfires, making potential solutions to the problem increasingly difficult. Many hundreds of homes have been destroyed by wildfires in the Sierra Nevada over the past few decades (e.g., 148 homes and 164 other structures were destroyed in the 1988 49er fire near Nevada City).

In short, we have three major fire-related "problems" in

reduce the fire hazard to property and lives in developed areas as well as reduce the total acreage burned at high severity. It might actually increase the total area burned compared with the past few decades. Such a program would, by necessity, require the effective development of institutional frameworks to facilitate interaction, financial support, and cooperation among agencies, local governments, and private interests. It is inconceivable that fire in its presettlement extent and frequencies could be restored fully to the Sierra Nevada.

The following are possible solutions addressing the identified problems:

- Prioritize fuel treatment areas to minimize the likelihood and spread of large, severe fires, based on broad, landscape-level analyses of risk and hazard to both human settlements and wildlands.

- Develop a system of "defensible fuel profile zones" (DFPZs), initially using a variety of silvicultural treatments, to limit the spread of large, severe fires. Once developed, these DFPZs will serve as areas of entry into larger landscapes to facilitate more widespread fuel treatments, such as prescribed fire, and will allow more widespread use of wildfire to meet management objectives.

- Increase substantially the use of prescribed fire (natural or management ignition) in areas where restoration of natural processes is emphasized.

- Develop programs for the increased use (through containment and confinement strategies) of low- and moderate-intensity wildfires to achieve goals of restored ecosystem processes, resource management, and human safety.

- Develop fuel-management demonstration areas. For the purpose of public education, some demonstration areas would illustrate vegetative conditions necessary to reduce the severity and extent of large, severe wildfires. These areas would be developed by a suite of treatment methods so that the public can adequately observe and managers can learn from the various resulting conditions. Other demonstration areas would be located to provide a social arena for developing the institutional framework necessary to carry out large, strategic fuel-management projects. Of particular value in this context may be projects in wildland-urban intermix areas such as those found in Nevada, Placer, and El Dorado Counties.

- Develop a collaborative institutional structure (e.g., an "Issue Command Structure," similar to the Incident Command System used for fire suppression and other emergencies) so that federal, state, and local agencies and communities could join together to plan, establish goals, finance, and execute programs to accomplish the fire-safety objectives.

- Make visible those counties (e.g., El Dorado) and communities (e.g., Incline Village, Lake Tahoe, Nevada, and Pine

Mountain Lake Development, Tuolumne County, California) that have implemented effective programs through General Plans, ordinances, and actions that either avoid new development in high fire-hazard zones, require full mitigation of the hazards concurrent with development, or are correcting hazardous fuel conditions in existing developments.

Defensible Fuel Profile Zones in Support of Goals 1 and 3

A key component of the proposed strategies is development of a network of broad DFPZs. Whereas initially addressing goals 1 and 3, the DFPZs will actually help to address all of the stated fire-related goals. Fuel-reduction treatments will be designed to address the specific local issues (e.g., establishing a community defense zone, or breaking up areas of continuous high-hazard fuels, or designating a strip or block of land to form a zone of defensible space where both live and dead fuels are reduced).

Such DFPZs are best initially placed primarily on ridges and upper south and west slopes and, where possible, along existing roads. They also should be located with respect to urban-wildland intermix and other high-value areas (such as old-growth or wildlife habitat areas), areas of high historical fire occurrence, and/or areas of heavy fuel concentration. Thinning from below and treatment of surface fuels should result in fairly open stands, dominated mostly by larger trees of fire-tolerant species. DFPZs need not be uniform, monotonous areas, however, but may encompass considerable diversity in ages, sizes, and distributions of trees. The key feature should be the general openness and discontinuity of crown fuels, both horizontally and vertically, producing a very low probability of sustained crown fire. Care must be exercised in the design and construction so that forest aesthetic values are largely retained and watershed values are not impaired. The open-canopied conditions would favor relatively abundant herbaceous growth. Stands probably would be somewhat similar to those that dominated many ridges and upper south slopes in presettlement times (on average, more open than on other sites because of more xeric conditions and more frequent fires). The heavy thinning will promote faster growth of trees into large size classes less susceptible to fire damage. Further details of this approach are provided in volume II, chapter 56.

DFPZs should offer multiple benefits by providing not only local protection to treated areas (as with any fuel-management treatment) but also (1) safe zones within which firefighters have improved odds of stopping a fire, (2) interruption of the continuity of hazardous fuels across a landscape, and (3) various benefits not related to fire, including, for example, improved forest health, greater landscape diversity, and increased availability of relatively open forest habitats dominated by large trees.

DFPZs are an initial, not an exclusive, focus for fuel-man-

A defensible fuel profile zone would be dominated by relatively large trees but would encompass considerable diversity in ages, sizes, and distributions of trees. The key feature would be the general openness and discontinuity of crown fuels, both horizontally and vertically. (Photo by Douglas Leisz.)

agement activities. The DFPZs are not a final solution. Rather, they should be viewed as an initial step in bringing large portions of landscapes into more defensible and fire-resilient condition. As the hazard level of various landscapes is brought down, the DFPZs will tend to blend into the surrounding landscapes. It must be recognized that desirable fuels conditions, once achieved, will require periodic maintenance or conditions will revert to hazardous states.

How will society pay for all the fuels management that will be necessary, given the huge areas that need to be treated? Given historical levels of funding and the current direction of federal budgets, it seems highly unlikely that federally appropriated funds will make more than a dent in the problem. Most of the limited appropriated funds are probably best spent to support prescribed burning in natural fuels where there is a special emphasis on reestablishing natural processes (goal 2). Existing cooperatively funded programs of the Forest Service and the California Department of Forestry and Fire Protection might be restructured to assist in funding some of the private landowner share. Significant progress on large-scale fuels treatments will have to be an economically self-sustaining enterprise, supported largely from the sale of forest products. Part of this can come from multiproduct sales, in which sawtimber and other high-value products subsidize the removal of lower-value material. Local property owners and communities may need to provide most of the support for treatments in the intermix areas.

In some portions of the Sierra Nevada, especially higher-elevation areas, including substantial acreage of red fir and other high-elevation vegetation types, large, high-severity fires are not as serious a concern. Thus neither goals 1, 3, and 4 nor DFPZs are particularly applicable. Many such areas are located in national parks and wilderness areas. The proposed strategy in these areas involves extending the use of prescribed

natural fire (PNF) as much as possible (including appropriate areas outside parks and wildernesses) and augmenting PNFs with management-ignited prescribed fires (MIPFs) as needed to reestablish near-natural fire regimes. MIPF also should become a key part of the management of other areas in which restoration of natural processes is a major management objective. Recently approved new federal policies will permit wildfires to be "managed" if they meet resource objectives and if fire-hazard conditions elsewhere are not likely to require the deployment of suppression forces from the "managed fire" unit.

Implications

Continuation of current fire-management strategies (i.e., primarily fire suppression with spatially sporadic and limited fuels management) will have important implications in a number of areas. First, there will continue to be periods in many years, especially dry ones, when weather and fuels will combine to produce fire behavior beyond the technological capability of fire-suppression forces to respond effectively. The strategies described here are intended to modify the fuel conditions that support the severe events, thus reducing their magnitude and frequency of occurrence. However, fire suppression has been quite effective in limiting the total area burned in the Sierra Nevada during the twentieth century. Ecological considerations aside, continuing current management strategies might produce similar results, at least in the near term. The primary difference will be in the increasing threat to human lives, forest resources, and property as more people move into the wildland-urban intermix without adequate hazard reduction. This threat could probably be dealt with by treating the wildland-urban intermix areas, instituting economic incentives for stakeholders to take part, and continuing an aggressive suppression strategy.

However, there is strong evidence that fire once was a major ecological process in the Sierra Nevada with profound influences on many, if not most, Sierran ecosystems. The success of fire suppression has altered, and will continue to alter, Sierran ecosystems, with various consequences in regard to ecological function (e.g., nutrient cycling, successional pathways, forest structural development, biodiversity, hydrology). Many of the consequences probably have not yet been described. Regardless of what combinations of strategies are ultimately used, only wide-scale, extensive landscape treatments (e.g., prescribed fire, fuel treatments) can approach the level of influence that fire once had on the Sierran environment.

Ideally, work on all goals should progress concurrently. Where possible, opportunities should be sought that provide the greatest gain toward all goals. Where this is not possible, however, goals 1, 3, and 4 should generally be given higher priority in the short term, to reduce losses of lives, property, and resources and to make it possible to work more effectively toward achieving goal 2, thus improving the overall health and sustainability of Sierra Nevada ecosystems. Stated in another way, protection is a prerequisite to restoration in many areas. Regardless of what strategies and priorities are adopted, it is essential for the wildland fire agencies to continue strong support for suppression and prevention activities.

Fire-related evaluation criteria that can be used to monitor progress toward the goals presented include (1) area and distribution of burned areas by severity classes (e.g., high sever-ity usually detrimental, low severity usually beneficial), (2) area and/or distribution of "desirable" fuel profiles, and (3) number of counties and communities adopting fuel-hazard reduction standards and participating in correcting hazard-ous fuel conditions in the wildland-urban intermix. The data required to apply these criteria should be part of a comprehensive temporal GIS database that would integrate, at a minimum, vegetation, fuels, fires, ecological and human values, and management activities.

CHAPTER 5

Plants and Terrestrial Wildlife

Plant Diversity Of California's 7,000 vascular plant species, about 50% occur in the Sierra Nevada. Of these, more than 400 species are found only in the Sierra Nevada, and 200 are rare.

Threats to Plant Diversity Three plant species marginally within the Sierra Nevada (*Monardella leucocephala, Mimulus whipplei,* and *Erigeron mariposanus*) appear to have become extinct in the last hundred years.

Vertebrate Diversity About 300 terrestrial vertebrate species (including mammals, birds, reptiles, and amphibians) use the Sierra Nevada as a significant part of their range, although more than 100 others include the Sierra Nevada as a minor part of more extensive ranges elsewhere.

Extinction Three modern vertebrate species once well distributed in the range are now extinct from the Sierra Nevada: Bell's vireo, California condor, and grizzly bear.

Vertebrate Species at Risk Sixty-nine species of terrestrial vertebrates (17% of the Sierra fauna) are considered at risk by state or federal agencies, which list them as endangered, threatened, of "special concern," or "sensitive."

Loss of Foothill Habitat Eighty-five terrestrial vertebrate species require west-slope foothill savanna, woodland, chaparral, or riparian habitats to retain population viability; 14% of these are considered at risk.

Loss of Riparian and Old-Growth Habitat The most important identified cause of the decline of Sierran vertebrates has been loss of habitat, especially foothill and riparian habitats and late successional forests.

Genetic Diversity Activities occurring in the Sierra Nevada that pose the greatest indirect and direct threats to genetic diversity are those that break the chain of natural selection and adaptation.

Genetic Management Genetic guidelines that alert managers to activities likely to have genetic consequences and inform managers about preferred management of seeds, plants, mushrooms, animals, insects, and other germ plasm have been mostly lacking, inadequate, or poorly implemented in land management of the Sierra.

Community Distribution Excluding marginal plant communities mainly distributed in the Mojave Desert and Great Basin, the Sierra Nevada encompasses eighty-eight plant community types as defined by California's Natural Heritage Division.

Private Ownership of Plant Communities Many of the foothill community types fall largely within private lands, notably grassland (88% of the mapped distribution on private lands), valley oak woodland (98%), blue oak woodland (89%), interior live oak woodland (71%), and foothill pine–oak woodland (82%).

Grazing Livestock grazing has been implicated in plant compositional and structural changes in foothill community types, meadows, and riparian systems, and grazing is the primary negative factor affecting the viability of native Sierran land bird populations.

Timber Harvest Six forest types are mostly found on lands available for firewood cutting or timber harvest, including interior live oak (81%), black oak (56%), east-side ponderosa pine (72%), Sierran mixed conifer (67%), Sierran white fir (62%), and lower cismontane mixed conifer–oak (70%).

Type Conversions Nearly 800,000 acres of oak woodlands in the Sierra Nevada have been converted to other land uses and vegetation types over the last forty years, a decline of almost 16%.

ASSESSMENTS

Sierra Nevada Plant Communities

The Sierra Nevada Ecosystem Project assessed all vegetated areas of the Sierra Nevada (15.6 million acres); 89.7% of the region is covered by plants (plate 5.1). The rest is rocky barrens, water, or settled lands. Eighty-eight natural plant community types have been described within the Sierra; about one-quarter of them have ranges of less than 6,000 acres. Conversely, twelve community types collectively contribute two-thirds of the region's total vegetated acreage (table 5.1).

Ownership and Management of Sierran Plant Communities

The SNEP assessment of terrestrial biodiversity focused mainly on the structure of commercial forest types, such as Sierran mixed conifer and red fir, and on the condition of selected rangeland communities, such as meadow and riparian types. Our findings are presented in more detail in chapters 23 and 58 of volume II. We did not systematically investigate the condition and trends of many of the region's ecosystems, but we did map the general distribution of all widespread plant communities, which we used as coarse surrogates for terrestrial ecosystems and wildlife habitats. We analyzed the distribution of each widespread type with respect to land

TABLE 5.1

Twelve major vegetation types of the Sierra Nevada.

Plant Community	Percentage of Total Vegetated Area in Sierra
Sierran mixed conifer forest	10
Blue oak woodland	10
West-side ponderosa pine forest	8
Lower montane mixed conifer–oak forest	7
Red fir forest	6
Foothill pine–oak woodland	5
Jeffrey pine–fir forest	5
Lodgepole pine forest	4
Jeffrey pine forest	3
East-side pine forest	3
Red fir, western white pine, and lodgepole pine–western white pine forest	3
Non-native annual grassland	3

ownership and management. Our objective was to identify types that might be especially vulnerable to land-use conversion or degradation because they are not well represented in existing designated conservation areas or are largely on land available for uses that could negatively impact native biodiversity. This map-based conservation risk-assessment method is known as *gap analysis* because it seeks to identify gaps in the representation of native biota in protected areas. Gap analysis is not a substitute for a detailed biological inventory, but it provides a useful description of regional vegetation patterns and helps to identify vulnerable plant communities and habitats. Our study was a collaboration with the National Biological Service's Gap Analysis Program (GAP).

The GAP uses land-management classes as a coarse measure for assessing the viability of plant communities. Communities that fall in lands allocated to certain extractive uses are likely to be more vulnerable than those in nature reserves, for example. Five ownership/management classes, based on fire policy and on potentials for development, timber harvest, and grazing were used for assessments:

Class 1: Public or private lands formally designated for conservation of native biodiversity. Development, grazing, and timber harvest are excluded. Examples include national parks, research natural areas, and Nature Conservancy preserves.

Class 2: National forest land that is generally managed for natural values but not formally designated for conservation. Development and grazing are excluded, and timber harvest is generally excluded.

Class 3: Public land that is generally managed for natural values, is currently classed as suitable for timber harvest, and may be grazed. Examples include grazing allotments in national forest wilderness, and Bureau of Land Management wilderness areas.

Class 4: Other public lands not included in Classes 1–3, mainly multiple-use lands.

Class 5: Private lands other than those in Class 1.

Use of these management classes as surrogates for biodiversity vulnerability is subject to many exceptions, and generalization is implicit. We do not intend to imply that timber harvest, grazing, or other activities are necessarily detrimental to biodiversity. Further, although the databases used in this analysis are the most comprehensive ever assembled for the region, producing the maps and analyzing the data at this scale require assumptions and simplifications, which need to be verified on the ground for local accuracy.

The GAP mapped 15% of the Sierra Nevada region as Class 1 lands. Yosemite, Sequoia, and Kings Canyon National Parks account for most (89%) of this area. These parks are an important source of large, continuous protected habitat. Nearly

---

✳ *Natural Diversity Database*

Plant community types are often used as a coarse descriptor of biotic and underlying environmental conditions. Since 1986, California's Natural Heritage Program has classified the state's plant communities into roughly 400 community types, using the Natural Diversity Data Base (NDDB) Plant Community Classification System (recently the California Native Plant Society has devised an alternative classification system that serves a similar purpose). To be consistent with the statewide gap analysis of California, SNEP employed the NDDB system. Excluding marginal communities mainly distributed in the Mojave Desert and the Great Basin, the Sierra Nevada encompasses eighty-eight plant community types.

The Heritage Program ranks each community type, much as species are ranked, to indicate its overall condition throughout its range in the state. Geographically restricted community types listed as very threatened by the Natural Heritage Division include Gabbroic northern mixed chaparral and Ione chaparral. More widespread Sierran community types listed as very threatened or threatened include sagebrush steppe, Sierra Tehachapi saltbrush scrub, big tree forest, west-side ponderosa pine forest, and east-side ponderosa pine forest. Types listed as threatened that are widespread in the Sierra Nevada but also have wide occurrence elsewhere include aspen forest, aspen riparian forest, black oak woodland, blue oak woodland, valley oak woodland, interior live oak woodland, serpentine foothill pine–chaparral woodland, wet or dry montane meadow, wet or dry subalpine meadow, and montane black cottonwood riparian forest.

half of the total units grouped as Class 1 lands, however, are small parcels, less than 100 acres, meaning that they may be unable to contribute to landscape-level ecosystem functions (migration, dispersal, metapopulation maintenance, animal habitat quality, recruitment). An additional 7% of the Sierra Nevada region is in Class 2 lands.

By adding the areas in Classes 3–5, we estimate that about 80% of the region, or 89% of the vegetated land, is available for grazing. Similarly, summing Classes 4–5, we find that about 57% of the land area is available for timber harvest.

The ownership of Sierran plant communities varies in a way that reflects the concentration of private lands at lower elevations and of National Park Service lands in the central and southern portions of the range. Many of the foothill plant community types fall largely within private lands, notably non-native grassland (88% of the mapped distribution on private lands), valley oak woodland (98%), blue oak woodland (89%), interior live oak woodland (71%), and foothill pine–oak woodland (82%).

A number of widespread community types occur disproportionately on national forest lands, notably low sagebrush scrub (79%), rabbitbrush scrub (93%), mountain mahogany woodland (94%), mixed montane chaparral and montane ceanothus chaparral (73%), bush chinquapin chaparral (85%), cismontane juniper woodland (86%), northern juniper woodland (85%), aspen (89%), east-side ponderosa pine (76%), Jeffrey pine forest (75%), Jeffrey pine–fir forest (80%), western white pine forest (75%), whitebark pine–lodgepole pine forest (86%), and alpine dwarf scrub (99%). Foxtail pine forest is the only type whose distribution falls mainly within the national parks (77%).

These results call attention to three conditions of special concern, and a fourth of relative security:

1. *Upland rangeland plant community types occupying more than 6,000 acres, with more than 90% mapped distribution potentially grazed.* Some 28% of Sierran plant communities are in this group and would be thus flagged for special concern about grazing management. Notable among these are black oak woodland, valley oak woodland, blue oak woodland, interior live oak woodland, and east-side ponderosa pine forest.

2. *Forest types occupying more than 6,000 acres, with less than 10% of their distribution in Class 1 areas.* Six widespread, lower-elevation Sierran forest types are largely available for timber harvest and are not well represented in Class 1 areas: interior live oak forest, black oak forest, east-side ponderosa pine forest, Sierran mixed conifer forest, Sierran white fir forest, and lower cismontane mixed conifer–oak forest.

3. *Chaparral types occupying more than 6,000 acres, with less than 10% of distribution in Class 1 areas.* The policy of suppressing wildfire and the widespread conversion of low-elevation chaparral to grasslands raise concern about the

long-term sustainability of at least eight of these fire-adapted ecosystems.

4. *Community types that are well represented in Class 1 areas (more than 25% of their distribution is in Class 1).* Viewed Sierrawide, thirteen types can be considered relatively low priority for additional land acquisition, administrative redesignation, or change in management in order to protect biodiversity. These include montane meadow, cismontane juniper woodlands, big tree (giant sequoia) forest, red fir–western white pine forest, red fir forest, lodgepole pine forest, whitebark pine–mountain hemlock forest, whitebark pine–lodgepole pine forest, foxtail pine forest, whitebark pine forest, Sierra Nevada fell field, and alpine dwarf scrub. All of these, of course, may be subject to local impacts that are not directly related to land classification, such as the spread of white pine blister rust, which disregards land-allocation boundaries.

Major differences exist in the representation of plant communities on the different land areas among regions of the Sierra. In general, the northern subregion is largely private or national forest land, and only 2.1% of this subregion is Class 1 land. These Class 1 areas are concentrated at higher elevations in the northern subregion. Potentially grazed lands (Classes 3–5) account for 88% of the area, while 71% is eligible for intensive timber harvest (Classes 4–5). Many types are almost wholly restricted to low-elevation private lands, including interior live oak (90%) and west-side ponderosa pine. Middle-elevation forests are more concentrated on the national forests (60%–90% on public lands). Because Yosemite, Sequoia, and Kings Canyon National Parks fall within the central and southern Sierra, the land-management profile of that subregion is strikingly different from that of the northern subregion. Class 1 areas and private areas are roughly equal in extent, covering 26% and 30% of the land, respectively. Roughly 75% of the area is available for grazing. The largest difference between the northern and the central-southern subregions lies in the management profiles of the major forest types. Virtually all of the community types possessing commercial forest species in the central-southern subregion have at least 20% of their areas in Class 1 lands.

Plant Species

Plants of the Sierra Nevada have provided food and shelter to humans for nearly 10,000 years and to wildlife for much longer. For more than a century the Sierran flora has attracted botanists from around the world; many of their names mark the scientific nomenclature of the species they described. Visions of giant sequoias, vast conifer forests, and open vistas of alpine tundra have added to the botanical allure of the range. Spanning nearly 300 miles from south to north and more than 14,000 feet in elevation, encompassing a wide range of soil and vegetation conditions and human land-use histories, the Sierra possesses a high diversity of plant species, and many species are endemic (restricted) to the range. Supporting more than 3,500 native vascular plants, the Sierra Nevada contains 50% of California's plant species, yet it comprises only 20% of the land base of the state. This species richness is greater than the total number of plant species growing in the entire state of Florida, which is considered the third most floristically diverse of the coterminous states.

Despite the attention of botanists, and perhaps because of the Sierra's diversity, floristic knowledge of the range is still so incomplete that species previously unrecorded in the Sierra, and new range extensions for those already known, are documented annually. For example, between 1968 and 1986, sixty-five new plants were described for the Sierra Nevada, and the trend continues. Studies of species viability and range expansions or contractions are exceedingly sparse. The nonvascular plants (lichens and mosses) are known even less. For these and other reasons, assessments of plants in the Sierra are highly provisional and concentrate mostly on entire plant communities, rare plants, and those with known conservation concerns.

About four hundred plant species occur only in the Sierra Nevada, including three trees, twenty shrub species, several hundred herbaceous plants, and at least two lichens and two mosses. Of this total, two hundred eighteen are considered rare or threatened by the California Native Plant Society or by state or federal agencies (figure 5 1). Within the Sierra, both genetic and species-level composition of Sierran plant community types change progressively from the southern to the northern end of the range. The plant species composition within any plant community type (for example, Sierran mixed conifer forest) changes systematically from north to south at a rate of roughly two plant species per mile. Consequently the Sierran mixed conifer flora of the far northern Sierra Nevada shares only half of its plant species with its southern counterpart. Of the geographic regions of the Sierra, the south is richest in species generally, as well as in numbers of rare species and species found only in the Sierra. The Owens River basin in the eastern Sierra is also an area of rarity and uniqueness for plant species.

Status of Rare Plants and Threatened Species

As a group, Sierran plants are most at risk where habitat has been reduced or substantially altered. Rare plants are scattered throughout the range in many different habitats and on both public and private lands. However, rare local geologic formations and their derived unique soils, such as the Ione Formation, have led to the evolution of ensembles of plant species restricted to these habitats. For most species, conservation status is a function of local land use, from past activities to future plans. Of the habitat types most frequently documented to contain rare and unique species, the foothill woodland and chaparral communities have been particularly altered and fragmented by changes in agriculture and settlement on the western slopes of the Sierra, including the introduction of Eurasian herbs and grasses and changes in the fire

regimes required by many native plants. Timber harvest and fire suppression have altered the patchiness and complexity of conifer forests, degrading habitat for some plant species that rely on the natural forest mosaic, while stimulating habitat for other species. Overgrazing in mountain meadows is a threat to many rare species that are restricted to these habitats. Aside from land use that converts habitat (e.g., settlement), activities such as grazing, logging, mining, and recreation can be compatible with plant conservation as long as the ecology of rare species is taken into account. However, interactions among the timing, intensity, and frequency of these activities can well lead to cumulative adverse impacts on rare and common species and ultimately bring about the loss of entire populations if these impacts are not understood.

Sugar pine, a much-beloved tree and highly valuable timber species widely distributed in the Sierra, deserves note for the threat from a fatal non-native disease pathogen, white pine blister rust. This disease, native to Asia, was introduced accidentally to the United States via nursery stock early in the century and has spread throughout the range of native white (five-needle) pines. Sugar pine seedlings and young trees are killed outright, whereas older trees progressively lose portions of their crowns and may eventually die. The disease has spread in "wave years" when climate conditions are advantageous for the pathogen, and it is now widespread throughout sugar pine populations in the Sierra. A small proportion of sugar pines in most populations contains genetic resistance to the disease, and an active breeding and planting program has been developed from these resistant individuals. Resistance also provides a supply of sugar pines for natural regeneration that probably will survive the epidemic. Although sugar pine populations throughout the range are likely to experience severe declines in number as the epidemic spreads, the long-term prospects for this economically and ecologically important species in the Sierra are good, since natural resistance will be strongly selected for, and the efforts of the control program will provide supplements. Retention of large sugar pines, both resistant and not, throughout the range over the next half-century will play a critical role in maintaining the genetic diversity of the species and its ability to cope with new adversities.

White pine blister rust attacks other species of native white pines in the Sierra, and this may prove a far worse problem in the future than the attack on sugar pine. Although little research has been conducted, the other species do not appear to have native genetic resistance. In the Rocky Mountains, whitebark pine populations have suffered widespread die-offs in a remarkably short time, threatening a variety of wildlife species that depend on pine nuts. Should this situation occur in the Sierra, there would be little opportunity to apply the silvicultural techniques that have been used for sugar pine, since the other white pines exist in remote upper-elevation habitats and their silvic and genetic behaviors are little known.

Another group of species experiencing threat in the Sierra is lichens. Lichens have been used in air-quality monitoring

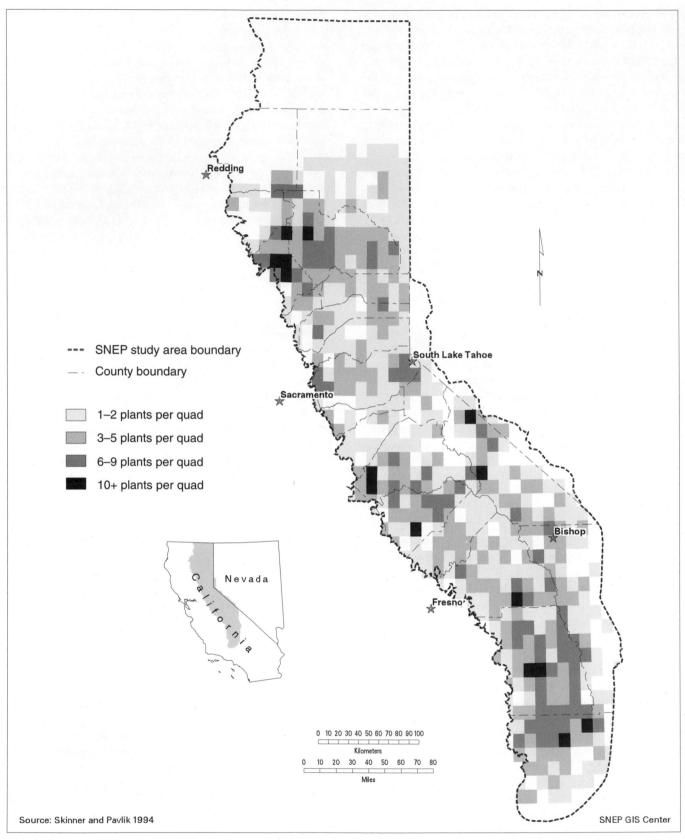

Legend:

--- SNEP study area boundary
— County boundary

1–2 plants per quad
3–5 plants per quad
6–9 plants per quad
10+ plants per quad

Redding
South Lake Tahoe
Sacramento
Bishop
Fresno

Nevada
California

0 10 20 30 40 50 60 70 80 90 100
Kilometers
0 10 20 30 40 50 60 70 80
Miles

Source: Skinner and Pavlik 1994

SNEP GIS Center

FIGURE 5.1

Distribution of rare plants by topographic quadrangle in the Sierra Nevada. (From volume II, chapter 24.)

studies because many species show physiological damage caused by air pollution. Air-quality degradation in the Sierra Nevada appears to be adversely affecting some lichens. Local extinctions of lichens are likely in the Sierra, similar to those that have occurred in southern California, if trends in air quality continue.

Terrestrial Vertebrate Species and Wildlife Habitats

Unlike plants, which generally stay in place long enough to be inventoried and mapped, animals move about, are often difficult to observe or capture, and vary naturally in population size from year to year. Hence, measuring populations, assessing geographic distributions, and assessing species and population viabilities are especially problematic for animals. Our assessments of the 400 species of terrestrial vertebrates that live in the Sierra Nevada depended upon a variety of published and direct sources, including databases from public agencies. For the vast majority of wildlife species, the quality and quantity of information on numbers and range are far below those necessary to make meaningful statements about status or distribution. The situation is even worse for trend data—monitoring over time. What little trend information exists is confined to such local sites that it seldom can be extrapolated to the entire Sierra. Ultimately, our most important source of information on viability of vertebrates at the scale of the Sierra Nevada was to infer distribution from habitat (mainly plant community information), using the California Wildlife Habitat Relationships (CWHR) computer database and model. Because animals depend on plant communities and their environments for habitat, they can be assessed indirectly by analyzing the status of those habitats. SNEP contributed to refining the portion of CWHR based on studies of species-habitat relationships in the Sierra Nevada to provide the most current available information. Although the information on the habitat requirements of many species is somewhat more complete than that for their population dynamics, unfortunately information on the distribution and quality of those habitat elements—riparian vegetation, large snags, montane meadows, vertical cliff faces, and myriad other factors that constitute viable habitat for a particular wildlife species—must presently be inferred from the gross vegetation types that represent most mapped habitat data.

Species Diversity

Of the four hundred species that use the Sierra to a greater or lesser extent, two hundred thirty-two are birds, one hundred twelve are mammals, thirty-two are reptiles, and twenty-five are amphibians (amphibians are treated at greater length in chapter 8 of this volume) (plate 5.2). However, only two hundred seventy-eight of these species use the Sierra as a principal part of their range and only thirteen are essentially restricted to the Sierra in California. During the Pleistocene, California's megafauna included camels, horses, giant ground

sloths, mammoths, bison, and saber-toothed cats, all of which became extinct about 10,000 years ago. These animals largely occupied the valleys and coastal plains, but they undoubtedly lapped up into the foothills of the Sierra Nevada on both sides, although few remains have been found there. The causes for extinction of these large mammals are only surmised, but climate change and predation by early human arrivals are implicated.

At the time of European settlement of the area, large herds of tule elk and pronghorn were still present, especially in the interior valleys; mule deer dominated the foothills, and mountain sheep occupied the crest and eastern slopes. All four of these ungulates were hunted heavily by Spanish and other European settlers.

Modern Extinctions in the Sierra Nevada

Three modern species once well-distributed are now gone from the Sierra Nevada. These are the grizzly bear, least Bell's vireo, and California condor. Grizzly bears were well distributed in California at the time of Spanish settlement, recorded everywhere but the Great Basin, deserts, and eastern Modoc Plateau. In the Sierra they were reported most frequently in the foothill woodlands and chaparral, but they appear to have been distributed throughout the range. Spanish and later European settlers set out systematically to exterminate them. The last California grizzly bear identified with reasonable certainty was killed in Sequoia National Forest in August 1922. The closest known surviving grizzly populations are in northeastern Washington and the northern Rocky Mountains.

The least Bell's vireo was historically distributed widely in riparian habitat of the San Joaquin valley, southern Coast Range, and southwestern California, as well as the lower foothills of the Sierra Nevada. Small numbers of this species persist in southern California and along the California coast. The extinction of least Bell's vireo in the Sierra appears most likely related to nest parasitism by brown-headed cowbirds, although destruction of willow-dominated riparian corridors, which were fragmented by grazing, greatly reduced its habitat.

The last wild California condor was captured in Kern County in 1987, one of twenty-seven birds removed to captivity in an effort to save the species from extinction through captive breeding. The condor is a forager of open plains and savannas, where it once fed on the carcasses of Pleistocene megafauna and later the cattle and sheep that replaced them. In the twentieth century, it ranged widely if sparsely over the southern San Joaquin valley, southern coast ranges, and southern California. Condors selected nest sites in cliffs and even in giant sequoias, which brought them well into the west slope of the Sierra as far north as Tuolumne County. It is most likely that the decline of vast herds of Pleistocene ungulates made condors rare by the time of European exploration. Efforts to reintroduce California condors from the captive population are presently under way.

The factors that led to extinction of each of these animals

❄ *Terrestrial Vertebrates Restricted to the Sierra Nevada*

Thirteen vertebrates are essentially restricted to (live only in) the Sierra Nevada:

Amphibians: Yosemite toad, Kern County slender salamander, relictual slender salamander, Mount Lyell salamander, limestone salamander, Owens Valley web-toed salamander

Mammals: alpine chipmunk, long-eared chipmunk, Mount Lyell shrew, yellow-eared pocket-mouse, heather vole

Birds: pine grosbeak, white-tailed ptarmigan (non-native)

---

in the Sierra were different: For grizzly bears, it was direct, intentional extirpation by killing; for least Bell's vireos, it was habitat disturbance, both directly and indirectly through modifications that encouraged the spread of the brown-headed cowbird into vireo habitat; and for California condors, it was climate change and the arrival of humans to the New World, which led to the demise of the condor's prey, although the coup de grâce appears to have come from modern phenomena, such as condor ingestion of lead slugs in game carcasses and contact with power lines. Because all three species exist elsewhere, should society wish to do so and bear the costs, all three could be reintroduced to the Sierra Nevada.

Non-Native (Alien) Species and Their Effects

Fifteen terrestrial vertebrate species now well established in the Sierra are not native to the region. Several of these have had significant detrimental impacts on the ecology of the Sierra Nevada and its native species. The most serious effects have been produced by the brown-headed cowbird, which was self-introduced early in the century. The spread of this nest-parasitizing bird in the Sierra (and the West in general) has mirrored the spread of farmland, livestock grazing, clear-cut logging, and suburban development. Cowbirds are implicated in or directly charged with the decline of several songbirds in the Sierra Nevada, especially the willow flycatcher, least Bell's vireo, yellow warbler, chipping sparrow, and song sparrow. Many songbirds beyond these are susceptible, although the effects of parasitism can be highly local. Parasitism rates (proportion of native species' eggs replaced by cowbirds' eggs in a nest) in excess of 10% are cause for concern, and those over 30% are a serious problem.

Cowbirds were first reported in the western Sierra foothills in 1915 and at Mono Lake in 1916. The species is now widespread throughout the lower and middle elevations of the Sierra. Cowbirds travel as far as three miles from feeding sites to host nests. Preferred foraging areas for cowbirds in the Sierra include heavily grazed meadows, recent clear-cuts (especially those that are grazed), open forest with short grass understory, pack stations and stables, picnic areas and campgrounds, lawns and golf courses, and residential areas with bird feeders. Closed-canopy and multilayered forests, forests with shrub understory, tall grass meadows, and clear-cuts after shrubs and trees are established do not provide cowbird feeding habitat, but these areas can be parasitized if they lie within a three-mile radius of feeding habitat.

Several other non-native species have significant locally negative effects on native species. European starlings and house sparrows compete aggressively for nest sites with several native Sierran bird species, and starlings particularly may reduce the nesting success of native cavity nesters. These aliens are abundant in the Sierran foothills in and adjacent to urban and agricultural lands. Bullfrogs, native to the eastern United States, have completely replaced Sierran native red-legged frogs and foothill yellow-legged frogs in many locations. Bullfrogs also prey on western pond turtles and other aquatic and riparian wildlife species. Wild pigs are increasing in the Sierra foothills, where they compete for forage with native species, destroy herbaceous vegetation, and root extensively.

Changes in Sierran Habitats and Habitat Dependency

The extreme and systematic alteration of several life zones in the Sierra has had significant impacts on terrestrial vertebrates. Some impacts are likely irreversible; others are on a threshold trending toward this condition. Oak savannas, oak woodlands, and foothill chaparral on the west slopes of the Sierra have been extensively modified. The herbaceous understory in these communities was virtually replaced by introduced Eurasian grasses and herbs (dicots) in the mid-nineteenth century. Most of these areas have been grazed heavily for many years or converted to agriculture; some former chaparral has been converted to grazing land, and much of the rest has grown decadent or succeeded to conifer forest, owing to the suppression of fires. Local firewood collection has reduced the abundance of large old trees, snags, and fallen logs. These foothill communities have been extensively settled. Historically the habitats were extremely important to many birds and mammals that wintered at lower elevations where winters are mild and production of food remains high enough to support them.

Riparian habitats, those areas associated with streams, lakeshores, and other wetlands, have similarly suffered proportionately greater reduction through human modification than many other Sierran habitats. These habitats are critical to many Sierran species, not only because of the availability of water itself in a region with six months of drought but also because of their milder temperatures during the summer, higher production of food, hiding cover, insect prey, variety of nest sites, and opportunities for migration and local movement along the east-west riparian corridor. Losses have occurred through water diversions, the drowning of bottomlands by reservoirs, long-term grazing in riparian zones, timber harvest, and settlement.

Conifer forest habitats in general have been less extensively and less severely modified than foothills and riparian communities. Timber harvest, combined with fire suppression, has modified important animal habitat elements: tree size, tree density, and the presence of large logs and snags in west-side and east-side pine, mixed conifer, and red fir forests. Widespread simplification of forest structure, especially loss of the natural forest mosaic, and the reduction of late successional forest areas through harvest have adversely affected species that use these habitats.

In the Sierra, eighty-two terrestrial vertebrate species are considered to be dependent on riparian habitat to sustain viable populations; 24% of these are listed as species "at risk" (see the next section). Eighteen species are similarly dependent on late successional forests; 28% of these are at risk. Eighty-four species require west-slope foothill savanna, woodland, chaparral, or riparian habitat (some are double-counted with species requiring riparian habitat) for Sierran population viability; 16% of these are at risk. This last number is misleadingly low because many species at risk in the Sierra are more widely distributed elsewhere, such as in the Coast Range.

Status of Sierran Terrestrial Vertebrates at Risk

Species considered at risk in the Sierra, because they are listed by state or federal governments as endangered or threatened, listed by California as being of "special concern," or listed by federal land managers as "sensitive," include thirty-three birds, nineteen mammals, four reptiles, and thirteen amphibians; these constitute 17% of the Sierran terrestrial fauna. For California as a whole, about 30% of the fauna are so listed. Thus, based on this administrative criterion alone, Sierran terrestrial vertebrates are nearly twice as secure under present conditions as is the full state fauna. When other information is brought to bear, however, a rather more complex picture emerges. A brief summary by groups follows.

Mammals. The one hundred twelve species of mammals that regularly use the Sierra Nevada are dominated in number by the smallest of them, including seven shrews, seventeen bats, seven rabbits, and fifty-six rodents. Most of these are nocturnal and seldom seen. Bat numbers seem to be declining in recent decades, perhaps because of use of pesticides, loss of the large old trees and snags associated with late successional conifer forests, and loss of riparian habitats.

Of the larger mammals, including the forest carnivores red fox, fisher, marten, and wolverine, marten continue to occupy their historic range in the Sierra Nevada; fisher populations appear to be persisting in the south but are largely gone from their former ranges north of Yosemite National Park. The de-

cline of fisher is associated with (among other causes) heavy trapping and changes in the structure of their habitat due to timber harvest and other activities that use resources. Red fox and wolverine have been so little studied that changes in their status cannot be determined.

Mountain sheep, once ranging the high Sierra south of Sonora Pass, were decimated by hunting, severe overgrazing by domestic sheep, and transmission of respiratory bacteria from domestic sheep following the arrival of Europeans in the mid-nineteenth century. Bighorn sheep were reintroduced in several locations in the southern Sierra (figure 5.2). Populations increased steadily until the early 1990s, when multiple causes seriously reduced herds. The current total Sierran population is well below the 250 recorded when reintroductions began in 1979, leaving the prospect of secure reestablishment in the wild distinctly pessimistic. A captive breeding program recently has been proposed as an emergency stop-gap measure.

Birds. Of all the vertebrate groups in the Sierra Nevada, breeding land birds are the best monitored. The Breeding Bird

FIGURE 5.2

By the 1970s, Sierra Nevada bighorn sheep, which had once widely populated the crest of the range, were reduced to two populations totaling about 250 individuals. Beginning in the late 1970s, individuals such as this one from the large Baxter Mountain herd (Kings Canyon National Park/Inyo National Forest) were introduced into former Sierra habitats. By 1990, there were five bighorn sheep herds in the central and southern Sierra Nevada. Unfortunately, since that time, probably because of weather, mountain lion predation, and other factors, the herds—including the Baxter Mountain herd—are greatly reduced in numbers and have been at risk of extirpation. (Photo by David Graber.)

Survey (BBS) has maintained systematic monitoring over seventeen routes in the entire Sierra Nevada since 1966. The data collected indicate species that are likely in decline (table 5.2) and species probably increasing (table 5.3). Although this monitoring is more robust than that done for any other group of vertebrates Sierra-wide, it fails to detect birds in adequate numbers, and thus fails to assess trends, when bird species are already uncommon or when too few of the seventeen monitored routes (transects) intersect the appropriate habitat of a species. Ironically, as a result, many species that are on state or federal risk lists are not shown on the BBS; examples include the black swift, purple martin, and yellow-breasted chat. Moreover, raptors and waterbirds are not monitored by the BBS. Populations of listed birds, including the raptors (e.g., prairie falcon, osprey, long-eared owl, and spotted owl) and waterbirds (e.g., harlequin duck, Barrow's goldeneye), are often monitored at local levels, but rangewide trends are largely unavailable.

A review of the birds in tables 5.2 and 5.3 shows that neotropical migrant birds (i.e., those that migrate to the tropics after breeding) in the Sierra, despite their reported vulnerability, do not seem to be faring worse than other species. By contrast, short-distance migrants (e.g., the red-breasted sapsucker and white-crowned sparrow, which winter in the foothills and valleys) seem, as a group, to be doing most poorly in the Sierra. This is not to say that individual neotropical migrant species might not be declining or that tropical deforestation is not a problem for Sierran land birds, but merely that any generalizations about massive declines in neotropical land birds in the Sierra may be unfounded.

Among the potential risks faced by Sierran land birds, grazing and its secondary effects appear to be the single most significant negative factor. Montane meadows and montane riparian habitats are extremely important for Sierran birds; by midsummer, montane meadows may be the single most critical Sierran habitat requirement for many species that do not use this habitat during the actual breeding season. Grazing catalyzes changes in meadow plant species and cover, with cascading effects on birds. Changes in herbaceous and shrubby growth in meadows potentially alter the levels of prey insects, change use patterns by predatory birds, alter nest-building opportunities, and change the water relations of meadows, which sometimes leads ultimately to loss of meadow area. Nest parasitism by non-native cowbirds may be increased by grazing, although grazing itself is not as important to the spread of cowbirds as are agricultural practices and feedlot distribution in the regions adjacent to the Sierra. Local cowbird-control programs related to grazing practices and aimed at certain critical meadows and riparian habitats may be necessary to protect remnant populations of some rare Sierran birds and already show promise where they have been tried. In recent decades cowbird populations on the Sierran transects have been declining, perhaps from reductions in grazing and logging disturbances where those transects occur. However, cowbird populations are still plentiful and widely distributed in the Sierra Nevada, and anecdotal reports suggest they may be occupying higher elevations than they previously did.

Forest management practices, particularly logging and fire suppression, can have a profound effect on land bird populations in the Sierra. Large clear-cut blocks (not widely found in the Sierra) entirely remove forest habitat. Even-aged forests and forests with a structural diversity that has been simplified both spatially and vertically (loss of crown layers, snags, multiple-aged trees, diverse understory layers, coarse woody debris) by selective logging and fire suppression also result in decreased habitat for many forest species. In addition to complex forest structure, large trees and snags are especially important for land birds. Beyond increasing the potential for large, severe wildfires that destroy large blocks of habitat, fire suppression has led to forest and chaparral conditions inimical to many Sierran land birds, conditions in which highly localized habitat elements have been lost.

Pressure for increased development throughout the Sierra, but especially in the foothills and lower elevations of the west slope, is an increasingly significant threat to Sierran land birds.

TABLE 5.2

Breeding land birds in potential decline in the Sierra Nevada. (Data from the Breeding Bird Survey, 1966–91; table from volume II, chapter 25.)

Species Decreasing[a]	Mean Annual Trend (Percentage)	Species Likely Decreasing[b]	Mean Annual Trend (Percentage)
Band-tailed pigeon	−5.5	Mourning dove	−1.8
American robin	−2.7	Mountain chickadee	−1.2
Red-breasted sapsucker	−7.5	Dark-eyed junco	−2.7
Chipping sparrow	−5.0	Belted kingfisher	−7.6
Olive-sided flycatcher	−3.2	Golden-crowned kinglet	−3.3
White-crowned sparrow	−9.7	Brown-headed cowbird	−2.3
		Western wood peewee	−2.0
		Swainson's thrush	−2.6
		House finch	−8.5
		Steller's jay	−2.1
		Black-headed grosbeak	−1.7
		Lesser goldfinch	−4.0

[a]P<0.05 or <0.01 depending on number of transects.
[b]0.01<P<0.10 depending on number of transects.

TABLE 5.3

Land birds likely increasing in the Sierra Nevada. (Data from the Breeding Bird Survey, 1966–91; table from volume II, chapter 25.)

Species Increasing[a]	Mean Annual Trend (Percentage)
White-headed woodpecker	+3.4
Cliff swallow	+26.3
Hammond's flycatcher	+4.9
Common raven	+9.1
Fox sparrow	+3.2
Black phoebe	+3.9
House wren	+2.4
Solitary vireo	+5.5
Warbling vireo	+1.8
Yellow warbler	+3.1
Yellow-rumped warbler	+3.0
MacGillivray's warbler	+1.7

[a]$0.01<P<0.10$, depending on number of transects.

Woody riparian habitat, oak woodland, and chaparral are most affected. Many, perhaps most, Sierran species that specialize in oak woodland habitats seem to be decreasing in the Sierra. Because most of the original riparian habitat of the Central Valley is gone, the remaining habitat in the Sierra becomes all the more critical. Although loss of habitat is the most serious impact of human settlement, even low-density development produces a host of subtle but significant problems.

Reptiles. Of thirty-two native species of reptiles, four are considered at risk: western pond turtle, blunt-nosed leopard lizard, California horned lizard, and California legless lizard. All these species are found elsewhere, and, with the exception of western pond turtle, only marginally lap into the western Sierran foothills. Habitat alteration as a result of agriculture and development in the Central Valley and other parts of these species' ranges seems to be the primary cause of decline. For the remaining reptiles, especially the few that are truly montane, such as western rattlesnake and western terrestrial garter snake, little organized information exists and assessments are largely anecdotal.

Genetic Diversity

Genes are the fundamental unit of biodiversity, the raw material for evolution, and the source of the enormous variety of plants, animals, communities, and ecosystems that we seek to conserve and use in the Sierra Nevada. Genetic variation shapes and defines individuals, populations, subspecies, and ultimately all plant, animal, fungal, and bacterial life on earth. The gene pool (collection of all genes within a species) of a widespread species such as ponderosa pine consists of many populations; of a rare species, it may be only a single population. From one species to the next, the composition and structure of individual gene pools varies. Some species of plants and animals consist of populations each locally adapted to

its environment, while other species appear to be generalists, possessing relatively low overall diversity or showing genetic diversity mostly among individuals rather than among populations. Forces of natural selection and history shape gene pools in the continuous process of short-term adaptation and long-term evolutionary change. The composition and structure of the gene pool, as shaped by natural selection, has a unique relationship to viability and long-term survival of populations and ultimately each species.

Many human actions on the landscape have some genetic effect. While certain changes in genetic diversity occur naturally, some human activities in the Sierra Nevada accelerate or alter the direction of evolution in undesired ways. Gradual or rapid loss of genetic diversity (genetic erosion), introduction of ill-adapted genes (genetic contamination), and major shifts in gene pool structure are changes that have been brought about by human actions in the Sierra. With direct information on genetic diversity virtually nonexistent for all taxa except a few well-studied trees, fish, and scattered plants and animals, we are left to make indirect inferences about the potential effects of past human actions on gene pools and the future consequences of those effects.

In the Sierra, any human activity that breaks the chain of natural selection, or forces rapid changes in adaptation on populations, is potentially detrimental to gene pools in both the short and the long term. Such effects include habitat alteration (habitat destruction, degradation, and/or fragmentation); silviculture (tree harvest, seedling culture, and planting methods); severe wildfire (artificially large and stand-replacing fires); ecological restoration (planting); fish management (hatchery culture, fish stocking); range habitat management (shrub planting); and accidental introduction of non-native pathogens. While genetically aware programs exist for managing tree stock (tree planting) that likely mitigate most potentially detrimental effects to forests, attention to genetic consequences is mostly lacking in other forest- and range-management activities. Introduction of salmonid fish to Sierran waterways, in addition to its cascading effects on invertebrates and amphibians, has resulted in hybridization with native trout and led to the loss of local distinctiveness of most native Sierran stocks, as well as threatening the very existence of some species, such as the Little Kern golden trout, through genetic swamping. Transmission of disease pathogens from domestic sheep to native bighorn sheep has caused high mortality in the latter species, which had evolved with little resistance to Eurasian diseases. This has probably caused severe losses of genetic diversity in the small populations, as well as the more obvious immediate effect of population extinctions. Direct knowledge of genetic diversity and its implications for adaptation will likely never be well known for most Sierran taxa. In light of this, however, preventive actions can be taken and genetic guidelines followed in many forms of management to mimic natural selection and the evolutionary process in preserving as much genetic diversity as possible.

MANAGEMENT STRATEGY

Biodiversity Management Areas

As summarized in the previous sections, human activities are exerting significant impacts on native Sierran plant and animal biodiversity. In addition to outright habitat conversion to residential or agricultural use, impacts accompany extractive activities such as grazing and timber harvest. The effects of these activities, however, depend on their timing, duration, and intensity. It appears that many native species are compatible with renewable uses, given appropriate management practices. On the other hand, SNEP's gap analysis indicates that many Sierran plant community types, which are crude surrogates for total biodiversity, are not well represented in areas where maintenance or restoration of native biodiversity is the primary management emphasis. As a result, some environments and species are more vulnerable to conflicting land uses than others, and there is very uneven knowledge of status and trends among community types.

One strategy that could contribute to conservation of Sierran biodiversity would be to improve the representation of plant community types in areas whose primary management foci are restoration and maintenance of native biodiversity. Design and implementation of a system of such areas would likely require a large investment of land and financial resources. Many questions would need to be addressed before committing to such a system. Which environments and community types are most vulnerable and in need of additional representation? How much area is required to meet specific conservation goals? Where should new Biodiversity Management Areas (BMAs) be located? Can representation of biodiversity be achieved using only public lands? How well could such areas address other concerns raised by SNEP related to forest structure, aquatic biodiversity, and areas of special ecological interest?

Goals

The following pertain to all strategies using BMA methods:

1. Represent all plant community types, as defined by the state of California Natural Heritage Division, in a regionally designed set of BMAs whose main objective would be restoring and/or maintaining native biodiversity.

2. Locate the BMAs as efficiently as possible in terms of both size and suitability of the area selected to meet a specified target for representation.

Possible Solutions

BMAs can be defined as specially designated public or private lands with an active ecosystem management plan in operation whose purpose is to contribute to regional maintenance of native genetic, species population, and community levels of biodiversity and the processes that maintain biodiversity. Each BMA is part of a regional system of BMAs and is located and managed to minimize the total risk to regional biodiversity. A BMA may target specific organisms or community types for restoration and management but not to the exclusion of other components of local biodiversity. Management may include programs to test and refine best management practices for extracting renewable natural resources. Economic activities are not necessarily precluded, but they are subordinate to the goal of maintaining native biodiversity.

The system of BMAs is designed to be representative of biodiversity but is not intended as a comprehensive reserve strategy that in itself can guarantee the viability of the native biodiversity of the Sierra Nevada. The SNEP BMA strategy assumes that the region will remain largely rural in character and managed for renewable resources in a way that sustains many if not most elements of native biodiversity. Given this scenario, a BMA system could not only provide sanctuaries for some species least compatible with human activities in the region but also provide a kind of insurance policy for maintaining native species and ecosystems. It is then largely a societal decision how much land to allocate to BMA status.

Designing a BMA system requires definition of a planning region, a starting set of BMAs, a set of sites within the region from which to select new BMAs, target levels for representing plant communities in BMAs, a means of comparing the suitability of different sites for BMA status, and a means of comparing the desirability of alternative BMA systems that all meet the stated goal for representing biodiversity.

SNEP developed and tested a computer siting model to explore opportunities for a comprehensive BMA system for the Sierra, in the following manner:

❋ SNEP Significant Areas Inventory

In addition to specific inventories of features such as old-growth forests and wildlife, SNEP mapped 945 areas of special interest on the national forests and national parks of the Sierra Nevada (figure 5.3). These areas contain features of special ecological, cultural, or geological diversity. A feature was considered significant if it was unusually rare, diverse, or representative of natural (including cultural) diversity. The average size of the areas was 3,349 acres for ecological features, 5,804 acres for cultural features, and 9,443 acres for geological features. More than 70% of the areas were newly recognized. Although more than a third of these areas are in "protected" categories of land designation (wilderness, natural reserves, parks, etc.), more than half were recorded as having had past or continuing impacts from intensive human uses, including recreation and grazing.

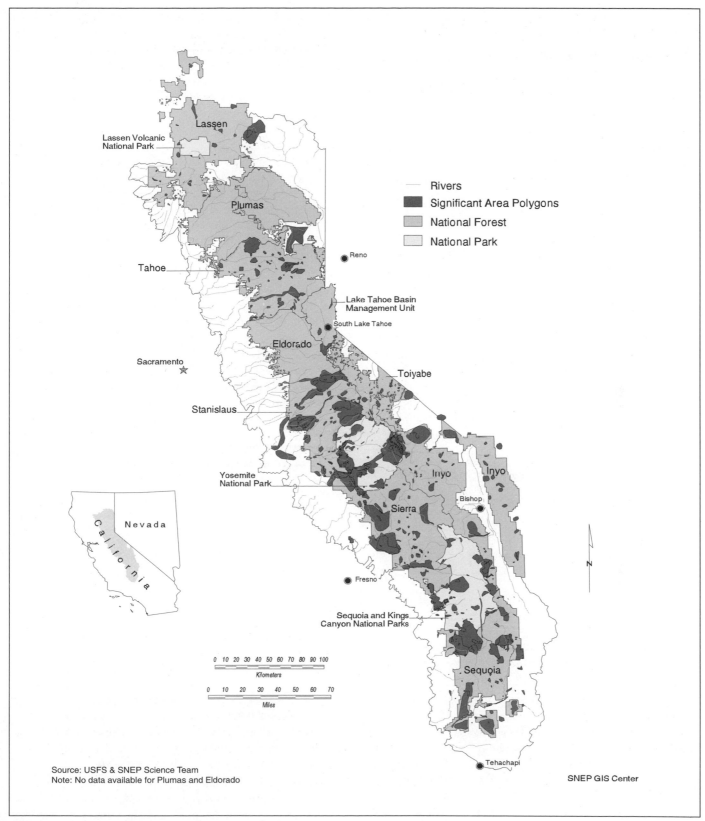

FIGURE 5.3

Ecologically significant areas mapped by SNEP. (From volume II, chapter 29.)

- The range was divided into northern, central, and southern regions.

- Each region was divided into planning watersheds averaging 7,500 acres in size. These watersheds form the set of sites for selecting new BMAs. (Only entire watersheds were selected.)

- A watershed suitability index was devised based on human population density, road density, the proportion of the watershed in private lands, and the degree of intermingling of public and private lands.

- Several starting BMA systems were compared. For example, one alternative assumed no existing BMAs. Another considered all parks, designated nature reserves, and ungrazed designated wilderness areas as BMA lands.

- We compared two target levels for representing plant community types in BMAs: 10% versus 25% of the distribution of each plant community type as mapped in the GAP database.

- The best (optimal) BMA system was the set of sites that required the least total area to meet the representation target and also had the highest total suitability. (In practice there is a trade-off between reducing the area required and maximizing the suitability of the solution.)

This strategy is not directed at a specific ecosystem problem. Instead, it is formulated as a proactive conservation approach to reduce the vulnerability of Sierran biodiversity to conflicting land uses—and to do so efficiently. The specific ecological concerns and management responses would vary among the different BMAs, which would be located to represent the full array of Sierran plant community types. SNEP addressed five specific questions related to the likely scope of a BMA system, depending on different assumptions and priorities.

1. What is the minimum area required to represent all Sierran plant community types in BMAs? How does a representative BMA system compare to the existing set of parks, wilderness areas, and reserves in the region?

If one ignores current land ownership and management designations and sets out to represent plant communities proportionately in a BMA system based on watersheds whose average size is 7,500 acres, an efficient BMA system requires land in direct proportion to the target level, at least over the range of target levels examined in this study. In other words, it takes roughly 10% of the region to meet a 10% goal, and 25% of the region to meet a 25% goal. The pattern of selected watersheds is very different from the current distribution of parks and wilderness areas, which are concentrated at middle and high elevations in the central and southern portion of the range.

In the northern Sierra, if one starts with a BMA system composed of Class 1 lands as defined by the Gap Analysis Project

(see "Ownership and Management of Sierran Plant Communities" earlier in this chapter), only five of fifty-nine plant community types exceed a 10% target level. At a minimum, a representative BMA system to meet this target level would require roughly 500,000 acres to include all plant community types. This is an area roughly two-thirds the size of Yosemite National Park.

In the central and southern Sierra, Yosemite, Sequoia, and Kings Canyon National Parks, despite their large size, do not encompass the full suite of plant community types. Roughly half of the native plant community types in these regions do not meet or exceed a 10% target. Meeting that target would require a minimum of roughly 370,000 acres of additional BMA land, 30% of which is currently privately owned.

Increasing the size of the BMA units by a factor of three, from "planning watersheds" to "superplanning watersheds" (approximately 22,500 acres) has a surprisingly large effect on the distribution and areal efficiency of the solution, increasing the area required to reach a 10% target by 27%. This illustrates both the sensitivity of the model results to the choice of planning sites and the trade-off between increased BMA size and decreased efficiency for representing regionally dispersed elements of biodiversity. However, the preservation of many elements of biodiversity (such as large animals) and processes (such as fire) requires units at least as large as superplanning watersheds.

2. How does the location of BMAs relate to the distribution of areas of special interest that have been identified in other SNEP assessments and scenarios?

Solutions using the BMA model show only a modest degree of overlap with other SNEP biodiversity strategies, unless the model weighting factors are adjusted to favor those areas (e.g., Aquatic Diversity Management Areas and Areas of Late Successional Emphasis). Overlap is slight because the latter designations are predominantly located on public lands, whereas many plant communities can be adequately represented only if private lands are included in the solution. However, BMAs can be selected that not only aim to preserve biodiveristy but also favor other SNEP areas of emphasis, especially in the northern region.

3. Can a representative BMA system be established on public lands only? If not, what area of private lands is required? How does the area requirement change if lands that are currently administratively withdrawn from grazing and timber harvest are classified as BMA lands?

Public lands alone are insufficient to create a BMA system that adequately represents all plant community types of the Sierra Nevada, even if administratively withdrawn lands are included in the solution. Many of the foothill plant community types occur almost exclusively on private lands.

4. How sensitive is the siting of BMAs to the way in which biodiversity is measured? Specifically, how do solutions designed to represent plant community types compare to solutions designed to represent vertebrate species?

Terrestrial vertebrates are reasonably well represented in a BMA system selected for plant communities. A BMA system selected for vertebrates alone, however, has little overlap with the one for plant communities. Although the two types of solutions were comparable in the area required, there were considerable differences in the sites selected as optimal for representing vertebrates versus those for representing plant communities. Because BMAs are based on watersheds and thus implicitly include stream systems and their adjacent riparian zones, they can be designed to provide for the large proportion of wildlife dependent upon riparian habitats; their weakness in this regard is that no account is taken of upstream conditions and their potential impacts on the BMA watershed, unless explicit measures are included to consider those factors.

5. Do some areas emerge from the analysis that appear especially well suited to serve as BMAs?

Although the modeling exercise has real limitations, certain geographic areas were consistently identified in the alternatives as well suited to become BMAs, based on the biological, efficiency, and suitability criteria, and these areas therefore were less sensitive to changes in model assumptions and objectives. In the northern region, these general areas include the lower elevations in Calaveras County and portions of the Cosumnes River basin, the middle elevations of Sierra County north of Highway 49, and parts of Plumas County east of Highway 89 and south of Highway 70. Frequently selected watersheds in the central region are scattered along Highway 49, particularly in Mariposa County. Few watersheds are needed from higher-elevation zones because Yosemite National Park provides coverage for most conifer and subalpine community types. Likewise in the southern region, higher-elevation communities are generally well represented in the national parks. The areas of BMAs from the alternatives for this region tend to concentrate along the South Fork of the Kern River to Walker Pass and along the Greenhorn Mountains.

Implications

The criteria for evaluating different model alternatives were simply the area required and the total suitability of the selected watersheds. The solutions are sensitive to the size of the planning region and of the planning units (watersheds), the weights used to assign suitability, the starting BMA system, and the measures of biodiversity. The model was designed to produce solutions with minimum area and maximum suitability. However, the solutions may not be optimal with respect to other design criteria—for example, social desirability, political feasibility, economic cost, spatial arrangement of the sites to provide connected biological (especially vertebrate) habitat, or future changes in the distribution of habitats and suitability factors. The model weighting factors can be adjusted to favor certain goals, such as upstream aquatic conservation or connected riparian systems. Again, we emphasize that the purpose of the modeling was to explore possible dimensions of plausible BMA systems, rather than to identify the specific set of sites that would best meet the stated goals.

Case Study of the BMA Strategy Applied to El Dorado County

The Biodiversity Management Area strategy represents one possible management and policy solution to attain a specific set of objectives aimed at maintaining the health and sustainability of Sierra Nevada ecosystems. This strategy was formulated from a regionwide perspective, using relatively coarse ecological and social information. Implementation could require major location-specific changes in public and private institutions, economic activities, land allocations, and resource management practices.

Due to time and resource limitations, we could not analyze how the BMA strategy would play out in each local setting within the region. However, we did undertake a case study in El Dorado County. The goal in this case study was to expose some of the local ecological, economic, and institutional issues and opportunities that might arise should the BMA approach be pursued.

We examined the solutions for two BMA alternatives for the northern region (figure 5.4). The objective of both alternatives was to include at least 10% of the mapped distribution of each plant community type in lands designated as BMAs, while minimizing the total area and maximizing the suitability of the solution to meet the 10% goal. The first alternative (A, in figure 5.4) is based on a starting BMA system of designated parks, reserves, and ungrazed wilderness areas (Class 1 lands in SNEP's gap analysis). The second alternative (B, in figure 5.4) includes both Class 1 lands and Class 2 lands (national forest lands that are administratively withdrawn from intensive timber management and grazing) based on current land suitability class maps and grazing allotment boundaries.

For alternative A, fifty-four of fifty-nine mapped plant community types do not meet the 10% target for representation on initial BMA lands. The 10% solution requires fifty-five additional watersheds whose combined area is 467,000 acres or an area roughly three-fourths the size of Yosemite National Park. In this alternative, 41% of the new BMA acreage has to be on private lands, in order to cover foothill woodland, shrubland, grassland, and meadow community types that are largely in private ownership. Only 37,393 acres (18.6%) of the final BMA solution are administratively withdrawn national forest lands. Five of the selected watersheds fall within the case study area in El Dorado County.

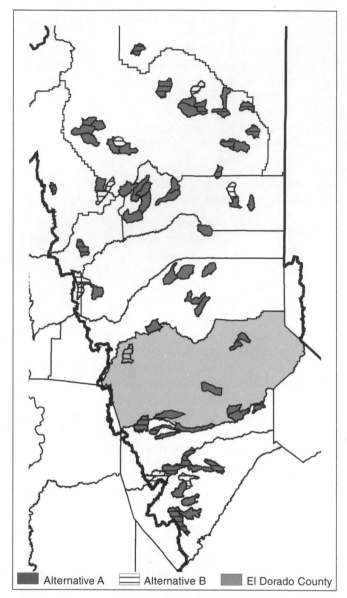

FIGURE 5.4

Case study of the BMA strategy. Two alternative BMA networks for the northern region, both of which have objectives of including at least 10% of the mapped distribution of each plant community type in lands designated as BMAs, while minimizing the total area and maximizing the suitability of the solution. Alternative A (darkly shaded polygons) shows BMAs needed in addition to Class 1 lands (designated parks, reserves, and ungrazed wilderness areas). Alternative B (cross-hatched polygons) shows BMAs needed in addition to Class 1 lands and Class 2 lands (national forest lands that are administratively withdrawn from intensive timber harvest and grazing). Class 1 and Class 2 lands are not shown. El Dorado County is shaded for reference. (From volume II, chapter 58.)

The area required in alternative B, which begins with Class 1 and Class 2 lands, is considerably less than that of alternative A, because the Class 2 lands account for many of the middle-elevation forest and shrubland community types. Under this alternative, 10% of the region is initial BMA lands and only thirty-six of fifty-five plant community types require additional representation. The solution requires twenty-five additional watersheds whose area totals 216,029 acres. Because middle- and high-elevation types are relatively well covered, watersheds are selected mainly from the foothill zone. Nearly half of the new area is selected from private lands in order to represent foothill plant community types.

Black Rock Creek Watershed

The solutions to BMA alternatives A and B were examined from a more local perspective using census and zoning data for El Dorado County. For example, one of the watersheds selected in a BMA alternative (see volume II, chapter 58) is the Black Rock Creek watershed near the towns of Cool and Pilot Hill (plate 5.3). This watershed, which was selected in four of nine model BMA alternatives for the northern region, is 9,312 acres and is entirely privately owned. The vegetation cover is a mosaic of foothill types dominated by foothill pine–oak woodland, interior live oak woodland, black oak woodland, annual grassland, and riparian woodland. Despite the lack of public lands, the watershed suitability index (WSI) is relatively low (i.e., the predicted suitability of this watershed for BMA status is high) based on mapped population density and roads.

For the Black Rock Creek watershed to meet the definition of a BMA it would have to be managed holistically to maintain native biodiversity associated with oak woodlands, grasslands, and riparian ecosystems. This might include such activities as (1) limiting and consolidating any future road construction and residential development to minimize fragmentation of habitats, (2) adaptive management of livestock grazing in upland environments to ensure adequate oak regeneration, promote native herbs, and reduce cover by noxious, non-native weeds, (3) enhanced protection and restoration of riparian areas, (4) controlled burning to restore or maintain specific upland plant and animal communities, and (5) systematic ecological monitoring of upland, riparian, and aquatic environments.

Although at present the watershed has many biological and environmental attributes that make it attractive for BMA status, the presence of multiple private landowners and the proximity to Auburn and other expanding municipal areas would require collaborative planning for BMA management, especially in the future. In the General Plan for El Dorado County, Black Rock Creek watershed is zoned primarily low-density residential and rural residential, with the exception of areas in the vicinity of Cool and Pilot Hill that are zoned medium- to high-density residential (plate 5.4). In contrast, the Alternative General Plan calls for a large block of open space in the southern half of the watershed and an increase in medium-density residential zoning in the eastern watershed. Full buildout based on either of these county plans would require extensive road construction and new housing and would lower the suitability of the watershed for BMA status. On the other hand, the high land values in these areas may provide an opportunity: nearby lands might be sold for development and the proceeds used as a conservation land bank to fund creation and maintenance of a BMA in this area.

Prothro Creek Watershed

Prothro Creek watershed is one of several selected from the upper Cosumnes Basin as part of the solution to one BMA alternative (see volume II, chapter 58) (plate 5.5). As we noted earlier, this alternative starts with Class 1 lands as the BMA system and requires additional area for most middle- and high-elevation forest types as well as for foothill plant community types. The Prothro Creek watershed was selected to contribute area in Sierran mixed conifer forest, west-side ponderosa pine forest, Jeffrey pine forest, red fir forest, mixed montane chaparral, and montane manzanita chaparral. The watershed is located on the southern edge of El Dorado County, just northwest of Lower Bear River Reservoir. It is 9,257 acres in area and is 92% public land, 8% industrial timberland. Population density is very low, but 34% of the watershed was mapped in roaded area.

Management of the Prothro Creek watershed as a BMA would likely be oriented toward maintaining native biodiversity in montane forest, notably Sierran mixed conifer and red fir types. This could include (1) fire management to reduce the likelihood of severe, stand-replacing fires, (2) implementing silvicultural systems to attain desired forest compositional and structural properties on different sites, (3) removal or repair of some logging roads, (4) protection and restoration of aquatic systems and riparian buffers, (5) systematic monitoring and adaptive management of biota and ecosystem processes.

Roughly 10% of the watershed is mapped by the Eldorado National Forest as unsuitable for intensive timber harvest (plate 5.6), including a large Spotted Owl Habitat Area (SOHA) in the western half and riparian zones throughout the watershed. The late successional old-growth (LSOG) mapping team divided the Prothro Creek watershed into three polygons: two lower-elevation polygons mapped as montane mixed conifer and one higher-elevation polygon mapped as upper montane red fir. These labels are consistent with the GAP vegetation map, which divided the watershed into ten polygons. The LSOG mappers assigned the red fir polygon a rank of 3, and the two mixed conifer polygons ranks of 1 and 4 (see chapter 6). The two mixed conifer polygons were included in an Area of Late Successional Emphasis (ALSE) that extends to the south and west.

The Prothro Creek watershed highlights several features of the BMA strategy. First, the watershed encompasses a wide range of elevations and ecosystem types, and an effective management plan would have to account for these different types and their juxtaposition in the landscape. In this sense a BMA is quite different from many reserves—for example, U.S. Forest Service Research Natural Areas—that target one or a few ecosystem types. The presence of industrial timberland adds another layer of management complexity to this watershed.

Much of the lower watershed was recently harvested for timber, and, although the area is included in at least one proposed ALSE system, it was given an LSOG rank of 1. This illustrates the point that, because the GAP vegetation database does not include detailed structural information, the BMA solutions do not account for seral stage in representing forest types and thus could include recently burned or logged areas. Perhaps 60% of the Prothro watershed is in rank 3 red fir or rank 4 mixed conifer forestlands that are also classified as suitable for intensive timber management. Thus another concern in designating this watershed as a BMA is possible reduction of the commercial timber base in the Eldorado National Forest.

Management Implications

The case study of watersheds in El Dorado County (only two of which are summarized here; for more, see volume II) serves to emphasize the multisector, multijurisdictional nature of biodiversity conservation in the Sierra Nevada. Virtually every BMA that was examined included both private and public lands. One BMA spanned two counties, and another included both public and private industrial timberlands. It is difficult to envision how a regionally designed BMA strategy, implemented in the form of watershed-based ecosystem management aimed at native biodiversity, could be undertaken or succeed without transfer of management rights to a single administering agency, unless much more effective interaction and collaboration occur between the public and the private sectors and among local, state, and federal agencies.

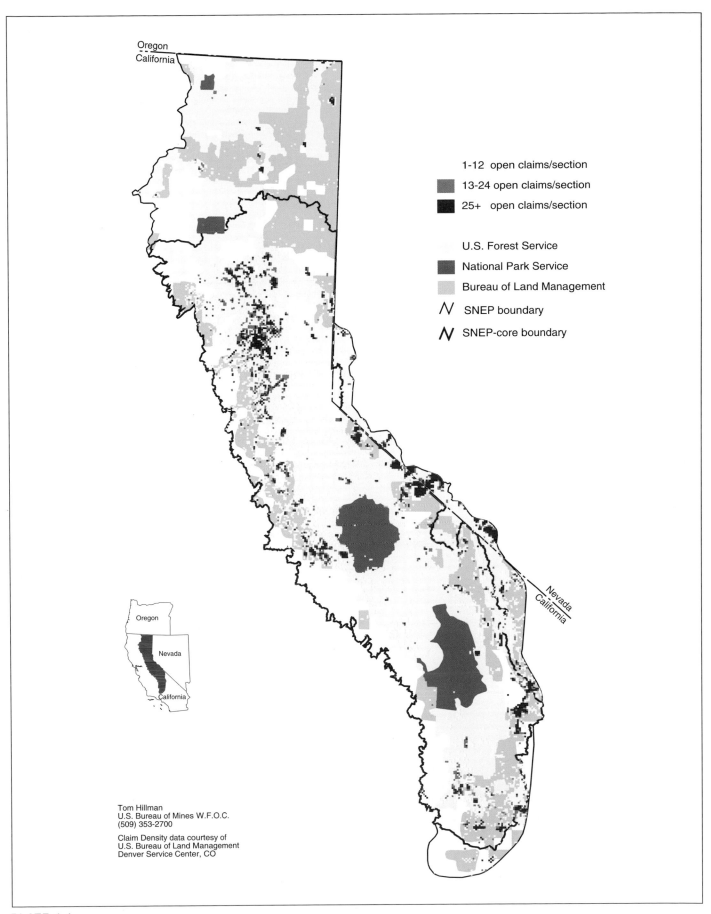

Oregon
California

1-12 open claims/section

13-24 open claims/section

25+ open claims/section

U.S. Forest Service

National Park Service

Bureau of Land Management

N SNEP boundary

N SNEP-core boundary

Oregon

Nevada

California

Nevada
California

Tom Hillman
U.S. Bureau of Mines W.F.O.C.
(509) 353-2700

Claim Density data courtesy of
U.S. Bureau of Land Management
Denver Service Center, CO

PLATE 1.1

Total mineral claim density per section in the SNEP study area. (From volume II, chapter 18.)

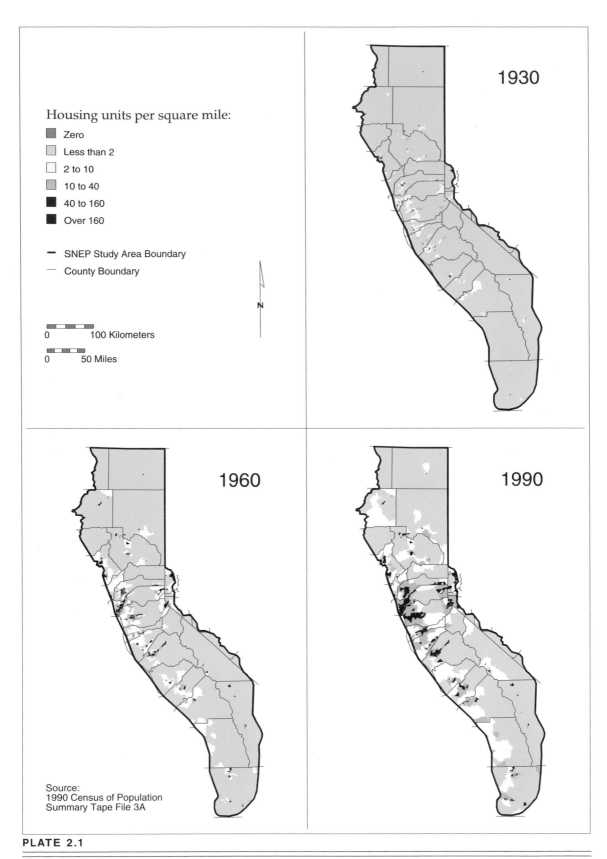

Housing units per square mile:
- Zero
- Less than 2
- 2 to 10
- 10 to 40
- 40 to 160
- Over 160

— SNEP Study Area Boundary
— County Boundary

0   100 Kilometers

0   50 Miles

1930

1960

1990

Source:
1990 Census of Population
Summary Tape File 3A

PLATE 2.1

Change in housing density in the Sierra Nevada at three different times: 1930, 1960, and 1990. (From volume II, chapter 11.)

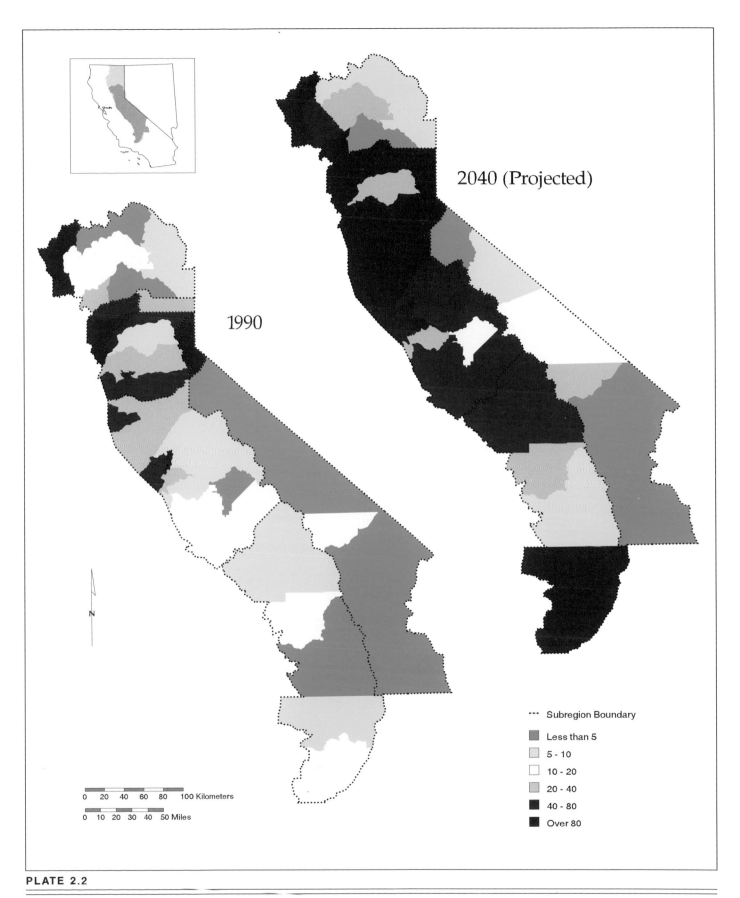

2040 (Projected)

1990

Subregion Boundary

Less than 5

5 - 10

10 - 20

20 - 40

40 - 80

Over 80

0 20 40 60 80 100 Kilometers

0 10 20 30 40 50 Miles

PLATE 2.2

Current and projected population density (persons per square mile), 1990 and 2040. (From volume II, chapter 11.)

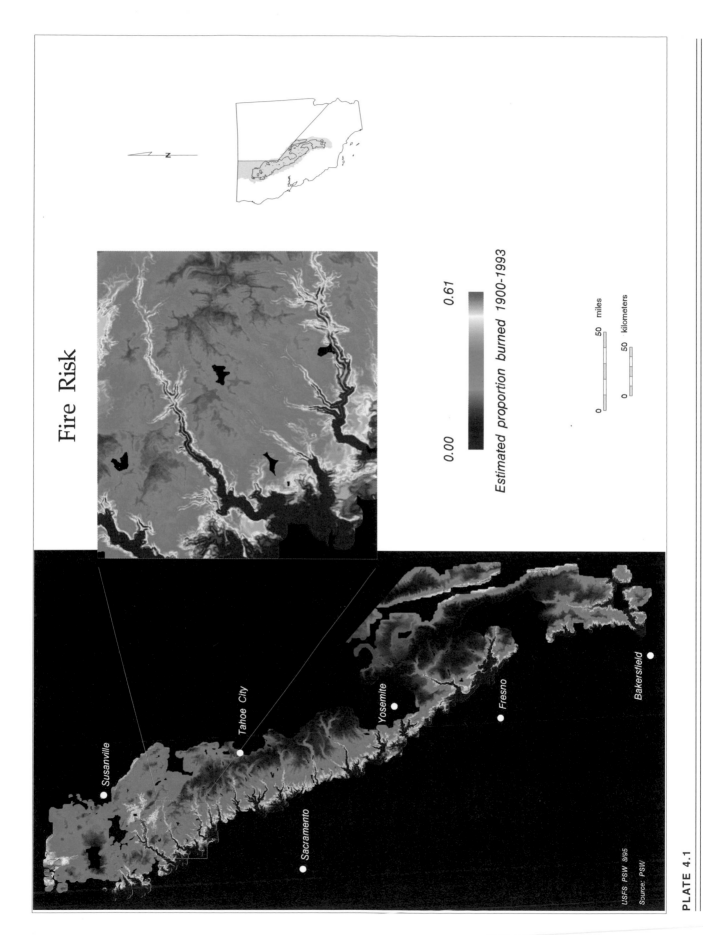

Fire Risk

Estimated proportion burned 1900-1993

0.00   0.61

Susanville

Tahoe City

Sacramento

Yosemite

Fresno

Bakersfield

USFS PSW 8/95

Source: PSW

N

0   50   miles

0   50   kilometers

PLATE 4.1

Fire risk in the Sierra Nevada based on model projections for fire frequency. Risk levels were based on fire frequencies for the period 1908–93, using elevation, slope, and rainfall as independent variables. (From volume II, chapter 41.)

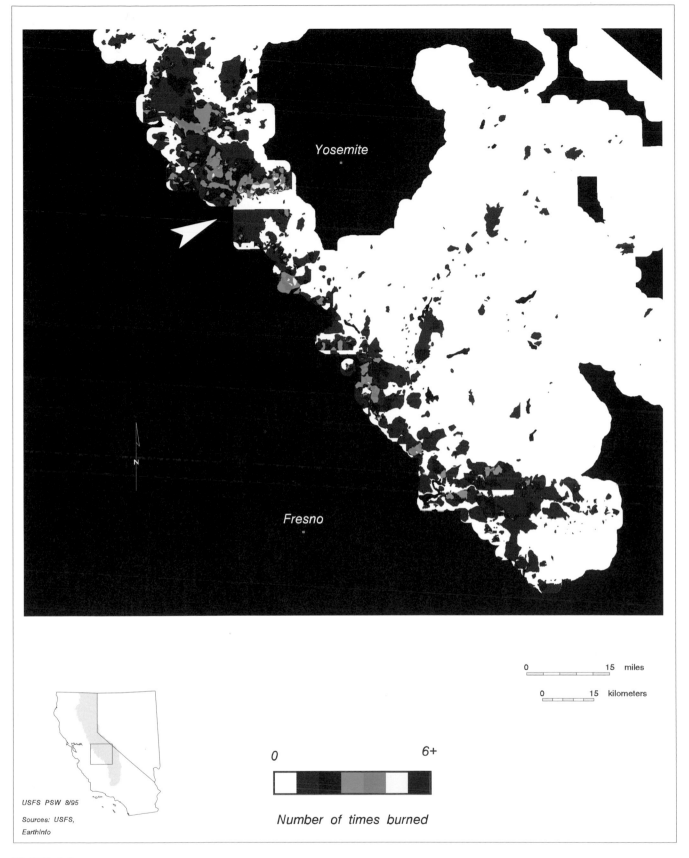

Yosemite

Fresno

0 _____ 15 miles

0 _____ 15 kilometers

USFS PSW 8/95

Sources: USFS,
EarthInfo

0   6+

Number of times burned

PLATE 4.2

Fire recurrence map for an area of high fire activity in the southern Sierra Nevada. The area, which reburned more than five times, is confined to a small section on the north side of the Merced River immediately adjacent to State Highway 140, a major route into Yosemite National Park (see arrow). (From volume II, chapter 41.)

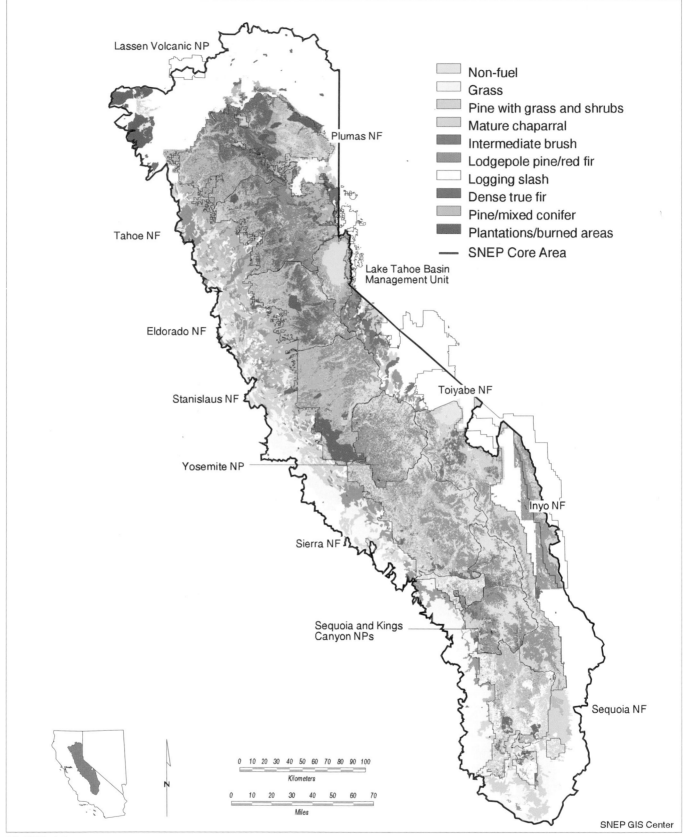

Legend:
- Non-fuel
- Grass
- Pine with grass and shrubs
- Mature chaparral
- Intermediate brush
- Lodgepole pine/red fir
- Logging slash
- Dense true fir
- Pine/mixed conifer
- Plantations/burned areas
- ⎯ SNEP Core Area

Lassen Volcanic NP

Plumas NF

Tahoe NF

Lake Tahoe Basin
Management Unit

Eldorado NF

Stanislaus NF

Toiyabe NF

Yosemite NP

Inyo NF

Sierra NF

Sequoia and Kings
Canyon NPs

Sequoia NF

0 10 20 30 40 50 60 70 80 90 100
Kilometers

0 10 20 30 40 50 60 70
Miles

N

SNEP GIS Center

PLATE 4.3

Generalized surface fuel characteristics as expressed by the composition and structure of the dominant vegetation occurring in the SNEP core area. Sites dominated by grass, lodgepole pine/red fir, and plantation represent relatively low hazard areas. Dense true fir and intermediate brush types indicate areas of moderate hazard. Pine with grass and shrub understory, pine/mixed conifer, logging slash, and mature chaparral represent areas of high to extreme fire hazard. (From volume III, chapter 19.)

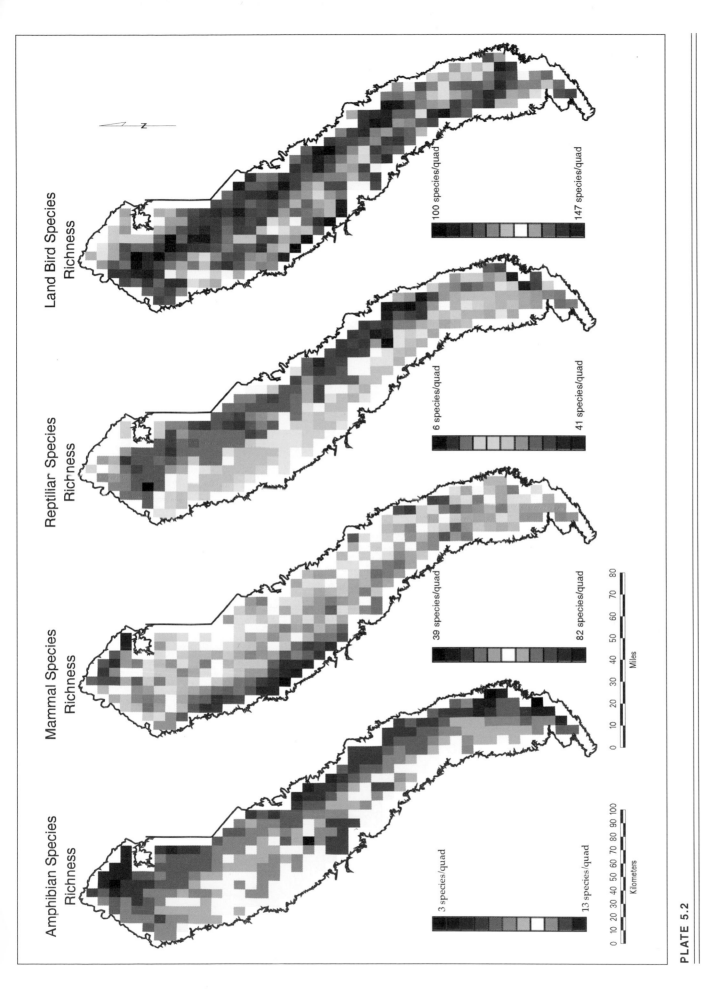

PLATE 5.2

Diversity (richness) of terrestrial vertebrate species in the Sierra Nevada: amphibians, mammals, reptiles, and birds. (From volume II, chapters 23 and 25.)

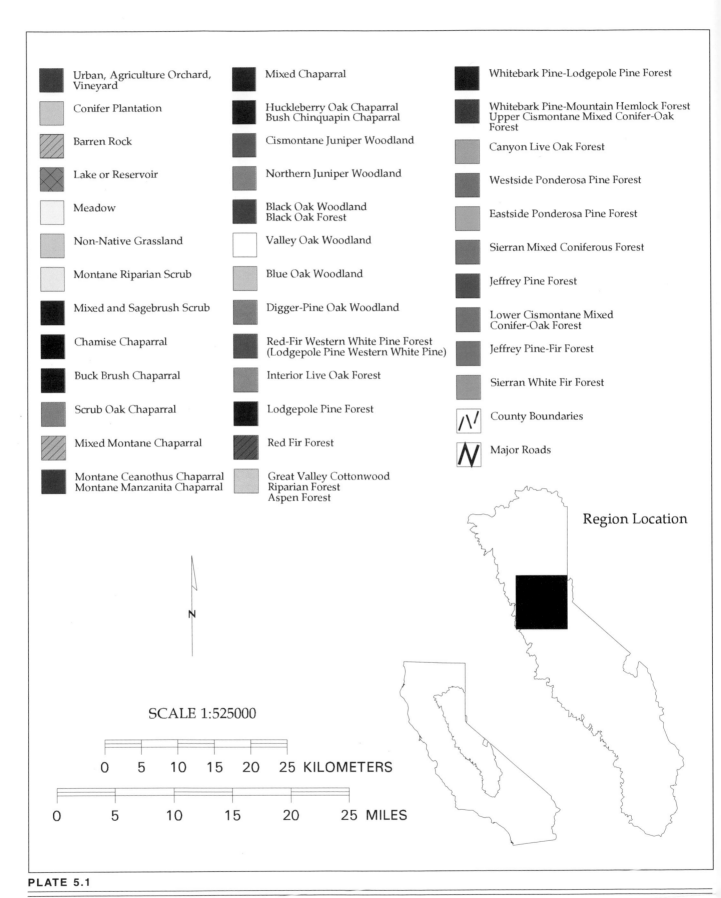

Legend:

- Urban, Agriculture Orchard, Vineyard
- Conifer Plantation
- Barren Rock
- Lake or Reservoir
- Meadow
- Non-Native Grassland
- Montane Riparian Scrub
- Mixed and Sagebrush Scrub
- Chamise Chaparral
- Buck Brush Chaparral
- Scrub Oak Chaparral
- Mixed Montane Chaparral
- Montane Ceanothus Chaparral Montane Manzanita Chaparral

- Mixed Chaparral
- Huckleberry Oak Chaparral Bush Chinquapin Chaparral
- Cismontane Juniper Woodland
- Northern Juniper Woodland
- Black Oak Woodland Black Oak Forest
- Valley Oak Woodland
- Blue Oak Woodland
- Digger-Pine Oak Woodland
- Red-Fir Western White Pine Forest (Lodgepole Pine Western White Pine)
- Interior Live Oak Forest
- Lodgepole Pine Forest
- Red Fir Forest
- Great Valley Cottonwood Riparian Forest Aspen Forest

- Whitebark Pine-Lodgepole Pine Forest
- Whitebark Pine-Mountain Hemlock Forest Upper Cismontane Mixed Conifer-Oak Forest
- Canyon Live Oak Forest
- Westside Ponderosa Pine Forest
- Eastside Ponderosa Pine Forest
- Sierran Mixed Coniferous Forest
- Jeffrey Pine Forest
- Lower Cismontane Mixed Conifer-Oak Forest
- Jeffrey Pine-Fir Forest
- Sierran White Fir Forest
- County Boundaries
- Major Roads

Region Location

SCALE 1:525000

0 5 10 15 20 25 KILOMETERS

0 5 10 15 20 25 MILES

N

PLATE 5.1

Distribution of plant communities in the west-central Sierra Nevada. (From volume II, chapter 23.)

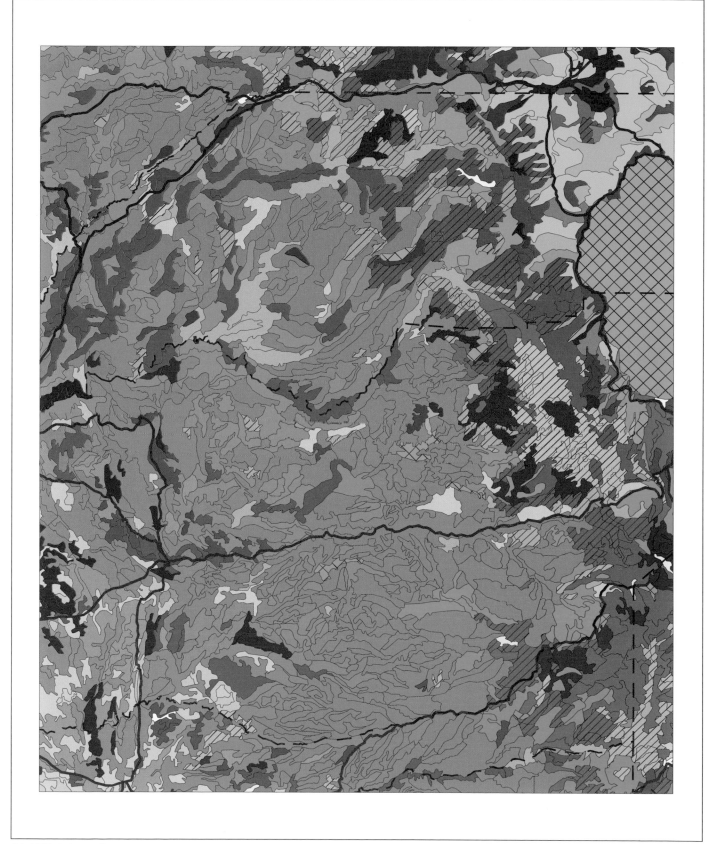

PLATE 5.1 continued

PLATE 5.4

Land zoning in the Black Rock Creek watershed under the proposed general plan for El Dorado County, Biodiversity Management Areas Case Study. R = rural residential, L = light residential, M = medium residential, O = open space. (From volume II, chapter 58.)

PLATE 5.3

Satellite image (from Thematic Mapper) of the Black Rock Creek planning watershed, Biodiversity Management Areas Case Study for El Dorado County, showing the watershed boundary (yellow line), vegetation units (red lines), and roads (black lines). (From volume II, chapter 58.)

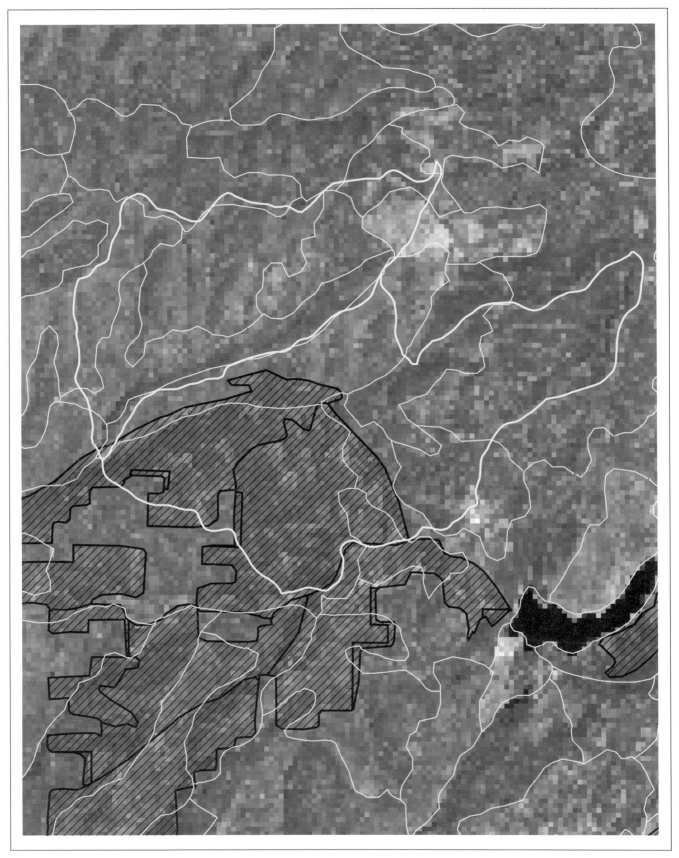

PLATE 5.5

Satellite image (from Thematic Mapper) of the Prothro Creek planning watershed, Biodiversity Management Areas Case Study for El Dorado County, showing the watershed boundaries (thick yellow lines), vegetation units (thin yellow lines), and SNEP Areas of Late-Successional Emphasis (purple hatching). (From volume II, chapter 58.)

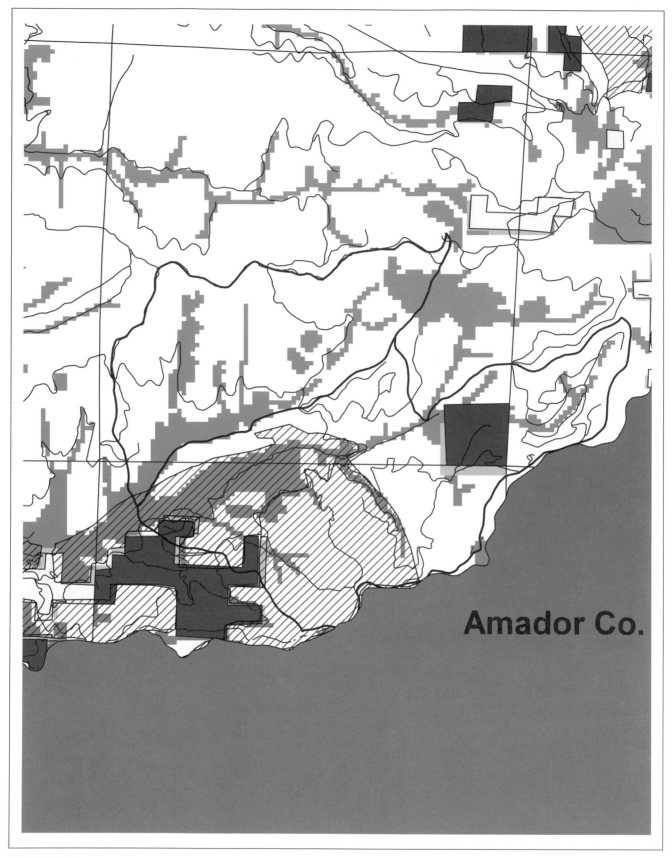

Amador Co.

PLATE 5.6

Map of the Prothro Creek planning watershed, Biodiversity Management Areas Case Study for El Dorado County, showing private industrial timberlands (gray-green), USFS lands classified as suitable (white) or unsuitable (bright green) for intensive timber harvest, other ownership (light yellow), roads (black lines), BMA watersheds (red lines), and Areas of Late-Successional Emphasis (hatching). (From volume II, chapter 58.)

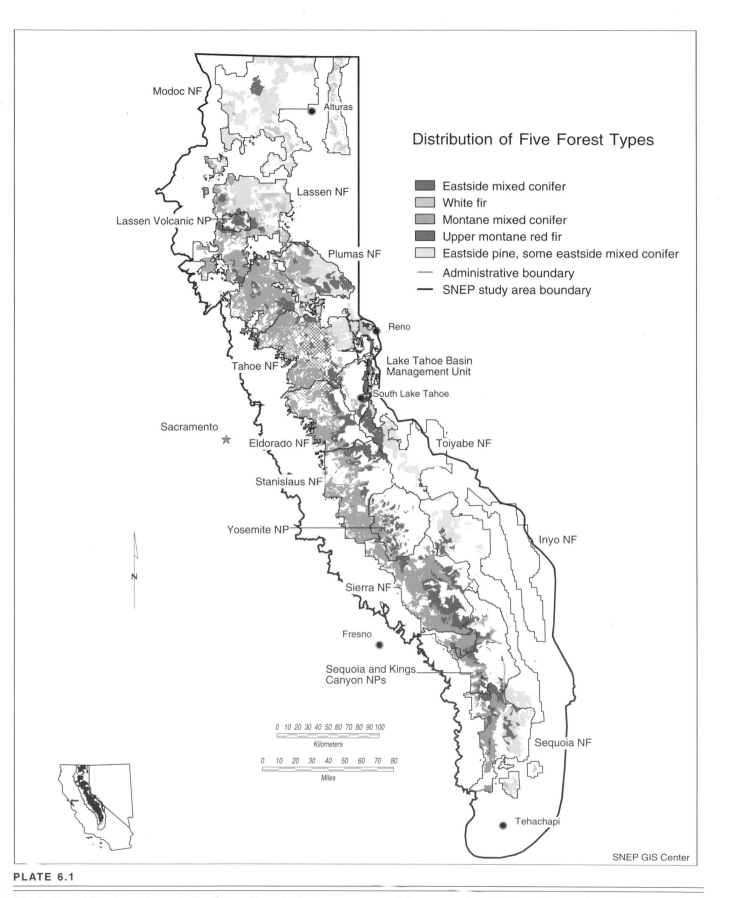

Distribution of Five Forest Types

■ Eastside mixed conifer
■ White fir
■ Montane mixed conifer
■ Upper montane red fir
■ Eastside pine, some eastside mixed conifer
— Administrative boundary
━ SNEP study area boundary

Modoc NF

Alturas

Lassen NF

Lassen Volcanic NP

Plumas NF

Reno

Tahoe NF

Lake Tahoe Basin
Management Unit

South Lake Tahoe

Sacramento

Eldorado NF

Toiyabe NF

Stanislaus NF

Yosemite NP

Inyo NF

Sierra NF

Fresno

Sequoia and Kings
Canyon NPs

0 10 20 30 40 50 60 70 80 90 100
Kilometers

0 10 20 30 40 50 60 70 80
Miles

Sequoia NF

Tehachapi

SNEP GIS Center

PLATE 6.1

Distribution of five forest types in the Sierra Nevada that were assessed for successional status. (From volume II, chapter 21.)

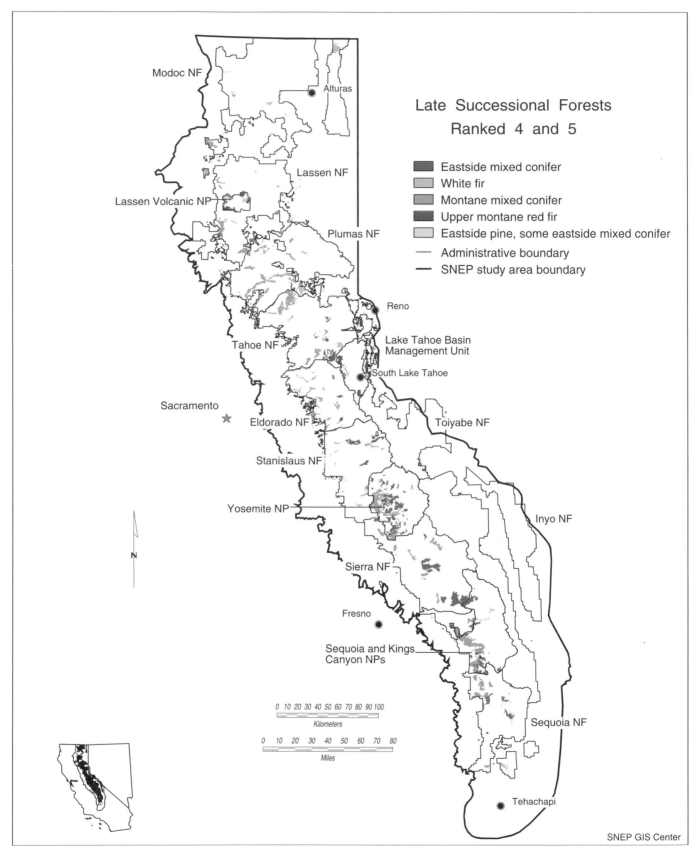

Late Successional Forests
Ranked 4 and 5

- ■ Eastside mixed conifer
- □ White fir
- ▨ Montane mixed conifer
- ▩ Upper montane red fir
- ▤ Eastside pine, some eastside mixed conifer
- —— Administrative boundary
- —— SNEP study area boundary

Modoc NF

Alturas

Lassen NF

Lassen Volcanic NP

Plumas NF

Reno

Tahoe NF

Lake Tahoe Basin
Management Unit

South Lake Tahoe

Sacramento

Eldorado NF

Toiyabe NF

Stanislaus NF

Yosemite NP

Inyo NF

Sierra NF

Fresno

Sequoia and Kings
Canyon NPs

0 10 20 30 40 50 60 70 80 90 100
Kilometers

0 10 20 30 40 50 60 70 80
Miles

Sequoia NF

Tehachapi

SNEP GIS Center

PLATE 6.2

High quality (ranks 4 and 5) late successional middle-elevation conifer forests of the Sierra Nevada ranked by SNEP. (From volume II, chapter 21.)

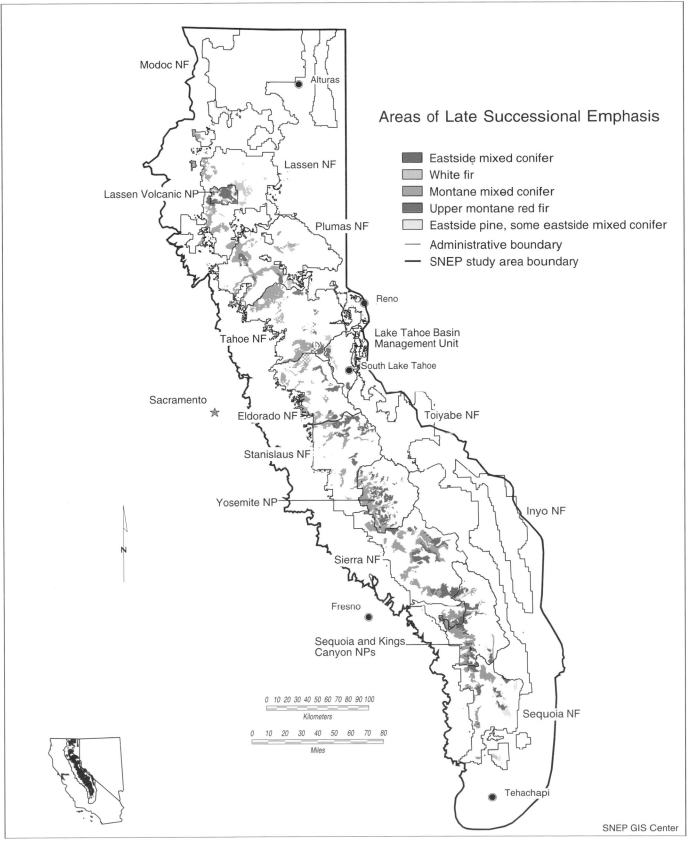

Areas of Late Successional Emphasis

Eastside mixed conifer
White fir
Montane mixed conifer
Upper montane red fir
Eastside pine, some eastside mixed conifer
— Administrative boundary
— SNEP study area boundary

Modoc NF
Alturas
Lassen NF
Lassen Volcanic NP
Plumas NF
Reno
Tahoe NF
Lake Tahoe Basin Management Unit
South Lake Tahoe
Sacramento
Eldorado NF
Toiyabe NF
Stanislaus NF
Yosemite NP
Inyo NF
Sierra NF
Fresno
Sequoia and Kings Canyon NPs
Sequoia NF
Tehachapi

SNEP GIS Center

0 10 20 30 40 50 60 70 80 90 100
Kilometers

0 10 20 30 40 50 60 70 80
Miles

PLATE 6.3

Network of areas of late successional emphasis (ALSEs) in middle-elevation conifer forests developed by SNEP as one landscape design for maintaining late successional forests. (From volume II, chapter 21.)

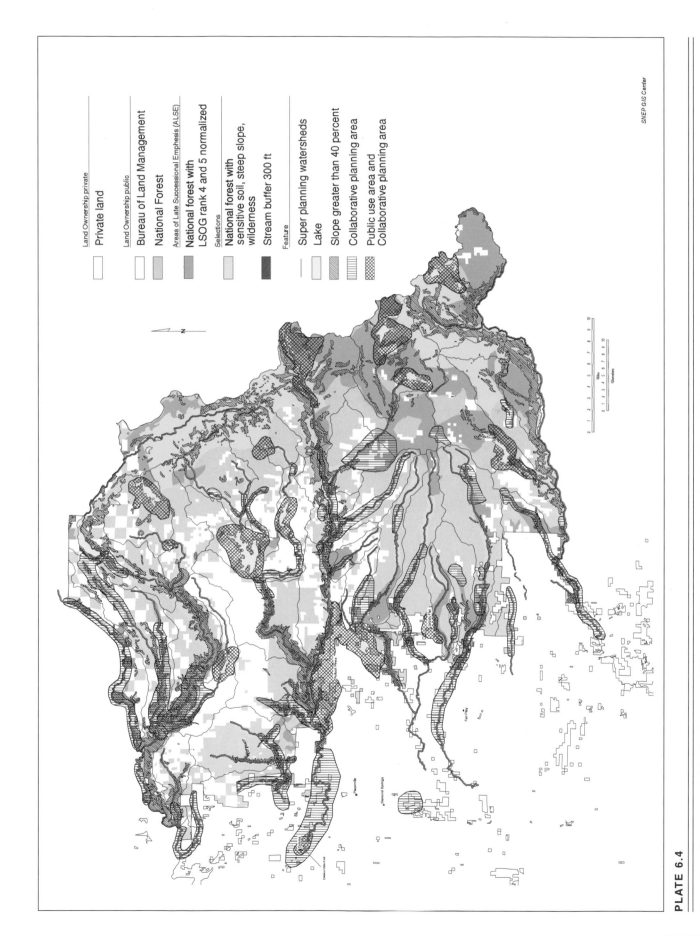

Land Ownership private

☐ Private land

Land Ownership public

☐ Bureau of Land Management

☐ National Forest

Areas of Late Successional Emphasis (ALSE)

☐ National forest with
LSOG rank 4 and 5 normalized

Selections

☐ National forest with
sensitive soil, steep slope,
wilderness

☐ Stream buffer 300 ft

Feature

— Super planning watersheds

☐ Lake

☐ Slope greater than 40 percent

☐ Collaborative planning area

☐ Public use area and
Collaborative planning area

N

0 1 2 3 4 5 6 7 8 9 10
Miles
0 1 2 3 4 5 6 7 8 9 10
Kilometers

SNEP GIS Center

PLATE 6.4

One alternative suggested by the Integrated Watershed Strategy/Case Study for the Eldorado National Forest.

CHAPTER 6

Late Successional Old-Growth Forest Conditions

❊ CRITICAL FINDINGS

Status of Current Late Successional Forests   Late successional old-growth forests of middle elevations (west-side mixed conifer, red fir, white fir, east-side mixed conifer, and east-side pine types) at present constitute 7%–30% of the forest cover, depending on forest type. On average, national forests have about 25% the amount of the national parks, which is an approximate benchmark for pre-contact forest conditions. East-side pine forests have been especially altered.

Forest Simplification   The primary impact of 150 years of forestry on middle-elevation conifer forests has been to simplify structure (including large trees, snags, woody debris of large diameter, canopies of multiple heights and closures, and complex spatial mosaics of vegetation), and presumably function, of these forests.

Distribution of Late Successional Forests   Four Sierran national parks, Lassen Volcanic, Yosemite, Sequoia, and Kings Canyon, provide most of the remaining large contiguous areas of late successional forests in middle-elevation conifer types.

Historic Conditions of Federal Lands   Much of the best of the accessible pine forest was cut before the national forests were created. Many national forest lands were created from the leavings: cutover lands, steep canyon walls, high montane forests, and relatively inaccessible timberlands.

Continuous Forest Cover   Despite 150 years of Euro-American timber harvest activity in the Sierra Nevada, clear-cut blocks larger than 5–10 acres are at present uncommon in the conifer forests of the Sierra Nevada, and tree cover is relatively continuous.

Forest Mortality   Over the past decade, as they have many times in the past, Sierra Nevada conifer forests have experienced widespread, locally severe mortality caused principally by bark beetles infesting trees stressed by drought, overdense stands, and pathogens.

ASSESSMENT

The forests of the Sierra Nevada are complex in composition, structure, and function, reflecting wide variations in environmental conditions on both local and regional scales, and varied histories of natural and human disturbance. This complexity makes an assessment of forest conditions challenging. The term *old growth* has, in common parlance, suggested ancient forests undisturbed and unaltered through time. In re-

ality, all forests are dynamic, although the rate and spatial distribution of change varies widely from region to region. Under ideal conditions, Sierran trees may live from several centuries (common) to several thousand years (uncommon), depending on species. Changes in climate over the past 10,000 years (after the end of the Pleistocene) have resulted in a continuously changing mix of species aggregations. Fire, drought, insect attacks, wind, avalanches, and other disturbances—often in combination—have typically modified and not infrequently destroyed entire stands of trees. As seedling trees are added and other trees in a stand grow, mature, and eventually die, both the appearance and the ecological function of the stand and the forest of which it is a part evolve until they reach a condition we refer to as late successional.

Old growth is incorporated within the broader category of late successional forest conditions in the following analysis. Contribution to late successional forest function refers to the ability of a stand or landscape to provide habitat for species that prefer or require late successional forest conditions and to carry out ecological functions of the types and at levels characteristic of late successional forest ecosystems, such as regulation of hydrologic regimes. Thus *old growth* and *late successional* are used as interchangeable terms here. Some of the ecological functions peculiar to the late successional stage can operate at the scale of an individual stand; others require much larger landscapes of intact forest.

SNEP used ten principal forest types for late successional analysis in the Sierra Nevada (table 6.1). Of these, our assessment of late successional old-growth (LSOG) forests has been directed principally toward the conifer forest types growing at middle elevations, the commercially important west-side mixed conifer, white fir, red fir, east-side mixed conifer, and east-side pine forests (plate 6.1). These are forest types in which structural complexity continues to increase with stand age for at least several centuries, and for which the ecological differences between late successional and earlier successional stages are distinctive and relatively well understood.

Conifer forests within the middle-elevation forested zones of the Sierra Nevada that are not disturbed by logging, clearing, or severe fire tend to develop complex structures over time. That is, most often the trees reflect a variety of sizes and conditions and, especially in the case of mixed conifer types, variety of species as well. There are large standing dead trees and down logs present, not as a by-product of timber harvest but through the natural processes of senescence and decay. Patches dominated by large, mature, and old trees are interspersed with openings and younger stands (or even single trees), forming a fine-scale mosaic resulting in both complexity from ground to tree canopy (vertical complexity) and spatial (horizontal) complexity (figure 6.1). The forest floor itself becomes more complex through the accumulation of organic

TABLE 6.1

Characteristics of the major forest type groups of the Sierra Nevada. (From volume II, chapter 21.)

| Forest Type | Dominant Trees | | Landscape Patterns | Primary Disturbances | Presettlement Fire Regime | | |
	Northern Sierra	Southern Sierra			Northern Sierra	Southern Sierra
Foothill pine and oak	Foothill pine, ponderosa pine, blue oak, live oak, Douglas fir	Foothill pine, ponderosa pine, blue oak, live oak	Mostly open structure, limited patches of dense forest, frequent natural openings (chaparral and outcrops)	Fire, insects, pathogens, drought	Low-severity regime: frequent, low-intensity fires	Same
West-side mixed conifer	Douglas fir, ponderosa pine, sugar pine, white fir, incense cedar, black oak, tan oak	Ponderosa pine, sugar pine, incense cedar, black oak, giant sequoia, Jeffrey pine	Primarily continuous forest with few extensive natural openings (e.g., outcrops)	Fire, insects, pathogens, drought	Low- to moderate-severity regimes: areas > 50 inches annual precipitation likely mixture of low- and moderate-intensity fires in complex mosaic with sufficient variability in interval to perpetuate Douglas fir; areas < 50 inches annual precipitation likely more dominantly low-intensity fires; infrequent large-scale high-severity fires	Low-severity regime: dominantly low-intensity fires
White fir	White fir	Same	Same as west-side mixed conifer	Insects, pathogens, fire, drought	Moderate-severity regime: frequent but variable extent or frequency, variable intensity with small patches of moderate to high intensity	Same?
Red fir	Red fir, lodgepole pine, western white pine	Same	Fine- to moderate-scale high patch diversity of natural openings (meadows, outcrops) and open or closed forest; large, extensive patches limited	Insects, pathogens, fire, drought, wind, avalanche	Moderate-severity regime (same as white fir)	Moderate-severity regime (same as white fir)
Jeffrey pine (upper montane)	Jeffrey pine	Same	Generally extensive uniform patches of very open forest or woodland interspersed with small pockets of denser forest	Insects, pathogens, fire, drought	Low-severity regime: low intensity and/or small extent of fires due to discontinuous fuels	Low-severity regime
Subalpine	Lodgepole pine, mountain hemlock, western white pine, whitebark pine	Lodgepole pine, mountain hemlock, western white pine, whitebark pine, foxtail pine, limber pine, western juniper	Highly variable patterns but generally diverse patch mosaic with large meadows; small patches of dense forest embedded in a large matrix of open forest or scattered trees and rock outcrop	Avalanche, wind	Low-severity regime: low intensity and/or small extent of fires due to discontinuous fuels and infrequent ignitions (due to precipitation associated with lightning)	

continued

TABLE 6.1 (continued)

Forest Type	Dominant Trees		Landscape Patterns	Primary Disturbances	Presettlement Fire Regime	
	Northern Sierra	Southern Sierra			Northern Sierra	Southern Sierra
East-side mixed conifer and white fir	White fir, ponderosa pine, Jeffrey pine (some Douglas fir, sugar pine, incense cedar)	White fir, Jeffrey pine	Variable patterns, most often occur in a coarse-scale mosaic with east-side pine related to aspect	Fire, insects, pathogens, drought	Low- to moderate-severity regime: dominantly frequent low-intensity fires but with variable intervals, enabling recruitment of Douglas fir and white fir to large sizes; greater proportion of moderate-intensity fires than in east-side pine due to greater productivity and fuel accumulations from variable intervals	Same
East-side pine	Ponderosa pine, Jeffrey pine, lodgepole pine	Jeffrey pine, lodgepole pine	Large, continuous patches of open forest that are often interspersed with large meadows, grasslands/shrublands	Fire, insects, pathogens, drought	Low-severity regime: dominantly frequent, low-severity fires	Same
Piñon and juniper	Western juniper	Utah and western juniper, piñon pine	Large, continuous savannas and woodlands	Fire, grazing, woodcutting	Low-severity regime: frequent low-intensity fires	Same
Riparian hardwood	Black cottonwood, aspen	Water birch, black cottonwood, aspen	Streamside strips	Flood, debris flow	Low-severity regime: infrequent fire	Same

FIGURE 6.1

Schematic cross section of typical west-side mixed conifer forest illustrating the structural complexity and spatial patterning characteristic of high-quality late successional stands ranked 4 and 5. (From volume II, chapter 21. Drawing by Robert VanPelt.)

matter and associated organisms. These late successional forests provide habitats for animals and plants that are not available in areas of extensive young forests, as well as regulating snowmelt, modifying biochemical processes, and moderating temperatures below their canopies.

Forests and woodlands composed of other tree species, such as foothill pine woodlands and oak woodlands and forests, riparian hardwood forests, piñon-juniper woodlands, and the several types of subalpine woodlands (e.g., whitebark pine) and forests (e.g., lodgepole pine) represent 40% of the Sierra Nevada's tree-dominated vegetation. These types also undergo structural succession that results in trees that are often very old and very large. They produce ecologically and aesthetically important structural elements, such as large snags and logs, but they generally do not develop the canopy cover, tree density, structural complexity, or patch dynamics over the substantial areas associated with middle-elevation late successional conifer forests. Our understanding of differences in ecology between early and late successional stages of these types is only partial, and although SNEP classified structural complexity in these forests, interpretations about successional status are not discussed here.

The structural complexity of natural stands reflects local environmental conditions, such as microclimate, soil depth and chemistry, water table, and disturbance patterns. Particularly at higher elevations, rock outcrops, thin soils, wetlands, and frost pockets further enrich the forest mosaic while constraining the size of the trees themselves (figure 6.2). Prior to the mid-1800s, the most significant disturbances at lower and middle elevations were apparently frequent, usually light to moderately severe fire, which thinned stands, created (usu-

ally) small openings, and generated as well as consumed snags and logs. Drought, insects, and disease killed individual trees or aggregations, providing another source of dead woody debris. Large, severe, forest-destroying fire events resulting from the interaction of drought, insect outbreaks, and extreme weather undoubtedly occurred in the Sierra Nevada, but their importance in constructing its successional landscape is a matter of conjecture.

In contrast, human activities have altered the structure of many forests in the Sierra Nevada directly and indirectly. Timber harvest has removed trees, snags, and logs, especially of larger diameters, simplifying forest structure. Denser and less diverse stands have been purposely created following harvest to accelerate timber production. The period of aboriginal occupation likely was one of increased fire frequency, with consequent lower fire intensities. Modern fire suppression has led to the invasion of shade-tolerant trees into existing older stands, producing greater vertical and horizontal continuity in canopies and largely excluding shrubs and herbs. This dense in-growth lacks the structural and ecological diversity of naturally disturbed forests and is vulnerable to high-intensity, stand-destroying fire.

Most of the timber harvest for the last half-century in the Sierra Nevada (on private and public lands) has been selective (partial) cutting rather than clear-cutting, although early logging (1850–1920) was often by clear-cutting of large areas. As a consequence, harvested forest stands often contain substantially more structural complexity, and more elements of a natural late successional stand, than would have been the case following clear-cutting. The potential contribution of these managed stands toward late successional ecological

composition) and for species that depend upon late successional forest but that are difficult to observe directly.

Major elements of the SNEP analysis were (1) adoption of structural complexity as the measure and surrogate for level of late successional function; (2) creation of a six-point ranking scale for structural complexity; and (3) identification, mapping, and characterization of landscape-level units ("polygons" of 1,000 acres or larger) to serve as the basic units of analysis (see volume II, chapter 21, for detail on methods). SNEP mapped conditions on public lands, including national forests, national park lands, and national resources lands (BLM) of the Sierra.

An experimental pilot mapping effort was applied to the Eldorado National Forest to test and refine procedures. This pilot effort led to rules and standards for structural complexity to ensure consistency in mapping over the range. Subsequently, mapping and characterization were carried out by a large team of resource specialists assembled from the federal and state land units of the Sierra, directed by members of SNEP. These specialists were used because of their familiarity with on-the-ground conditions. A wide variety of source materials, including aerial photographs, satellite imagery, and maps showing forest conditions and habitat suitability as well as personal knowledge of forest conditions, was used by the specialists to delineate landscape polygons and characterize the patches within them.

The polygons, generally of several thousand acres each (although significantly smaller in the national parks), were delineated on maps based upon overall forest type and characteristics of structural complexity. More than 2,800 such polygons were mapped on the public lands of the Sierra Nevada. For each polygon, mappers described and ranked several large, relatively homogeneous units called "patches" using late successional structural features, including numbers of large trees, numbers of large snags and logs, degree of canopy closure, and history of human disturbances. The ranks of these patches were then aggregated to provide an overall rank for the larger polygon in which they occur. Thus the landscape polygons were usually mixes of forest and nonforest vegetation of varying composition and structure.

The six-point scale for ranking structural complexity and contribution to late successional forest function in the Sierra Nevada ranged from 0 (low complexity, no contribution) to 5 (very high complexity and contribution). Examples of areas that received low ratings were structurally simple forests, such as young plantations, areas recently burned and salvaged, and landscapes that were largely nonforested, such as rock outcrops. Ranking of 2 included maturing even-aged forests lacking large-diameter trees, snags, and logs. Ranking of 3 included areas that had been selectively logged or burned but retained significant numbers of large trees and snags or where second-growth forests were approaching maturity. Old-growth mixed conifer forests with open, parklike structures often produced by frequent low-intensity fire were typically given a ranking of 4. Forests with the highest levels of struc-

FIGURE 6.2

An example of an area of higher elevation forest with low structural complexity. Exposed granitic outcrops dominate the site. (Photo by Jerry F. Franklin.)

functions of the Sierra depends greatly upon their size and on the forest matrix in which they occur, but they are an important legacy in the Sierra and are considered along with the contribution of unharvested stands.

Approach to Late Successional Analysis

In recent years late successional stands in the Sierra were mapped, largely using remote sensing imagery from satellite and ground sampling and subsequent computer-assisted classification. SNEP used a novel approach to identify and map remaining late successional forests on Sierran public lands. New approaches were necessary because of the size of the range itself and the complex spatial distribution of late successional elements on the landscape. In middle-elevation conifer forests, late successional forest structures, especially elements of structural complexity, provide readily observed surrogates for ecological functions (e.g., nutrient cycling, de-

tural complexity, including many large trees, were typical of areas given a ranking of 5. For example, many national park areas outside zones where aggressive fire suppression has occurred were ranked 5.

High-quality late successional polygons included patches with structural rankings of 4 and 5 intermixed with many 3-ranked stands, thus they often contained a mix of variously ranked patches. Some low-ranked polygons also contained small patches of superlative (rank 4 or 5) old growth. Stands with the highest level of structural development (rank 5) are not necessarily those stemming from natural conditions; they may reflect past fire suppression and excess numbers of smaller trees at the expense of more open understories and horizontal complexity. Many of the more open stands (rank 4) with large-diameter trees, small gaps, and open understories of low shrubs or herbs contribute more useful late successional habitat than some of those ranked 5 and are less vulnerable to stand-destroying fire.

The initial mapping was followed by extensive field checking, revisions, review by knowledgeable individuals outside SNEP, and final revision. An independent statistical analysis of the mapping project, based on a small number of field plots, was conducted to test the validity of the classification procedure (reported in volume II, chapter 22). The fact that patches were not specifically delineated on the maps (such an effort would have been impossibly laborious) made assessment of the polygon rankings difficult, as these ranks were composites of the patch values. Moreover, for reasons of past inventory practices, polygons on the national parks were generally smaller, about the size of national forest patches. These differences may have biased comparisons between national parks and national forests, because polygons tended to be ranked lower if late successional patches were comparatively smaller and fragmented, a problem in larger polygons. Although limited in scope, the validation study found less reliable discrimination of the middle-ranked polygons (2 and 3), than those with low (0–1) or high (4–5) rankings. Also, the degree of past human influence on polygons was a strong component of the rankings; a polygon that had experienced significant past human-caused disturbance tended to be

ranked lower than an otherwise similar polygon without such influences. SNEP also compared maps produced by this LSOG process with those produced using remote sensing by the Sierra Biodiversity Institute. We found substantial disparity in the mapped locations of late successional forests, but overall quantities were similar for most forest types.

Final maps showing landscape polygons at the scale of half an inch to one mile, GIS data layers, and characterizations of the patch conditions found within the polygons are available for individual national forests and parks. Only a sample is included here.

Status of Late Successional Middle-Elevation Forests

Only a small proportion of the middle-elevation conifer landscapes are at present high-quality late successional forest (plate 6.2; table 6.2): Nineteen percent of the mapped polygons were ranked as structural classes 4 and 5. Substantially more areas were rated as structural class 3 (29% of the total); these latter polygons represent a variety of conditions, including forests that have been selectively logged, productive lands that have regrown following earlier logging, and naturally fragmented landscapes in which high-quality stands are interspersed with nonforested areas. About half of the 3-rated polygons have a substantial proportion of their area (more than 25%) in patches ranked 4 and 5. Landscapes in which high-quality late successional patches are large, or are adjoined to patches of rank 3, function far more effectively as late successional landscapes (for example, by meeting the requirements of animals requiring large areas for support) than small or comparatively isolated high-ranked patches surrounded by large areas of low-ranked forest.

As expected, national parks provide the major concentrations of middle-elevation late successional conifer forests, especially at the landscape level, and, proportionally, they have about four times as much forest with high LSOG rankings as adjacent national forests (table 6.3). Within the parks, late successional forests of ranks 4 and 5 constituted 55% of the area in five forest types in Yosemite, Sequoia, Kings Canyon, and

TABLE 6.2

Proportion of polygons by major forest type group and late successional forest ranking for federal lands in the Sierra Nevada. (From volume II, chapter 21.)

Forest Type	Total Acres Classified	Percentage by Rank					
		0	1	2	3	4	5
West-side mixed conifer	3,344,960	4	12	33	31	15	5
White fir (west-side)	217,583	3	16	34	33	7	7
Red fir	1,476,390	0	9	28	34	17	13
East-side pine	2,776,024	9	24	45	14	5	2
East-side mixed conifer	711,982	4	22	39	26	9	0
All forest types	**8,526,939**	**4**	**14**	**34**	**29**	**13**	**6**

Lassen Volcanic National Parks (table 6.3). Despite reflecting increased forest density and fuel loadings due to fire suppression, forests in the national parks provide an instructive reference point for estimating pre-contact levels of high-quality late successional forests, as only minor areas have been subject to significant timber harvest. Fire suppression throughout most of the twentieth century is gradually giving way to prescribed management fire (controlled burns) and prescribed natural fire (lightning ignitions permitted to burn under constrained conditions), although many more forest stands in the national parks still carry excessive tree densities and unnatural fuel levels than have been restored to proximate pre-contact conditions, and extreme fire events continue to be suppressed. Although current conditions reduce the value of the national parks as indices of natural forest conditions, parks remain the best available benchmarks. The proportion of polygons (82%) with rankings of 3, 4, and 5 in the national parks is the best available indicator of conditions that prevailed in the Sierra Nevada before Euro-American settlement and is nearly twice the proportion on the national forest lands (42%).

The most commercially valuable forest types, such as the west-side mixed conifer and east-side pine forests, are proportionally the most deficient in high-quality late successional forest. These types have had the longest and most intense histories of timber harvest. Forests with high structural rankings are rarest in east-side pine: only 7% were ranked as structural class 4 and 5 (table 6.2). The west-side mixed conifer type has a greater proportion of high-ranked polygons: overall 20% are ranked 4 and 5, and red fir, with 30%, has the greatest proportion. One reason for this difference is the substantial representation of west-side mixed conifer protected within national parks.

Despite nearly 150 years of significant activity by Euro-Americans, there is still a high level of continuity in forest landscapes. The forest cover of the Sierra is relatively continuous, and most forested stands have sufficient structural complexity to provide for at least low levels of late successional forest functions. Fragmentation of forests through patch clear-cutting practices has been much less common in the Sierra than on federal forest lands in the Northwest. Though forest continuity is high, forest structure has been greatly simplified relative to pre-contact conditions; key structural features of late successional forests, such as large diameter trees, decadent trees, snags, and logs, are generally at low levels in the commercial forests of the Sierra Nevada. These forests thus do not provide the level of wildlife habitat and other ecological functions characteristic of high-quality late successional forests. In many areas, excessive stocking renders forests subject to severe wildfire and stand destruction rather than the stand-thinning fires more typical of natural Sierran conditions. Low levels of structural diversity are partially the legacy of acquired cutover lands and selective-removal timber harvest on the national forests.

Over the past decade, Sierra Nevada conifer forests have experienced widespread, locally severe levels of mortality caused principally by bark beetles infesting trees stressed by drought, overdense stands, and pathogens. Pine and fir forests in the Tahoe Basin and along the eastern slopes of the Sierra have been especially affected, although heavy losses to true fir have occurred in central western forests; 12%–15% of the forest inventory was lost in a recent 8-year period on the Eldorado National Forest. Along the western boundary of the southern Sierra, air pollution stress may have contributed to extensive mortality. Although fire suppression and forestry practices leading to unhealthy tree densities are implicated in the current die-off, U.S. Forest Service records dating to the beginning of the century reveal that periodic insect outbreaks, often associated with droughts, have led to high levels of tree mortality over large areas. These outbreaks are usually specific to a particular species of tree, depending on the insect.

Somewhat less than half the high-ranked late successional forest on national forest lands is unreserved and potentially available for timber harvest. A fair proportion of west-side mixed conifer polygons ranked as classes 4 and 5 may remain in the "suitable" land class in national forest plans, depending on the outcome of the California spotted owl environmental impact statement, and thus be available for timber harvest. Conversely, there is very little west-side mixed conifer or east-side pine forest with high LSOG rankings found within congressionally reserved areas, such as designated wilderness, as most wilderness occurs at higher elevations than these types. Recent Forest Service directives specify increased retention of large trees and other late successional forest components in those areas available for timber harvest.

Many (but not all) high-ranked national forest polygons in the northern and central Sierra are associated with steep, relatively inaccessible river canyons on the western slope, such as portions of the American, Feather, Yuba, and Cosumnes

TABLE 6.3

Proportion (%) of polygons ranked 4 or 5 (highest contribution of late successional function) and proportion ranked 3, 4, or 5 (mature forest with late successional potential plus 4- and 5-ranked polygons) for five middle-elevation conifer forest types in national parks and adjacent national forests and for all (Sierran) national forests, national parks, and federal lands combined. (From volume II, chapter 21.)

Administrative Unit	Rank	
	3+4+5	4+5
Lassen National Forest	42	9
Lassen Volcanic National Park	96	79
Stanislaus and Sierra National Forests	49	15
Yosemite National Park	76	48
Sequoia National Forest	51	24
Sequoia and Kings Canyon National Parks	82	56
All national forests	*42*	*13*
All national parks	*82*	*55*
All federal lands	*47*	*19*

❋ *Logging in the Sierra Nevada*

The logging of the Sierra Nevada took place in several stages. The gold rush created an immediate demand for mining timbers and lumber for construction of towns. Large sugar pines were cut down for shakes. This was a time of small sawmills that moved frequently as timber nearby was exhausted. Logging and lumber transport was by ox team and horses. As the placers gave out, this form of logging continued at a slower pace until the Central Pacific Railroad was built across the Sierra in 1865–68. The railroad ushered in industrial logging with its own construction followed by logging of the Tahoe-Truckee Basin, from which huge amounts of timber and wood were removed for the Comstock Mines. The construction of the railroad up and down the Central Valley offered an opportunity for industrial logging of the Sierra. The industry expanded, using new methods developed in the Tahoe Basin, such as V flumes, chutes, and inclines, and later donkey engines and logging railroads. Expansion was aided by land disposal laws that favored development of large timber holdings. In 1890 and 1891 national parks were created and the forest reserves were authorized, yet millions of acres of Sierra timberlands were still being disposed of through 1905. In a 1902 U.S. Geological Report for the Northern Sierra, John Leiberg estimated that 44% of the areas he examined at the turn of the century had been logged. He noted "a large proportion of the remaining forest (30%) is on places inaccessible and will never be available for use." The U.S. Forest Service, created in 1905, began making timber sales soon after, but they were not a major factor in wood supply until World War II. The period after 1900 was the heyday of the logging railroad and high-speed cable yarder. This form of logging flourished until the mid-1920s, when tractor-truck logging began to increase. Markets continued to be mainly in California, where the major uses of lumber were for fruit packing boxes and for home building caused by rapid population growth. After a slowdown during the 1930s, logging in the Sierra picked up rapidly during World War II. Acquistions of private forestland by the Forest Service beginning in the depression years added hundreds of thousands of acres of cutover, partially cut, and understocked lands to the national forests. But it was the postwar population and building booms in California that caused the rapid expansion of logging in the Sierra. As a result of higher prices and great demand many private ownerships, small and large, were cutover and the national forests rose in the timber market. Production from national forests in California rose to a peak of 2 billion board feet by the late 1970s, about half from the Sierra Nevada forests. Since that time logging has steadily declined as public lands were set aside for wilderness, wildlife habitat, watershed protection, and other uses. Logging on private lands has also been impacted, first by a more comprehensive forest practices act in 1973, and later by sharp declines in national forest timber available for logging. Because of high prices resulting from short supplies of timber, much of the timber on small ownerships was cut during the late 1980s and early 1990s.

river drainages. Rather than occurring only in remote locations in the Sierra Nevada, many polygons ranked 4 and 5 are found along the western edges of the national forests. Because such areas are at the interface of rural and urban environments, they may be subject to higher fire risks, and protecting them in the future poses a major management challenge.

Summary of Late Successional Status

The current extent of structurally complex, late successional middle-elevation conifer forests in the Sierra Nevada is probably far below levels that existed prior to western settlement. The widespread occurrence of such forests can be inferred from historical accounts, the pre-contact fire regime, and current conditions in the national parks. Late successional forests (ranks 4 and 5) now occupy 19% of all federal lands comprising these middle-elevation forests, with 13% of those on the national forests versus 55% on the national parks. The amount of late successional forest on the national parks is an approximate benchmark for pre-contact conditions. Including polygons ranked 3 or higher, the proportion of late successional forest is 47% on all federal lands, 42% on national forests, and 82% in national parks. The lower values on the national forests reflect more than a century of harvest activity. Although densities have increased and composition has shifted toward shade-tolerant species in middle-elevation park forests as a result of fire suppression, it is nonetheless reasonable to infer that most Sierran forests of these types in pre-contact times maintained moderate to high structural complexity and high horizontal diversity through frequent low- or moderate-intensity fire. The collective inference is that stands with moderate (rank 3) to high levels (ranks 4 and 5) of late-successional-related structural complexity once occupied the majority of what are now middle-elevation commercial forest lands in the Sierra. The still-considerable area with polygons ranked 3 on the national forests offers significant promise for a future increase in late successional forest, should that be a policy goal.

Severe tree mortality resulting from insect damage to a dense stand of lodgepole pine, Lassen National Forest, 1907. (Photo courtesy of the U.S. Forest Service.)

MANAGEMENT STRATEGIES

Of the six strategies SNEP analyzed to counter the major declines in late successional forests that were found during the SNEP assessments, three are presented here. Each assumes that existing high-quality late successional forests must be retained and expanded to support the full range of organisms and functions into the future. In concept the strategies illustrate contrasting opportunities in a continuum of landscape designs to achieve similar goals. Although the strategies target different forest types or areas, the designs they use, as well as other combinations suggested by them, could apply to other forest types

in the Sierra. Here, as elsewhere in SNEP, we emphasize that actual solutions will depend on analysis of local conditions; the key when going to the ground is to adapt a Sierra-wide framework to local needs. We suggest here the framework of thinking as well as a range of options possible for maintaining and enhancing late successional forest representation at the Sierra-wide scale.

The first two strategies (areas of late successional emphasis and distributed forest conditions) emphasize landscape designs based on existing ecological conditions encountered in different forest types (west-side versus east-side forests). They represent primarily ecological solutions, with less consideration of other factors. The third approach (integrated case study) combines a strategy with a case study. It illustrates how modification of ecological designs might occur when one applies these strategies at a local level. Other factors (than ecological) must be contended with, and several of these are integrated in the case study. A "best fit" of the rangewide pattern for late successional forests is found for local conditions on the Eldorado National Forest.

Goals of Late Successional Forest Strategies

The forest condition strategies have the following goals:

- Maintain existing high-quality late successional forest stands in middle-elevation forests.

- Expand late successional representation by actively managing forest stands that have potential to contribute structure and function.

- Restore fire as an important process in maintaining and protecting late successional habitat.

- Restore structural complexity in "matrix" lands (forested areas not targeted for primary late successional representation).

- Distribute late successional representation across latitudinal and elevational ranges of the targeted forest types.

A recurring question in the development of forest condition strategies is whether provision of large blocks of contiguous late successional forest (several thousands of acres) is critical or whether necessary conditions can be provided with smaller blocks (less than a few hundred acres). Although there are ecological and practical arguments for both, it is clear that large areas of late successional forest were the aboriginal condition. These areas were complex, fine-scale mosaics of varied stand structures, including areas of high and low density, and patches with young and mixed-age trees. Thus, large blocks of late successional forest include many seral stages and structurally diverse patches. Because aboriginal late successional forests tended to be so varied, the ecological value of large, continuous undisturbed areas or "reserves" is less clear than in areas where homogeneous landscape is a natural condition. In the Sierra there is little scientific consensus on this issue, although it is clearer that disruption by roads, mechanical entry, harvest, or grazing reduces the habitat quality and function for some species.

Strong consensus exists, however, on the importance of a late successional strategy that is widely distributed throughout the latitudinal and elevational range of the forest types and incorporates representative cross-section habitat conditions, including different productivity classes, plant associations, slopes, and soils. It is critical to provide not only representation across the range of environments but also connectivity among late successional blocks. Thus, for any strategy, the matrix lands are extremely important parts of a rangewide network. Retaining and promoting late successional structure to some target amount in these forested areas is essential, in that many organisms will use this mosaic for habitat, either independently or as extension from primary late successional blocks. Further, fungi and other detritivores provide important ecosystem functions that will support productivity of soils, animals, and plant communities in the matrix.

Strategy 1. Areas of Late Successional Emphasis

The SNEP team developed one forest condition strategy, "areas of late successional emphasis" (ALSEs), in considerable detail, advancing new simulation models, developing multiple alternatives based on different starting points, and evaluating implications from various runs. These are described in detail in technical reports found in volumes II and III and the addendum to the SNEP final report. Only a brief summary is presented here. This strategy has been developed primarily for west-slope forests, specifically mixed conifer and red fir/white fir types, although in principle the design could apply to several other Sierran forest types. The strategy is targeted for public forest lands, but it could be adopted on private lands where conditions and goals permit.

This strategy stratifies forestland into two landscape categories: areas of late successional emphasis and matrix lands. Achievement of goals at the rangewide scale depends on an integrated network of ALSEs and managed matrix lands across the latitudinal and elevational distribution of the forest type. Different management applies, or is allowed, in ALSEs and matrix lands.

Possible Solutions

Areas of late successional emphasis are areas with a management emphasis on maintenance of structurally diverse forests that provide high levels of late successional function, including habitat for species requiring or preferring such conditions. ALSEs would be large landscape units, typically in the range of 20,000–60,000 acres (multi-polygons), distributed across the range of the forest types. Existing high-ranked polygons (4s and 5s) would be used as starting points for identifying ALSEs, with adjacent or intermixed polygons potential areas for enhancing late successional characteristics. It should be recalled that these areas would not be homogeneous continuous stands of old trees. Patches of lower-ranked stands are included in many 4 and 5 polygons; what is more important, as described earlier, the "natural" late successional condition of Sierran middle-elevation forests is defined by great spatial variability (patches of deep forest interspersed with treefall gaps, areas where fires burned at different intensities resulting in different densities, etc.).

The size of ALSEs and their distribution are based on several criteria. Large size (multi-polygon) is promoted for ecological reasons: large blocks are assumed to provide preferred habitat over small areas for some plants and animals. Large areas also allow better opportunity to protect against loss from catastrophic fire (fuel breaks, fuel reduction) than small areas; if, however, fire should be uncontainable within ALSEs, they are unlikely to be entirely consumed. ALSEs are distributed across the elevational and latitudinal range of the forest types in the western Sierra. Gaps in ALSE distribution at the rangewide scale would occur where large blocks of high-ranking stands do not at present exist to form the base of an ALSE network, or where intermixed land-ownership patterns and conflicting land-use objectives preclude development of large areas.

Management of ALSEs would emphasize treatments to maintain, enhance, and protect high-quality late successional conditions . Active management within ALSEs is anticipated in at least some areas, with prescribed fire being the primary tool. Mechanical fuel treatment (timber harvest) could be allowed if limited in intensity and extent so as to maintain conditions as near natural as possible.

Fire protection within and adjacent to ALSEs would be priority ranked for treatment depending on fire risk severity. Adjacent areas would be subject to active management, with treatments including fuels breaks and other fuel protection zones, timber harvests, and prescribed burning.

SNEP developed several ALSE configurations. One solution is illustrated in plate 6.3. If the ALSEs depicted here were actually grown out as indicated, they would about double the present amount of late successional forest. The exact areal extent of high-quality late successional forest ultimately needed to achieve the objectives cannot be determined from existing information. However, the design and approximate overall abundance of late successional forests are most important. Extent and location of ALSEs illustrated here provide one solution. Local conditions will present real constraints and opportunities. However, the current total acreage is far below levels that existed in the pre-contact landscape, outside what is believed to be the natural range of variability if the rough benchmark of the national parks can be used, and may be inadequately distributed to support plant and biodiversity needs or to be protected against catastrophic loss.

ALSEs as described would not be adequate to sustain

amounts or distribution of late successional forest near pre-contact levels; contribution of other forest lands is essential to a rangewide network. *Matrix lands* are forested areas outside of ALSEs and fuel protection zones, and they would typically have primary management objectives other than attaining late successional representation. These may be multiple-use forest lands: timber, recreation, firewood cutting, and so on. Although matrix lands have other primary objectives (e.g., wood production), restoration of late successional forest conditions in structurally simplified stands to the structural standards of rank 3 will be critical to achieving adequate amounts of late successional forest at the rangewide scale. Forests have undergone significant structural simplification as a result of timber harvest and other human-caused disturbance. Higher levels of structural complexity are needed in the matrix to maintain biodiversity and forest functions in managed stands that are more characteristic of natural forests. Some of these processes and species—such as the array of fungi that form mycorrhizae with trees—are of direct importance in maintaining the long-term productivity of these sites. Greater structural diversity may also be important to improve the degree of connection—which affects movement of organisms and materials—across the managed landscape.

Silvicultural harvest systems that provide for retention and long-term maintenance of important structures—including large-diameter trees and their derivatives (large snags and logs)—are one effective strategy for providing a structurally complex managed-forest matrix. Partial cutting, including retention of selected forest structures at time of harvest, is a promising approach to maintaining a structurally diverse forest matrix. Structural goals, such as numbers and distribution of large-diameter trees, would vary according to management objectives. Large-diameter trees and their derivatives, large snags and logs, are of particular importance because they fulfill many important ecosystem functions, including provision of wildlife habitat. Silvicultural prescriptions should also incorporate compositional objectives, such as maintenance and restoration of sugar pine populations and representation of other species.

Two general silvicultural prescriptions have been proposed for the Sierra Nevada that can be used to maintain structural complexity in the matrix. Group selection, which involves harvest of small forest areas, is one approach; keeping harvested patches very small and retaining some structural features within areas selected for harvest would assist in maintaining late successional forest functions and organisms. Silvicultural prescriptions that maintain or restore specific structures—such as large-diameter trees—are a second approach. The interim California spotted owl (CASPO) guidelines are one step in demonstrating the feasibility of such approaches. Multiple-entry prescriptions that will systematically provide replacements for the large-diameter tree population are also essential elements of such a strategy.

Implications

The strength of the ALSE strategy developed here is that it clearly delineates a spatially explicit rangewide strategy for retaining late successional forest conditions across the environmental diversity of the targeted forest types. For plants and animals that favor large areas of undisturbed late successional habitat (including the patch diversity inherent to this condition), the ALSE strategy by intent provides this. Large blocks of land such as ALSEs provide efficiency in delineating and systematically managing late successional forests. Large management units more effectively lend themselves both to effective presuppression activities to prevent catastrophic fires and to effective application of managed fire. Blocks of large enough size are developed such that even catastrophic fire would be unlikely to decimate entire ALSE areas. Roads may expand in some areas, primarily matrix, due to the need for fire protection activities or other forest uses. Economic considerations are recognized in the ALSE strategy; potential economic impact is designed to be minimized.

Strategy 2. Distributed Forest Conditions

Whereas in the ALSE strategy goals are met through a network of large ALSEs and matrix forest lands, the distributed forest conditions (DFC) strategy distributes small to medium-sized patches of early to late successional forests continuously over the landscape in a mosaic approximating pre-contact forest patterns.

Historic conditions in many of the fire-adapted forests of the eastern Sierra Nevada were characterized by relatively continuous forest cover at the landscape scale and extreme patchiness at the local scale. Several SNEP assessments draw attention to the importance of patchiness, patch size, and patch variability for maintaining aspects of health and sustainability. An important criterion is patch size and mixture relative to mobility of forest inhabitants. For instance, many large and small mammals, amphibians, and birds use patches of different size and structure for sustenance and reproduction and rely on continuously distributed patchiness rather than large blocks of uniform forest conditions. Forest patchiness is likely to be a critical element in sustaining metapopulation structure typical of many Sierran plant and animal species. Vascular and nonvascular plants, genetic diversity within species, and insects and fungi use, or are adapted to, this landscape pattern. Juxtaposition of openings and old forest patches, size of patch, patch attributes, and distribution of different patch types within the landscape are important elements for sustaining these populations or attributes. Further, many Sierran taxa are likely to be adapted to regular disturbances within some part of their habitat. An assumption is made in several assessments that many Sierran organisms evolved under selection pressure from fire.

✳ *Implementing SNEP Forest Strategies*

Implementation of the strategies summarized in this report and detailed in volume II would require considerable further planning by local managers. Some of the management aspects involve

Fuel reduction: Reduction of fuels that have accumulated from fire prevention and suppression policies and from timber harvest is called for to reduce the potential for widespread, intense, destructive fire. Programs of prescribed burning (figure 6.3) and thinning, including logging and mechanical removal of fuels, will be needed to reduce fuels. The spatial retention of large snags and down logs desirable for late successional functions will at times conflict with the need to eliminate these fuels throughout defensible fuel space zones.

Density management: There are many acres of young stands that were regenerated after timber harvest and wildfires (of 300,000 acres of plantations on national

FIGURE 6.4

Dense, young stands of ponderosa pine, established after a fire. (Photo by John C. Tappeiner.)

forests in the Sierra Nevada; about half are fire related and half harvest related). These stands are often very dense, and consequently susceptible to damage by insects and fire (figures 6.4 and 6.5). They are often quite vigorous and have the potential for producing substantial yields of wood. Thinning and reducing the density of these stands would increase the tree growth and vigor, reduce susceptibility to insects and fire, increase understory tree and shrub diversity, provide some opportunity to manage tree species composition, and produce commercial yields of wood. Density management in the stands shown in figures 6.4 and 6.5, and 6.6 will enable them to become like the stands shown in figure 6.7.

Riparian areas and ALSEs: Areas selected as ALSEs and riparian areas (described in chapter 8) will contain

FIGURE 6.3

A mixed conifer stand immediately after burning for fuel reduction. The stand was "salvaged" before burning to reduce fuel loading. This ensured a light burn and safer conditions for workers. (Photo by John C. Tappeiner.)

FIGURE 6.5

Mixed conifers regenerated after logging. The stand is quite dense and therefore susceptible to insects and fire. (Photo by John C. Tappeiner.)

many stand types, including stands of large old trees and often some hardwood mix; stands designated late successional (rank 4 or 5); young, dense stands regenerated after fire or timber harvest; and stands in which there has been salvage and partial cutting for timber production. Some of these stands have high concentrations of fuels that could be removed to reduce the threat of intense, destructive fire in ALSEs and riparian areas. Many are very dense and are not likely to provide large trees or diverse structures and contribute to the riparian and ALSE functions without density management (figures 6.8 and 6.9).

Management complexity and resource managers: Managing forest stands in riparian areas and ALSEs must

FIGURE 6.6

Mixed conifer stands with older (120+ years) sugar pine and ponderosa pine and younger fir and cedar. The trees could be thinned to promote growth of the larger pines, reduce the potential for mortality and fuel accumulation, and produce commercial wood. Underburning could follow thinning. (Photo by John C. Tappeiner.)

FIGURE 6.7

A stand that has been thinned and could be underburned to reduce fuels. (Photo by John C. Tappeiner.)

FIGURE 6.8

A group of large ponderosa pine and hardwoods (top) that are susceptible to fire because of dense fuel from shrubs and smaller conifers. An adjoining stand (bottom) of younger ponderosa pine that could be thinned to enhance tree growth and reduce insect susceptibility. The two stands could become one area of large ponderosa pine. Fuel reduction could be done in both stands. (Photos by John C. Tappeiner.)

FIGURE 6.9

High fuels (top) and dense, young stands (bottom) in a riparian area. Careful fuel removal, thinning, and prescribed burning in areas such as these may occasionally be needed to accomplish overall objectives of SNEP alternatives. (Photos by John C. Tappeiner.)

be approached cautiously and is likely to be controversial even if the purpose is to contribute to the function of these areas. For example, removing fuels in riparian areas (figure 6.9) may be needed to enhance their function in the future (figure 6.10). Managers will have to design, implement, and evaluate management strategies to ensure protection and function of these areas. Prescriptions will have to be developed case by case to address local variability in stand conditions, fire potential, wildlife habitat, and operational considerations.

SNEP has not provided prescriptions for accomplishing the objectives envisioned for the various strategies. Its philosophy has been that objectives can best be met by using local expertise to adapt to local conditions.

FIGURE 6.10

An older mixed conifer "ideal" stand in a riparian area: low density, low fuel accumulation. (Photo by John C. Tappeiner.)

Extensive harvest for over 100 years, fire suppression for upwards of 80 years, and grazing for nearly 150 years have greatly altered conditions for east-side conifer types from those indicated as important to organisms. On a regional basis, east-side pine has lost more late successional attributes in the last century than any other forest type analyzed. Small-scale patchiness characteristic of historic pine forests has been pervasively lost or reduced, extensive presence of old trees is gone, forest-floor characteristics and shrub layers have been simplified and altered, complexity of stands as a result of regular fire has been altered, and other ecological functions of fire (e.g., seed and spore germination, induction of sprouting, nutrient cycling, natural selection) have been disrupted.

Possible Solutions

The objective of the DFC strategy is to meet overall forest goals by creating a forest landscape on the east side of the Sierra

Nevada (primarily east-side pine) with the following attributes:

- Small patches of different seral ages distributed in an irregular mosaic across the forest.

- Structural diversity within patches appropriate to expected levels for seral stage.

- Fire reintroduced.

Specific desired conditions would vary with local conditions, including specific plant communities, species mixes, environmental variability, total forest extent, topography, environmental and human site history, local biodiversity, and social uses and desires.

For planning and management, the scale would be the CALWATER planning watershed units (a subdivision within the river basins used by SNEP and delineated by the California Department of Water Resources), which are about 5,000 acres. Actual boundaries would flexibly be adapted to local conditions: for example, where forest polygons extend across watershed boundaries, the planning unit might also extend beyond the watershed, accommodating the local forest pattern. Forest patches within the planning watersheds would be about 2–20 acres, uneven aged and multilayered, although in some cases, small (less than 2 acres) even-aged patches could occur. Density of trees within patches and mix of patch types within a watershed would vary with local conditions. Old trees would be maintained in all patches. Snags and downed logs and debris would be retained in locally appropriate amounts. Decadence from biotic and abiotic factors would be maintained in old stands, generally those older than 200 years.

As in the ALSE strategy, forest landscapes are divided into cores and matrix, which are managed differently. Within each planning watershed (or its equivalent), about 30% of the watershed (about 1,500 acres) would be core forests, where emphasis would be to maintain natural processes and develop natural forest spatial and vertical structure, meaning to favor the dominance of nonhuman ecological processes and structures. Areas within planning watersheds that are currently minimally disturbed, especially late successional stands and roadless areas, would be favored for core forests. Core forest acres would not need to be contiguous, but areas of more than 100 acres would be best for ecological and management efficiency. Managed fire would be encouraged in core areas, with the goal of reducing risk of severe fire to a point where managed fire or prescribed natural fire could burn eventually with minimal risk. Mechanical treatment of fuels, including removal by harvest, would not be prohibited but, to the degree practicable, would be limited in intensity and extent within core forests to maintain natural conditions.

Additional biodiversity values would be given high priority in core areas, including restoration and maintenance of native plant diversity and maintenance of genetic diversity. Wildlife habitat requirements would be considered in local evaluations; decisions about patchiness and forest structure would be developed primarily relative to inferences of historic habitat, not developed from a single-perspective goal of increased animal abundances. Grazing would not be allowed in core areas.

The remaining 70%–80% of the watershed, the matrix, would be available for more intensive uses. Local conditions would dictate the number, size, distribution, content, and spatial pattern of patches in the matrix. The constraining terms for management would be achievement of the overall goals for forest strategies and the specific objectives for this scenario, especially maintenance or development of a fine-scale mosaic of seral patches (small size, distribution, juxtaposition), maintenance or development of appropriate complex structure within patches, and reintroduction of fire. For example, timber harvest, livestock grazing, or developed recreation could be allowed subject to local evaluation. In many stands, maintenance of open stands and vigorous tree growth would be encouraged in the first 100 years.

Fuels treatment would be given high priority throughout the watershed units, both core and matrix areas. With local exceptions (to protect especially highly valued late successional stands or biodiversity areas), fuels treatment would not be concentrated geographically. That is, fuels treatment would not necessarily be designed to protect core areas generally but would follow reasonable strategies aimed to eventually address fire regimes in the whole watershed. Managed fire would be used to combine objectives of restoring ecological function, reducing fuels, thinning and sanitizing stands, preparing for reforestation, and maintaining fine-scale patchiness.

Maps are not presented for this strategy, because SNEP did not map successional status at the scale of small patches.

Implications

By intent, this DFC strategy distributes seral diversity across the landscape, benefiting those organisms and ecological functions that use a pattern of patchiness. Existing small patches of late successional forest would be maintained where they occur, and late successional forest stands would be evenly distributed over the landscape. Risk of loss of late successional forest is distributed differently than in ALSE strategies, in which areas are concentrated: individual core areas could be expended, because of replication. Fire-protection efforts can be scattered across the landscape rather than concentrated. Although patches are small and inventories would be needed at that scale, forest managers are more accustomed to working at the scale of stands.

This strategy would not rely on excessive coordination at the rangewide or regional scale. Coordination among landowners of units less than 5,000 acres would be necessary, but only minimal coordination would be necessary for areas larger than that. The strategy is flexible to local adaptation and would integrate relatively easily with other solutions that are less flexible, for instance, a Sierra-wide biodiversity management areas network (chapter 5).

Despite these positive benefits, several difficulties for implementation would arise from this strategy. First, managing at the scale implied by this scenario would be administratively challenging and costly. Many administrative and on-the-ground difficulties would arise from planning, tracking, and coordinating activities in patch sizes of 2–20 acres and watershed units of 5,000 acres. Ways of managing at a higher level (clusters of patches) may exist, and GIS/GPS technology would assist the process; however, new institutional capacities and staff organization would have to be developed.

Further, excluding livestock grazing from core areas but not matrix forests may prove prohibitively expensive and nearly impossible to enforce, especially if the units of the core forest in each watershed were not contiguous (i.e., fencing difficulties). On the other hand, if grazing could be eliminated from entire select watersheds or the entire forest, this problem could be managed.

Because this strategy gives little direction for where fuel reduction and managed fires should be conducted, the average rate of reintroduction of fire per watershed would probably be very low.

Success in adaptation and use of this strategy could be evaluated by monitoring

- number of watersheds treated (general strategy mapped, planned, treatments begun)

- average number of acres per watershed treated

- average number of acres per watershed managed for (and currently in) late successional seral patch status

- average number of acres managed for other seral stages

- average number of acres designated and managed as core forest per watershed

- distribution of late successional patches in the landscape; adjacency to diverse seral patches, pattern of patch mixture

- individual tree measures, such as size increase, structural complexity changes, number of snags and downed logs, forest health trends

- average acres per watershed burned, by intensity class

- plant diversity status landscape wide

- wildlife habitat ratios per watershed and actual animal use

- average riparian protection width managed per watershed

- average timber harvest amount per watershed, as a ratio of core to matrix

- average number of acres of livestock grazing per watershed as a ratio of core to matrix

- average number of miles of roads built or eliminated per watershed

- cost and administrative feasibility and efficiency

- social acceptability

Strategy 3. Integrated Case Study

A final forest-condition case study integrates seven of the SNEP strategies and illustrates how late successional goals could be integrated with other objectives in an application to the Eldorado National Forest. This case study illustrates some of the modifications and novel solutions that are possible when implementing regionwide strategies in practice locally.

Goals

This strategy/case study integrates goals for the following attributes:

1. Late successional forests
   - Provide a well-distributed network of late successional forests sufficient to sustain the organisms and functions associated with such ecosystems.

   - Include the full range of representative native vegetation in the selection of late successional areas.

   - Include aquatic areas as feasible in late successional area selections.

2. Vegetation
   - Restore and maintain Sierran plant communities with representation of all plant community types, emphasizing native biodiversity.

   - Recognize the need for regional representation in plant community maintenance throughout the Sierra Nevada.

   - Restore a species mix more representative of natural conditions and reduce influence of exotic species wherever feasible.

   - Maintain vegetation units on a large enough scale to promote genetic resilience and provide functional wildlife habitat.

   - Restore and maintain forest health to provide resistance to large-scale insect depredations and high resiliency to meet periodic droughts and wildfires.

3. Wildlife habitat
   - Restore and protect riparian corridors of vegetation.

   - Plan forest extractive uses to attain a dynamic flow of plant communities of different ages distributed across the landscape without unnaturally large openings or extensive areas of young forest.

   - Recognize unique habitat needs for certain wildlife species.

4. Watershed and aquatic areas
   - Maintain soil profiles intact.

   - Reduce sedimentation to minimal levels, as near the low range of natural levels as practicable.

   - Provide increased protection for both large and small aquatic systems, attaining high-quality habitat for both vertebrates and invertebrates.

   - Identify and take corrective action to eliminate contamination by toxic materials.

5. Fire protection
   - Reduce substantially the area and size of high-severity wildfires, giving priority to the fire safety of communities, forests at extreme risk, and watersheds with high erosion potential.

- Restore fire to something near its historic natural role, recognizing this may be possible for only a portion of the Sierra Nevada.

- Reduce the fire severity potential for areas of late succession emphasis (ALSEs).

6. Community well-being
   - Provide a continuing flow of forest resources to meet human needs.

   - Incorporate private landowners, residents, and interested parties into collaborative planning for both public and private lands.

   - Use forest management activities to build local socioeconomic status.

7. Private land contributions to ecosystem sustainability
   - Recognize that private land uses are a critical part of ecosystem sustainability in most parts of the Sierra Nevada and that mutually acceptable goals must be formulated.

   - Institutionalize collaborative planning wherever possible when it is clear that significant ecosystem functions are dependent upon intermixed ownerships.

Possible Solutions

This strategy incorporates a wide range of strategies to bring an integrated approach for systemwide benefits. Implementation of fire strategies is largely financed through commercial sales. Private land uses are important in the long-term sustainability of ecosystems of the entire range. Every major stream within the Eldorado National Forest has private lands somewhere along its length. Collaborative planning is essential to set effective goals and attain successful results. Core ALSEs include the best of late successional conifer and hardwood forests joined with areas exceeding 40% slope added to a 300-foot zone along major streams. Areas of concentrated public use (e.g., recreation centers, main roads, communities) are placed in the matrix, recognizing the need to provide for public safety (e.g., snag removal, fuel reduction).

Specific attention is paid to the following problems addressed in assessments:

- Structural characteristics, distribution, and spatial relation of forest habitat have been fractured or threatened through development and are at risk to large wildfire burns of high intensity.

- Fire hazard is unacceptably high for many areas that include forest communities, sensitive watersheds, and much of the mixed conifer type.

- The area of high-quality, structurally complex, late succession forests is quite limited in the mixed conifer type, well below the range of natural variability.

- Areas of steep slopes or highly erodible soils continue to yield unacceptable sediment loads, whenever disturbed, adversely affecting downstream values.

- Aquatic invertebrates and vertebrates are in continuing decline due, in part, to habitat loss, introduction of exotics, and modified stream flows.

- Forest yields of commercial products have been completely disrupted in the last five years while major forest plan adjustments are made.

- Population growth rates along the western forest edge and in the oak woodlands are putting enormous stress on public land management and dependent wildlife and are potentially threatening the continuity of large blocks of undeveloped or lightly developed land areas with major representations of native vegetation.

- Fire protection for the last half century has provided for the development of continuous dense forest stands, which are in need of thinning to accelerate growth, reduce fire hazard, provide more midsuccession forest habitat, and yield usable wood.

The Eldorado strategy/case study integrates fire protection, late succession emphasis, watershed and aquatic area protection and restoration, reintroduction of fire as an element of ecological importance, linkage of late succession vegetation of all species with riparian habitat, spatial distribution of various seral stages for desired wildlife habitat, recognition of the critical contribution of private lands in maintenance of the ecosystem, adoption of an adaptive management approach so that activities may move ahead without long delays, and involvement of local communities in restoring and maintaining ecosystem elements as well as resource utilization. The case study illustrates how solutions will play out differently in the various parts of the Sierra Nevada due to local conditions, opportunities, management objectives, and ecosystem conditions.

Late Successional Forest Strategy. The core areas for late succession management are derived by

- Setting goals of area representation (e.g., 20%–25% of mixed conifer forest in late successional condition).

- Using the late successional areas ranked 4 and 5 as bases for developing "watershed ALSEs," adding areas formed by the overlapping of slopes > 40% and high soil erodibility (K factor >0.28).

- Extending the area now formed to include a 300-foot strip along perennial streams. Mixed conifer ALSEs are joined with hardwood forest, chaparral, red fir, and subalpine to form, where possible, connected late successional vegetation. Wilderness, wild and scenic rivers, and other existing forest plan allocations retaining old-growth representation (e.g., spotted owl habitat areas) are included. The core areas are adjusted so that boundaries do not fall in the midpoint of steep slopes, are not intermixed with private lands, and do not include prominent ridgetops where fuel breaks must be constructed.

- Attempting to get some late successional representation for vegetation types occurring in each of the super planning watersheds of the California Department of Water and Resources (average about 14,000 acres).

- Accelerating the development of old-growth forest characteristics in ALSEs through thinning, favoring underrepresented tree species to attain natural species distribution. ALSE polygon boundaries are modified in some cases in order to attain practicable management boundaries.

Matrix Lands. Matrix management is prescribed to provide a full range of seral stages spatially arranged to avoid large, contiguous areas of a seral stage; protection is provided to both large and small aquatic systems, recognizing various levels of influence zones around streams.

Hardwoods are provided through silvicultural prescriptions in the conifer areas, by riparian protection along streams, and management of the oak woodland using best management practices. Rotation age is lengthened to 175–225 years for conifers. Within planning watersheds the goal is to attain and maintain more than 25% of the area in mature forest. Silvicultural prescriptions vary and include individual tree selection as well as small group harvests of 0.5 to less than 3 acres. Commercial yields are produced through silvicultural prescriptions to attain biodiversity objectives, reduce fuel hazards, and thin stands to accelerate growth and encourage stand health. Stand-terminating wildfires of substantial size (more than 1,000 acres) will require a review of both ALSE and matrix alignment. The special management areas (e.g., spotted owl habitat areas, undeveloped recreation areas) included at present in the Eldorado National Forest plan are placed in either ALSE core or matrix lands, depending on the most appropriate local fit.

Aquatic and Riparian Protection. All areas are provided increasing protection for both small and large aquatic habitats. Old-growth trees are left surrounding meadows and springs as well as along streams. Livestock grazing is eliminated from riparian areas in unstable or deteriorating condition. Watersheds with current high quality of aquatic biodiversity are maintained; those needing improvement are identified for appropriate restoration. Management direction incorporates the concepts of three zones of riparian influences; community, energy, and land-use zones associated with aquatic life.

Terrestrial Plant Representation. The biodiversity management area (BMA) selection approach developed in chapter 5 is used through a review of the ALSE design and a search for opportunities to incorporate BMA selections of local plant community types. Areas where both public and private lands are required to meet objectives are identified and favorable collaborative planning or exchange opportunities offered. BMAs require active, adaptive management with the management goal for renewable resources to sustain many if not most elements of native biodiversity. BMA selection may include either lands in the ALSE or in the matrix. For BMA matrix selections, special management provisions would be prescribed depending upon how well the present condition of the selected area matches the desired native biodiversity.

Fire Hazard Reduction. A fuel break system is incorporated that has two objectives. The first is to provide a separation between forest and developed communities that will minimize the threat of catastrophic fire to either area. The second is to break up the existing unacceptable fuel loads and thereby provide a safer place from which to apply managed fire and suppress wildfire. Prescriptions for fuel breaks will vary with the type of stand and its location. Treatments could include thinning young stands and then using prescribed fire to reduce fuels from slash, forest litter, and understory shrubs. Small patches of shrubs should be retained. Salvage of dead wood and removal of snags completes the fuel break until maintenance is required. Hazard reduction work is targeted for areas of high priority based on values at risk, likelihood of loss, or ecological benefits that justify costs. As practicable, fire is reintroduced as part of the management process to provide the natural effects of periodic low- and moderate-intensity fires.

Plate 6.4 depicts one solution possible for a portion of the Eldorado National Forest when these goals are integrated.

Implications

Implementation of an integrated strategy such as is suggested here implies the following:

- Silvicultural prescriptions must include development of structurally complex forest stands for various forest types. Opening sizes can be tailored to encourage successful reproduction and growth of both shade-tolerant and shade-intolerant species.

- Increased use of fire to reduce fuel hazard and for ecosystem health will bring substantial risk of escape fires and will probably be curtailed by air-quality regulations. Large-scale use of fire will require public education and further proof of air-quality benefit gained through prescribed fire as compared with wildfire.

- Fuel hazard reduction can be funded largely through resource extraction collections rather than through increased appropriations.

- Ecosystem restoration and maintenance will require more capital reinvestment in the system. All benefiting resource users must reinvest substantially in the maintenance of the system.

- Private and public landowners must be willing to join in collaborative planning and management toward mutually acceptable goals.

- Adaptive management will require the availability of research personnel to work periodically, but regularly, with land managers.

- Knowledge gaps must be identified and vigorously researched before major problems arise.

- Off-site air pollutants that drift into the Sierra Nevada largely from sources in the Central Valley and the Bay Area are not considered in the strategy.

The success of such a strategy/case study would be evaluated using the following criteria:

- Proposed activities are evaluated in context with landscape-scale strategies that reflect the goals for the larger area within the project objectives.

- Progress has been made in reducing the fuel hazards in selected areas, as measured by before and after fuel load; arrangement, continuity, and loss of desired structural components; and the distribution and area of attained desirable fuel profiles.

- Late successional forest areas including the existing concentrations of high-quality late successional forest are well distributed in the various watersheds. The network includes major riparian vegetation associations and areas of greatest soil sensitivity.

- A target level is established for plant community representation within major watersheds.

- Best management practices (BMPs) incorporate provisions for small and large aquatic zones, incorporating the concepts of riparian, community, and energy zones.

- Wildlife species associated with specific seral stages are supported adequately by the planned or established vegetation structure and distribution.

- Collaborative goal-setting and planning efforts are under way with private landowners and local communities.

- Local residents are involved in the various activities, including restoration, maintenance, and resource utilization.

- Baseline references have been established for key ecosystem features so that progress can be measured. A core of late succession forests (ALSE), well distributed in the super planning watersheds, is established. Matrix spatial vegetation targets are established and attainment is under way.

- Stream sedimentation levels are acceptable. There is progress in improving and maintaining local socioeconomic status.

- Resource use and output levels are meeting human needs and are consistent with ecosystem sustainability.

- Sufficient reinvestment resources are available for maintenance and some restoration progress.

Conclusions from Forest Conditions Strategies

None of the three strategies presented here or the six developed elsewhere is perfect in addressing all important design elements. In the samples presented in this chapter, it becomes clear that decision making about goals is a local and collaborative public process, although science can help understand how forested ecosystems work, defend scientific bases for setting management targets, and evaluate progress toward goals. Exact values about acres, boundaries, or locations that would guide restoration—that is, whether to use data from historical sources to guide restoration targets, ecological goals of maintaining biodiversity, or practical goals such as fire protection—are not determinable. This is partly because information is scanty, because some aspects of ecosystems are unknowable, and because in practice restoration targets are determined by local conditions. When pieces are considered collectively for a region or watershed, modifications and compromises result. What is most needed now is a collective will for collaborative goal-setting, integrated with scientific counsel and monitoring.

The best way to ensure that late successional forest conditions are available and maintained in the Sierra Nevada is to have this goal stated and explicitly addressed as part of any management strategy. It is highly unlikely that such forests will be present in the Sierran landscapes in the desired quantities if they are expected to be a by-product of other management objectives. A point of consensus is that an effective late successional strategy would start by retaining the best high-quality stands (ranks 4 and 5 and equivalents on other forest types) as core areas in any design.

How do the directions indicated in the present strategies compare with current practices? From federal policy (e.g., the new CalOwl plan) to revised state forest practices, although explicit goals for rangewide networks of late successional forests are not stated, the tendency is toward increased representation of late successional structures in Sierran landscapes, although not necessarily representation of full late successional ecosystems. The public has clearly indicated an interest in the continued existence of late successional forests both for their intrinsic interest and as habitat for associated species and processes. A pressing need is for development of a defensible rangewide strategy that explicitly recognizes the objective of maintaining late successional forests and is flexible enough to allow local adaptation and cross-ownership implementation.

CHAPTER 7

Rangelands

Historic Grazing Impacts Historic unregulated grazing, which ended in the early 1900s, created widespread, profound, and, in some places, irreversible ecological impacts. Foothill habitats have suffered physical and biological damage of many riparian systems and virtual replacement of the native perennial flora by Eurasian annuals.

Current Grazing Effects Current livestock grazing practices continue to exert reduced but significant impacts on the biodiversity and ecological processes of many middle- to high-elevation rangelands even though properly managed grazing (appropriate timing, intensity, duration of use, control of cowbirds, and exclusion from wetlands) can be compatible with sustainable ecological functions.

Restoration of Upland Rangelands Increases in native perennial grasses are occurring on some east-side sagebrush-steppe rangelands, but the continuing cheatgrass invasion of these habitats indicates that complete restoration of native plant communities is highly unlikely.

Restoration of Meadows and Riparian Systems Easily damaged by improper grazing, montane meadows and riparian systems are resilient relative to restoration of plant cover, but restoration of stream channel shape, system function, and biodiversity may take decades.

Conversion of Hardwood Rangelands Human settlement patterns represent the largest threat to continued sustainability of ecological functions on hardwood rangelands.

Oak Woodland Resiliency Oak woodlands (particularly blue oak) are much more stable than previously thought; concerns about regeneration are not well founded.

ASSESSMENT

Historic Rangeland Ecosystems

Poorly managed or unmanaged livestock use of Sierra Nevada rangelands, especially during the late 1800s, contributed to reduced productivity and impaired health of these ecosystems. Continuing problems in some riparian areas and the persistent dominance of exotic annual grasses in foothill and east-side rangelands, with the accompanying decline in potential productivity of these sites, warrants an examination of historical causes and possible remedies for these problems.

Historical accounts of rangeland condition and use in the late 1800s indicate that highly productive rangeland commu-

nities existed throughout the study area when Europeans arrived. Large elk herds were present on the west side of the range. Native perennial grasses were dominant in the grassland communities, although exotic annuals had begun their invasion even before the arrival of the first missions in 1769, evidently resulting from the travels of early Spanish explorers throughout the Southwest more than two hundred years earlier.

During the late Pleistocene (before 10,000 years ago), a grass-sagebrush rangeland existed where montane and subalpine forests occur today, while at lower elevations conifers occurred. The sagebrush grasslands supported a diverse ecosystem of now extinct megafauna, including a large number of herbivores and a formidable group of mammalian predators. The disturbance regime associated with these herbivores, quite unlike livestock disturbance under traditional livestock management, would have presumably provided several crucial functions for sustaining the high productivity of rangeland ecosystems, including the breakdown of dead plant material and the recycling of nutrients, while allowing seed germination and seedling establishment. These landscape-level energy and nutrient transfers increased energy flows and perennial plant cover, thereby increasing the net productivity of rangeland vegetation, improving the rangeland water cycle, and increasing water capture by plants. The synergistic nature of the relationship between Pleistocene herbivores and rangeland productivity, although not known for certain, is supported by recent research with alternative livestock management practices that have substituted high-intensity, short-duration grazing for the traditional low-level, chronic grazing disturbance. Also unknown is whether or not the Sierra Nevada grassland ecosystems encountered by Euro-Americans were disturbance adapted, as might have been the case prior to the extinction of the Pleistocene megafauna.

Effects of Early Use of Rangelands

The first extensive use of Sierra Nevada rangelands for livestock began in the 1860s. A number of observers reported severe and repeated overstocking until about 1900, due in part to a lack of regulation of the common rangelands. The combination of poor grazing practices and extended periods of drought contributed to the conversion of Sierra foothills from perennial to annual grasslands and is also implicated in the expansion of juniper woodlands on the east side of the range.

Without regulation of access during the late 1800s, overutilization of the common rangelands of the Sierra Nevada occurred. With unregulated use of this common-pool resource by many livestock operators, no user had incentive to reduce usage or conserve resources, because any benefit so conserved was quickly captured by other users. As a result,

A stream channel damaged by cattle grazing. Plumas National Forest, Milford Ranger District, Doyle Allotment. (Photo by John W. Menke.)

A healthy meadow on the Tahoe National Forest that was subjected to moderate levels of cattle grazing and then allowed to rest for five years. (Photo by John W. Menke.)

Sierra Nevada rangelands were overgrazed, in that native forage plants did not have enough time to recover after severe, repeated grazing. As unregulated grazing was eliminated, recovery of some of the rangeland vegetation in many areas was fairly rapid, at least in terms of forage production.

Fire has perhaps had the largest effect on Sierra Nevada rangeland. From 1880 to 1910 sheepherders set large fires every fall as they left the public lands. These fires opened vast areas of western montane slopes and foothill chaparral shrubland areas to livestock grazing and left large areas subject to erosion. Where there was regrowth of nutritious forbs and shrubs, deer numbers increased dramatically. In contrast, fire-suppression policy since that time has generally allowed decadent habitat conditions to develop except where wildfire or vegetation management programs have restored some of the natural role fire has in these ecosystems.

Until the Taylor Grazing Act of 1934, little attention was given to livestock grazing capacity limits. During World Wars I and II, increased livestock use occurred again on public rangelands, often without regard to appropriate stocking rates. It is clearly apparent from well-documented Forest Service allotment reports that managers recognized that grazing problems were occurring. Given the emphasis at the time, managers believed that transient cattle and sheep use and range depletion were jeopardizing the local livestock economy. From the 1950s through the early 1970s, stocking rates on many allotments were reduced to levels closer to sustainable grazing capacity but still above that threshold and without adequate safeguards for riparian habitats. Range improvement activities common during this period included water developments, range seedings, brush control, and other practices that attempted to restore former grazing capacities.

Sierra Nevada and Modoc Plateau rangelands are susceptible to exotic annual grass and forb invasion following depletion of native perennial grasses. Overgrazing can also influence soil compaction, erosion, and lowering of water

tables. Reducing perennial grasses allows for increased water availability in soil, which then promotes continued invasion by exotic annual plants, sagebrush, and juniper. For the same reason, yellow star thistle, an exotic annual forb, has spread and is altering native biodiversity and ecological functions of Sierra Nevada foothill annual grassland and oak woodlands. When short-season annual grasses and forbs replace perennial grasses, forage productivity and carrying capacity are reduced for livestock and wildlife.

In the 1970s, stream riparian wildlife and fisheries habitat concerns began to surface, and public land-management agencies developed various riparian initiatives. Following numerous demonstration projects, interdisciplinary research projects, symposia, and workshops, major new management actions began. Widespread adoption of practices is slow in coming, but riparian-sensitive management has continued to increase over the last twenty-five years. Today it is a prime factor in livestock grazing management.

Current Conditions

In the late 1940s and early 1950s the Forest Service began the largest vegetation and soil monitoring program ever mounted by an agency—the Parker Three-Step Rangeland Condition and Trend Monitoring program. Despite limitations of the Parker transect data, SNEP recognized that much valuable interpretation was possible from this large database of information. The SNEP assessment used several contemporary functional response indicators to evaluate the historic data for sagebrush-steppe uplands and mountain meadow riparian areas on ten national forests (see volume III, chapter 24, for the precise methods used for this assessment). Indicators included:

- A decrease in the ratio of sedge-to-grass without compensation by rush species, indicating loss or declines in water tables either from stream downcutting or from enhanced runoff due to compaction.

- Invasion of weedy forbs, indicating excess soil water supplies due to loss of keystone perennial grasses.

- Reductions in abundance of late seral grasses due to inadequate recovery times following repeated grazing events.

- Radical fluctuations of clover species in meadows due to excited nitrogen cycling and close grazing of taller vegetation that formerly buffered against such wide swings in botanical composition.

- A "red-flag" indicator of more than 7%–10% bare soil in wet meadows, indicating severe abuse beyond what burrowing rodents could account for.

- Native versus non-native species composition trends.

A major section of the SNEP rangeland assessment is a compendium of individual plant indicators of livestock grazing effects that serve as short-term indicators of changes in community composition.

Sagebrush-Steppe

From GIS interpretations of data developed by the gap analysis portion of the SNEP study, it was determined that 45% of Sierra Nevada sagebrush-steppe rangeland is managed by the Forest Service, 31% by the Bureau of Land Management, and 23% by private owners. SNEP evaluated only those lands represented by the Forest Service and accompanying Parker transect data. Seven attributes were analyzed from the Parker transect data for seven of the ten national forests with significant acreage of sagebrush-steppe, including big sagebrush composition, native perennial grass composition, forb composition, non-native species composition, litter cover, bare soil exposure, and erosion pavement (tables 7.1, 7.2, and 7.3).

From the mid-1950s to the present, big sagebrush cover declined on all seven forests; however, native perennial grass composition increased by at least one-third on the Modoc, Lassen, Toiyabe, and Inyo National Forests. Trends for native

TABLE 7.1

Percentage of big sagebrush, native perennial grass, and forb composition in sagebrush-steppe communities on seven national forests over five decades. (From volume III, chapter 22.)

National Forest			Decade		
	Before 1956	1956–65	1966–75	1976–85	1986–95
Modoc	(9)[a]	(3)	(0)	(1)	(11)
Big sagebrush	15.4	22.0	—	15.0	14.8
Perennial grasses	7.3	3.0	—	6.0	10.5
Forbs	21.7	24.3	—	27.0	18.2
Lassen	(0)	(12)	(2)	(0)	(8)
Big sagebrush	—	12.8	17.0	—	11.2
Perennial grasses	—	6.5	6.5	—	8.4
Forbs	—	19.8	20.0	—	22.1
Plumas	(0)	(11)	(3)	(3)	(3)
Big sagebrush	—	23.7	9.7	17.7	30.0
Perennial grasses	—	2.9	5.0	5.3	3.0
Forbs	—	35.0	19.7	22.3	38.0
Tahoe	(3)	(5)	(11)	(3)	(0)
Big sagebrush	1.7	20.8	14.3	16.7	—
Perennial grasses	1.7	2.8	3.0	1.7	—
Forbs	8.7	29.6	21.7	19.3	—
Stanislaus	(0)	(0)	(7)	(5)	(0)
Big sagebrush	—	—	31.7	19.0	—
Perennial grasses	—	—	7.1	4.2	—
Forbs	—	—	41.7	25.6	—
Toiyabe	(0)	(10)	(2)	(10)	(2)
Big sagebrush	—	24.4	32.0	20.4	21.0
Perennial grasses	—	2.8	2.0	5.2	0.5
Forbs	—	29.3	25.3	28.1	43.0
Inyo	(0)	(8)	(2)	(0)	(10)
Big sagebrush	—	16.9	14.0	—	13.4
Perennial grasses	—	0.4	0	—	3.3
Forbs	—	24.8	25.5	—	23.7
Weighted Average	(12)	(49)	(27)	(22)	(34)
Big sagebrush	12.0	19.7	19.8	19.0	15.2
Perennial grasses	5.9	3.3	4.2	4.5	6.6
Forbs	18.4	27.2	27.1	25.5	23.9

[a]Numbers in parentheses indicate the number of transects.

TABLE 7.2

Percentage of non-native species composition in sagebrush-steppe communities on seven national forests over five decades. (From volume III, chapter 22.)

National Forest	Before 1956	1956–65	1966–75	1976–85	1986–95
			Decade		
Modoc	(9)[a]	(3)	(0)	(1)	(11)
Cheatgrass	0.8	3.7	—	0	2.5
Medusahead	0	0	—	0	0.6
Filaree	0.1	0	—	0	0
Dandelion	0.1	0	—	0	0
Lassen	(0)	(12)	(2)	(0)	(8)
Cheatgrass	—	0	2.0	—	0.1
Filaree	—	0.4	0	—	0
Plumas	(0)	(11)	(3)	(3)	(3)
Cheatgrass	—	0	2.0	0	0.1
Filaree	—	0.6	0	0	0
Wheatgrass	—	0	0	9.0	0
Tahoe	(3)	(5)	(11)	(3)	(0)
Cheatgrass	2.3	0.2	5.5	0.3	—
Wheatgrass	0	0	0.3	0	—
Plantain	1.3	0	0	0	—
Stanislaus	(0)	(0)	(7)	(5)	(0)
Filaree	—	—	0.4	0	—
Toiyabe	(0)	(10)	(2)	(10)	(2)
Bull thistle	—	0	0	0.2	0
Inyo	(0)	(8)	(2)	(10)	(2)
Cheatgrass	—	0.9	0.5	0	4.8

[a]Numbers in parentheses indicate the number of transects.

perennial grasses on the other three forests appear to be static or downward. Overall forb composition has been remarkably stable, with a tendency for a small downward decline in abundance on most national forests.

Cheatgrass was the most common non-native component of the monitored sagebrush-steppe. Overall, weeds other than cheatgrass were not detected as a major problem.

Based on historical review of livestock grazing on what is now national forest land, the Modoc National Forest was the most disturbed in the sagebrush-steppe, and the Lassen, Inyo, and Toiyabe National Forests were not far behind. Although the Modoc and other forests are showing declines in sagebrush and increases in cheatgrass, the increase in native perennial grass on four of the forests is a positive finding of improving ecosystem biodiversity. The general reduction in sagebrush cover is ecologically desirable as long as it remains as a major component of the sagebrush-steppe. Excessive prescribed burning of sagebrush-steppe would likely result in additional spreading of cheatgrass; however, some reduction in sagebrush would free up water resources for maintenance of a larger composition of grasses (including perennials). The slowly declining forb composition is likely to contribute to poorer diets for ground-nesting birds in the future. The high and increasing cheatgrass component on many of the forests is alarming, especially as California becomes more populated

and even remote areas have greater probability of fire ignitions. In addition to contributing little value to biodiversity, cheatgrass is unpalatable to livestock, except for a short period during spring growth, and therefore accumulates as fuel that threatens the survival of other plant species in the event of fire.

Substantial reductions in livestock grazing intensity occurred during the five decades covered by this assessment; however, most ranges were stocked above carrying capacity as recently as the last one or two decades. The key positive indicator observed from the Parker transect data was the increase in native perennial grass composition on some of these upland rangelands. Thus, with continued improvement in management, there is reason to hope for reestablishment of more native grassland communities. The key negative indicator was the continued cheatgrass invasion. Use of livestock as a management tool to reduce cheatgrass appears to be limited.

Mountain Meadows

Transect data on mountain meadows for ten national forests of the Sierra Nevada and Modoc Plateau were analyzed for plant community composition attributes including grass, legumes, sedge, and rush species, non-native species, and exposed bare soil. The first set of indices used to indicate

TABLE 7.3

Percentage of litter, bare soil, and erosion pavement in sagebrush-steppe communities on seven national forests over five decades from transect data. (From volume III, chapter 22.)

National Forest	Before 1956	1956–65	1966–75	1976–85	1986–95
			Decade		
Modoc	(9)[a]	(3)	(0)	(1)	(11)
Litter	29.6	20.3	—	28.0	40.1
Bare soil	33.3	41.7	—	27.0	20.3
Erosion pavement	1.6	0.7	—	4.0	3.3
Lassen	(0)	(12)	(2)	(0)	(8)
Litter	—	24.4	16.0	—	38.9
Bare soil	—	18.2	2.0	—	9.6
Erosion pavement	—	12.3	0	—	10.5
Plumas	(0)	(11)	(3)	(3)	(3)
Litter	—	34.5	36.3	38.7	34.0
Bare soil	—	14.5	17.3	18.0	17.0
Erosion pavement	—	10.5	23.0	0	2.7
Tahoe	(3)	(5)	(11)	(3)	(0)
Litter	36.3	33.0	36.9	44.0	—
Bare soil	47.0	25.4	23.9	29.3	—
Erosion pavement	3.7	8.4	5.4	5.7	—
Stanislaus	(0)	(0)	(7)	(5)	(0)
Litter	—	—	16.1	14.2	—
Bare soil	—	—	9.0	19.4	—
Erosion pavement	—	—	24.7	34.4	—
Toiyabe	(0)	(10)	(2)	(10)	(2)
Litter	—	35.3	21.5	30.2	23.5
Bare soil	—	18.5	20.0	24.8	10.5
Erosion pavement	—	8.5	18.5	6.4	19.0
Inyo	(0)	(8)	(2)	(0)	(10)
Litter	—	19.9	29.5	—	23.5
Bare soil	—	19.2	23.5	—	26.5
Erosion pavement	—	32.9	20.5	—	17.4
Weighted Average	(12)	(49)	(27)	(22)	(34)
Litter	31.3	28.8	28.2	29.5	33.4
Bare soil	36.7	19.8	17.4	23.4	18.7
Erosion pavement	2.1	13.4	14.0	11.7	10.0

[a]Numbers in parentheses indicate the number of transects.

meadow functionality was grass, legume, sedge, and rush relative composition and trends. Wet and mesic meadow ecosystems, if overgrazed, show a trend of grass and legume composition increase at the expense of sedge and rush composition. Such trends usually result from soil compaction and stream downcutting; ultimately the result is drier site conditions, change in species composition, and lowered productivity. The opposite trend, however, typically indicates restoration of a water table, reduced runoff and increased infiltration, and gully repair. Given that livestock numbers have been reduced and many grazing systems and restoration projects have occurred during the five-decade monitoring period, we should expect some reversal of dewatering indicators, such as increases in moisture-loving sedges and rushes (grasslike plants). Two national forests, Modoc and Toiyabe, showed an apparent unfavorable meadow water-regime response: a reduction in sedges and an increase in grasses as an aggregate (table 7.4).

In mountain meadows on ten national forests, exposed bare soil has stabilized at around 5%, whereas before 1956 the average for all forests was about 11% (range, 1.5%–23%). Trends toward greater plant cover are most apparent on the Modoc, Lassen, Tahoe, Stanislaus, Sierra, and Sequoia National Forests.

Hardwood Rangelands

There are 4.7 million acres of hardwood rangelands (also known as oak woodlands) in the Sierra Nevada region. Data compiled by the California Integrated Hardwood Range Management Program (IHRMP) were used for SNEP's assessment of these significant areas.

These lands are concentrated in the western foothills (85% on private land) in a belt 20–30 miles wide from 450 to 4,500 feet in elevation. Nearly 800,000 acres of hardwood rangelands habitat in the Sierra Nevada were converted to other land uses and vegetation types over the last forty years, an

TABLE 7.4

Percentage of grass, legume, sedge, and rush species[a] composition in wet and mesic meadows on ten national forests over five decades from transect data. (From volume III, chapter 22.)

National Forest	Decade				
	Before 1956	1956–65	1966–75	1976–85	1986–95
Modoc	(2)[b]	(9)	(9)	(0)	(0)
Grasses	7.5	10.6	26.1	—	25.0
Legumes	5.0	7.0	10.3	—	9.0
Sedges	14.5	16.3	17.2	—	7.7
Rushes	4.5	5.0	6.1	—	2.5
Lassen	(0)	(13)	(13)	(1)	(15)
Grasses	—	22.6	19.9	31.0	29.4
Legumes	—	2.8	4.8	1.0	7.2
Sedges	—	20.4	22.0	26.0	19.6
Rushes	—	12.5	9.2	4.0	10.2
Plumas	(0)	(14)	(13)	(5)	(13)
Grasses	—	25.1	18.4	14.0	20.5
Legumes	—	6.6	3.4	4.0	13.0
Sedges	—	20.6	21.1	22.8	23.2
Rushes	—	13.1	16.1	9.6	11.1
Tahoe	(1)	(16)	(12)	(11)	(7)
Grasses	13.0	32.9	31.9	28.6	20.3
Legumes	0	10.1	4.8	3.9	15.0
Sedges	25.0	18.6	22.2	22.3	24.4
Rushes	19.0	2.9	11.8	10.1	11.0
Eldorado	(5)	(12)	(13)	(0)	(3)
Grasses	24.4	22.6	46.7	—	16.7
Legumes	4.6	6.0	8.0	—	4.0
Sedges	20.6	13.1	12.9	—	1.0
Rushes	0.4	0.1	10.0	—	0
Stanislaus	(1)	(8)	(14)	(10)	(2)
Grasses	10.0	27.4	20.3	19.1	7.5
Legumes	0	18.0	6.4	11.0	2.0
Sedges	2.0	28.8	35.6	31.7	30.5
Rushes	0	0.6	1.9	0.8	3.5
Sierra	(6)	(13)	(15)	(0)	(4)
Grasses	29.2	19.3	18.6	—	6.2
Legumes	10.3	3.6	4.3	—	4.5
Sedges	19.7	40.8	34.3	—	47.0
Rushes	1.7	4.6	6.1	—	9.0
Sequoia	(0)	(10)	(8)	(4)	(0)
Grasses	—	12.5	8.5	11.8	—
Legumes	—	8.0	8.8	8.0	—
Sedges	—	41.9	50.4	41.2	—
Rushes	—	10.8	6.1	6.2	—
Toiyabe	(0)	(10)	(1)	(10)	(0)
Grasses	—	16.3	17.0	24.8	—
Legumes	—	6.7	0	8.7	—
Sedges	—	26.4	44.0	22.4	—
Rushes	—	6.2	14.0	7.4	—
Inyo	(0)	(20)	(3)	(15)	(11)
Grasses	—	12.5	13.0	9.6	18.0
Legumes	—	6.9	5.0	10.2	2.5
Sedges	—	37.8	25.5	53.8	35.3
Rushes	—	8.6	33.5	3.4	8.1

[a]Grasses (Poaceae), legumes (Fabaceae, primarily *Trifolium* spp.), sedges (Cyperaceae; primarily *Carex*, *Scirpus*, and *Eleocharis*), and rushes (Juncaceae, primarily *Juncus*).
[b]Numbers in parentheses indicate the number of transects.

overall decline of almost 16% and highlighted by individual county losses as high as 42% (table 7.5). Major conversions from 1945 through 1973 were from rangeland clearing for enhancement of forage production. Since 1973, major losses have been from conversions to residential and industrial developments.

Introductions of domestic livestock and exotic annuals have led to dramatic changes in hardwood rangeland ecosystems.

TABLE 7.5

Changes in hardwood habitat in the Sierra Nevada region from 1945 to 1985. (From volume III, chapter 15.)

County	Percentage Change
Shasta	+7
Tehama	−23
Butte	−9
Yuba	−18
Nevada	−18
Placer	−32
El Dorado	+2
Amador	−28
Calaveras	−29
Tuolumne	−42
Mariposa	−21
Madera	−13
Fresno	−19
Tulare	−2
Kern	−15
Sierra total	−16

The herbaceous layer has changed from a perennial layer to an annual layer. Fire intervals have increased dramatically, and fire intensity has also increased. The overstory tree layer, if not converted to another land use, has generally increased. Soil moisture late in the growing season has decreased, and soil bulk density has increased due to compaction from higher herbivore densities. Riparian zones are now lower in vegetation density and diversity.

These major impacts of livestock grazing also suggest other ecosystem influences:

- More moisture may be available to oaks when the herbaceous layer is removed by grazing.

- Transpirational surface area of seedlings, reduced by grazing, may result in higher soil moisture later in the summer.

- Consumption of ladder fuels reduces the likelihood of crown fires in grazed woodlands.

- Grazing animals consume oak seedlings and acorns, thereby reducing their availability as food for rodents and other wildlife.

- Grazing may increase soil compaction, making root growth for developing oak seedlings more difficult.

- Less organic matter may be available for incorporation in soils.

Research on the effects of removing oak trees, particularly relative to forage production, has provided a number of general findings:

- There is little or no enhancement of forage value from removing blue oaks in areas with less than 20 inches of annual precipitation.

- For areas with greater than 20 inches of annual precipitation, thinning oaks where the canopy exceeds 50% will increase forage production.

- In areas thinned for forage enhancement, residual tree canopies of 25%–35% are able to maintain soil fertility, provide wildlife habitat, and minimize erosion processes.

Ironically, factors that cause livestock operations in hardwood rangelands to suffer low profitability and high risk are leading indirectly to conversion of these lands from extensively managed private ranches to suburban developments:

- Dramatic annual fluctuations in livestock markets.

- High variability in annual rainfall, leading to unpredictable forage shortages.

- Higher profitability potential from suburban development or intensive agriculture industries such as wine grapes.

- Uncertainties about federal grazing policies for public rangelands required for summer pasture.

At the individual stand or patch level, oak woodlands actually appear to be much more stable than previously thought. Concerns about oak regeneration are not well founded. Long-term trends reveal stand structures with recruitment into various size classes and increasing canopy density under typical livestock management practices. Technologies have been developed to carry out restoration of areas denuded of oaks in the past. Voluntary research and education programs such as the IHRMP have made dramatic, measured progress in accomplishing sustainable management practices by landowners. The major accomplishments have been made in the more rural areas of the state where livestock and natural resource management are predominant land uses. Where individual landowners have the ability to implement management activities that affect large acreages, education and research have contributed to decisions that favor conservation of hardwood rangelands.

Potential for Recovery and Sustainable Range Management

Patterns of increasing cheatgrass and other exotic plant invasion in sagebrush-steppe communities and associated increases in fire frequency due to increases in flashy fuels threaten to spread this condition throughout this community type. Extensive overgrazing of most Sierra Nevada and Modoc Plateau meadows, upland shrublands, and stream/riparian systems before 1920, followed by documented substantial reductions in domestic livestock numbers through the 1960s, still presents managers with many damaged meadow/riparian and upland rangeland conditions in need of restoration. Many meadows have downcut stream courses, compacted soils, altered plant community compositions, and diminished wildlife and aquatic habitats. Many uplands have excessive bare soil exposure dependent on annual grasses for their future stability.

The mechanisms involved with invasion by annual grasses defy the natural restoration capacity of Sierra Nevada upland rangelands. Even intense application of active management techniques will have uncertain success in restoring native plant communities. If grazing were completely eliminated from these ranges, the restoration task would be no less monumental.

In spite of persistent problems, the remarkably recovered condition of many ecosystem components of montane meadows and uplands today indicates that well-watered meadow/riparian ecosystems have tremendous potential for restoration of plant communities, while providing very important agricultural grazing values to society. Beginning about 1975 and continuing to today, land management agencies and ranchers have conducted numerous riparian restoration demonstration projects throughout the Sierra Nevada and Modoc Plateau. Public rangeland managers, allotment by allotment, have prioritized limited funding and gained cooperative support of permittees to target riparian restoration management on local problems within allotments. Though livestock exclusion from riparian pastures has been the common method, many other grazing management strategies, such as increased animal distribution control measures, sometimes with reductions in numbers of livestock, have resulted in favorable improvements. In some cases, grazing systems that variably adjust intensity and duration have resulted in increases in livestock carrying capacity while reducing environmental impacts.

Continuing efforts to reduce local undesirable grazing impacts to soils, streams, and habitats could return natural aquatic and terrestrial functionality where it is currently at less than its potential. Better management can increase not only native biodiversity, wildlife habitat, and nonforage values but also livestock performance. Forage plant vigor has as much to gain as riparian functionality.

The area of closely grazed rangeland and the length of damaged riparian/stream habitat is substantially higher than under presettlement conditions. The ecological function and agricultural productivity of Sierra Nevada and Modoc Plateau rangelands are depressed below their potential. Rangelands provide a wealth of habitat and aesthetic values to the general society, and grazing values to an important agricultural industry, but management directed to improve ecological functionality and agricultural productivity has not been realized to the extent possible.

A GRAZING AND RANGELAND STRATEGY

Goals

There are three goals for the grazing and rangeland strategy:

1. Improve soil and stream-bank stability and aquatic/terrestrial habitats on mountain meadows, upland shrublands, and stream/riparian ecosystems.

2. Prioritize restoration on meadow/riparian systems that are in an upward trend in functionality and on upland shrublands that show resistance to weed invasion and greater abundance of native perennial grasses.

3. Continue adherence to the mission of the California Integrated Hardwood Range Management Program (IHRMP): "To maintain, and where possible expand, the acreage of California's hardwood range resource to provide wildlife habitat, recreational opportunities, wood and livestock products, high quality water supply, and aesthetic value."

Possible Solutions

Operationally, the key management element is to ensure that the persons responsible for livestock management are knowledgeable about undesirable impacts and are dedicated to improving conditions. Training will need to be a large part of carrying out this strategy. Frequent monitoring of livestock impacts and rapid solutions are required.

Clearly articulated descriptions of what meadow, riparian, and upland conditions are desired, in proximate and ultimate terms, must be developed. That is, without expecting or proposing the impossible, it must be made clear in ecological and managerial terms the stages (state and transition seral stages and timing) each system can and should go through to achieve two goals concomitantly—increased ecosystem functionality and increased agricultural productivity.

The rancher/permittee and agency manager would take joint responsibility for understanding and seeking the proxi-

Livestock grazing in a mountain meadow. Headwaters of Willow Creek near Eagle Lake, Lassen County. (Photo by Michael Oliver.)

mate and ultimate rangeland conditions described. Operationally this task is a large one. Each party would become educated about rangeland ecosystem responses to management and other natural environmental forces, develop tolerance for practical versus technical understanding of ecological and agricultural aspects of range systems, and overcome tensions arising from diverse viewpoints about individual priorities.

Prescriptive and adaptive management could be implemented with an accountable system of ten-year allotment and annual operating plans supported by professional rapport among the rancher/permittee, the agency range manager, and the public at large. At the outset of this strategy, goal 1 seeks to reduce local forage overutilization and associated soil and stream-bank instability and undesirable aquatic/terrestrial habitat impacts on grazing allotments. Overutilization of forage is a temporal event never referencing longer than one growing season's production; however, it can occur in as short a time as a few days. What goal 1 focuses on is animal distribution control, using such means as herding, salting, fencing, water development to attract animals, and culling of individual unmanageable animals.

Currently, thirteen of fifteen Sierra Nevada counties have adopted or started the process of adopting local hardwood rangeland conservation strategies. Most have adopted voluntary guidelines, which should be continually monitored to measure their efficacy. Optionally, conservation strategies can be incorporated in ordinances or can become part of county general plan policies that govern land use.

Implications

As range managers have become more aware of short- and long-term undesirable impacts of grazing livestock on multiple-use public rangelands, animal management has become more complex, time-consuming, and expensive. Because rangelands are often remote, problem situations that could be easily managed too often go unnoticed for weeks, months, seasons, and sometimes even years.

The rancher may not perceive that problems even exist. What is recognized as a problem changes as understanding and standards change. Ranchers and agency managers would need to be in much closer touch with the resource and each other than they have been in the past.

On some allotments, herder/riders may need to be present much of the time to avoid undesirable impacts; this represents an additional cost to the rancher. One major potential trade-off for this additional management cost for the rancher is the proven increase in productivity possible with time-controlled grazing. Intensive grazing systems pay great dividends in forage productivity enhancement when plants are grazed heavily for a very few days and then have as much as a month to regrow before being grazed again. Such controlled grazing systems should offset some of the added cost of herding.

Using a suite of ecosystem functionality and livestock carrying capacity and performance criteria, trends in many redundant measures will corroborate whether management has been successful. Many of the criteria will be site-specific, but the conditions measured in the SNEP rangeland assessment, including bare soil exposure, width/depth ratios in meadow streams, and abundance of native perennial grasses and weeds, as well as fish and aquatic organism diversity and neotropical bird nesting success should be used. Monitoring (data compilation and analysis) of key associated ecosystem factors needs to be an integral part of this management strategy. The task of reading condition and trend transects is not unreasonable, but it must be done on at least a three-year schedule. Annual monitoring of other short-term indicators will also be a necessary part of the annual operating plan for the ranchers and range managers.

CHAPTER 8

Watersheds and Aquatic Biodiversity

Aquatic Habitats The aquatic/riparian systems are the most altered and impaired habitats of the Sierra.

Stream Flow Dams and diversions throughout most of the Sierra Nevada have profoundly altered stream-flow patterns (timing and amount of water) and water temperatures, with significant impacts to aquatic biodiversity.

Riparian Status Riparian areas have been damaged extensively by placer mining (northern and west-central Sierra) and grazing (Sierra-wide), and locally by dams, ditches, flumes, pipelines, roads, timber harvest, residential development, and recreational activities.

Sediment Excessive sediment yield into streams remains a widespread water-quality problem in the Sierra Nevada.

Water Quality Major water-quality impacts on the Sierra are (1) impairment of chemical water quality downstream of urban centers, mines, and intensive land-use zones, (2) accumulation of near toxic levels of mercury in many low- to middle-elevation reservoirs of the western Sierra, (3) widespread biological contamination by human pathogens (especially *Giardia*), and (4) increased salinity in east-side lakes as a result of water diversions.

Introduced Aquatics Introduction of non-native fishes (primarily trout) has greatly altered aquatic ecosystems through impacts on native fish, amphibians, and invertebrate assemblages.

Amphibian Status Amphibian species at all elevations have severely declined throughout the Sierra Nevada.

Anadromous Fish Anadromous fish (chinook salmon, steelhead), once native to most major Sierran rivers north of the Kings River, are now nearly extinct from Sierran rivers.

Aquatic Invertebrates Local degradation of habitats has led to significant impacts on aquatic invertebrates, which make up the vast majority of aquatic species in the Sierra Nevada.

ASSESSMENT

California's economy derives enormous benefits from water diverted from the streams, rivers, and lakes of the Sierra Nevada. A major cost associated with these benefits has been deterioration of the biotic integrity and sustainability of the aquatic systems, as reflected in declines in the distribution and abundance of native aquatic and riparian organisms. Water determines the distribution and abundance of many plants and animals throughout the Sierra Nevada by shaping and providing habitat. Lakes and streams support rich communities of native organisms both in the water and in adjoining riparian areas. These water bodies also support cities, farms, and industries within and distant from the mountains. Water was critical for development of the mining economy that dominated California for years after the gold rush. The Sierra Nevada has provided high-quality water for natural communities for millennia and for modern society for more than half a century. But in less than twenty years the risk of *Giardia* has spread to such an extent that virtually everywhere in the mountains one can no longer casually drink from a stream or lake, and concern for other microorganisms, such as *Microsporidium*, in water supplies is growing. Development of streams and other resources of the Sierra Nevada over the past 150 years has met the downstream demands of society throughout California but has impaired the quality and availability of water for both ecological and social needs in many parts of the mountain range.

Aquatic Ecosystems

Aquatic and riparian habitats are linked in direct and complex ways and are fundamentally dependent on natural flows of water. Natural supplies of water and its constituents (mineral particles, solutes, organic matter, biota) are highly variable over time, changing markedly between seasons and between years and over space. The native biota is well adapted to these seasonal patterns and extremes, but Californians have not been satisfied with the natural distribution of water and have engineered extensive control over the waters of the Sierra Nevada. Hydrologic processes have been further modified by side effects of the development of other natural resources of the Sierra Nevada. As human activities have altered characteristics of streams (such as volume of water, flood peaks, duration of low flows, seasonal timing, sediment supply, amounts of nutrients and organic matter, and water temperature) aquatic and riparian ecosystems have been forced to change. Other ecological changes have been deliberate, such as introduction of exotic species (e.g., brook trout, bullfrog), conversion of streams to lakes, and conversion of riparian zones to roads and structures.

In many respects aquatic systems have shown remarkable resilience. Vegetation along many streams gutted by mining has returned. Agencies are beginning to recognize the special nature of riparian areas, and some are developing practices intended to protect in-stream and associated resources.

❋ A Past View of Resources in the Lahontan Region

"A discussion of the economic value of the fishes of this region and any consideration of methods of propagation and protection must begin and end with the assumption that agricultural and manufacturing interests are of paramount importance. A considerable and constantly increasing amount of the flowing water must be used first for power and then for irrigation, and when any measure intended for the protection of fishes is found to seriously interfere with the working of power plants or the demands of agriculture it will have to be abandoned."

John Otterbein Snyder, Fish Biologist
Bulletin of the U.S. Bureau of Fisheries 1915/16

Present-day water projects at least recognize that the aquatic system requires some flows to exist. And some fisheries agencies personnel are becoming attuned to the needs of all organisms rather than the special management of a few. Nevertheless, the net results of a century and a half of these disturbances to the Sierra Nevada are greatly simplified and impaired aquatic ecosystems. Aquatic and riparian habitats have been severely altered and continue to deteriorate, leading to the loss of native species, ecosystem functions, and services to human society.

Invertebrates

The best indicators of the health of the aquatic system of the Sierra Nevada may be the group of organisms we know the least about—invertebrates. These small creatures are rarely seen or considered by most people, but they are central to aquatic ecosystems because they consume algae and organic matter and become food for fish, birds, mammals, amphibians, and reptiles. These organisms represent a great diversity of species. Species restricted to the Sierra Nevada (endemic) in two major groups of aquatic insects, the caddisflies and the stoneflies, were estimated for this report to be 19% (of 199 species) and 25% (of 122 species), respectively. A wealth of evolutionary, ecological, and biogeographical information is contained in Sierra aquatic invertebrates. Some species are highly specialized and are found only in a few wetlands, springs, or small streams. When these limited habitats are altered, their dependent invertebrates are likely to disappear.

Shifts in composition of invertebrate communities suggest changes in aquatic habitat or water quality, and invertebrates have been used to assess changes for many years. The great diversity of aquatic invertebrates makes them an especially valuable tool for monitoring almost any kind of aquatic habi-

tat. The invertebrate fauna of the Sierra Nevada has probably changed dramatically since the 1850s because of major changes in habitat, and some species have become extinct. However, few species-level inventories of aquatic invertebrates exist for the Sierra, and the distribution of most species is poorly known.

Fish

Native fishes are much better known than their invertebrate food supply and are also at risk from changes in water availability and quality, habitat alteration, and introduction of exotic species. Of the forty species of fishes native to the Sierra Nevada, six are formally listed as threatened or endangered and twelve others are candidates for listing. Four other fishes are in decline within the Sierra Nevada but are less threatened elsewhere. Less than half of the native fish species of the Sierra Nevada have secure populations. The long-term causes of the declines are introductions of exotic fishes, dams and diversions, alterations of stream channels, and watershed disturbance (grazing, mining, roads, logging, etc.). These different problems occur throughout the range and usually operate in combination to degrade and dissect aquatic habitat. This habitat fragmentation, in turn, allows piecemeal extirpation of local populations.

Chinook salmon are a principal example of the drastic declines in native fishes of the Sierra Nevada. In the nineteenth century, more than a million salmon spawned annually in the streams of the west slope, with some ascending to an elevation of 6,000 feet. However, the curtain of dams across the Sierra Nevada rivers blocked access to about 90% of the original spawning habitat (figure 8.1). Consequently, spring-run chinook salmon, present in less than 10% of their original numbers, have been virtually eliminated from the Sierra Nevada except for those spawning in a few undammed tributaries to the Sacramento River (such as Deer Creek and Mill Creek).

Fish are one of the most intensively managed components of the ecosystems of the Sierra Nevada. Occasional transfer of fish in buckets in the 1800s has exploded into hatchery production of millions of fish and mechanized stocking at hundreds of sites throughout the range. At least thirty non-native fishes have become established in the Sierra Nevada, and ten of these exotic species are now widespread and abundant. Before the active manipulation of fisheries, most of the Sierra Nevada above 6,000 feet lacked any fish fauna. Hundreds of miles of streams and almost all of the more than 4,000 natural lakes of the Sierra Nevada were dominated by invertebrates and frogs until widespread trout introductions began in the nineteenth century. Trout are now present almost everywhere in the range that is capable of supporting them. In Sequoia, Kings Canyon, and Yosemite National Parks fish stocking was terminated in the lakes in the 1980s. Recent regional surveys show that trout have disappeared naturally from 29%–44% of these previously stocked lakes. Many high-elevation lakes

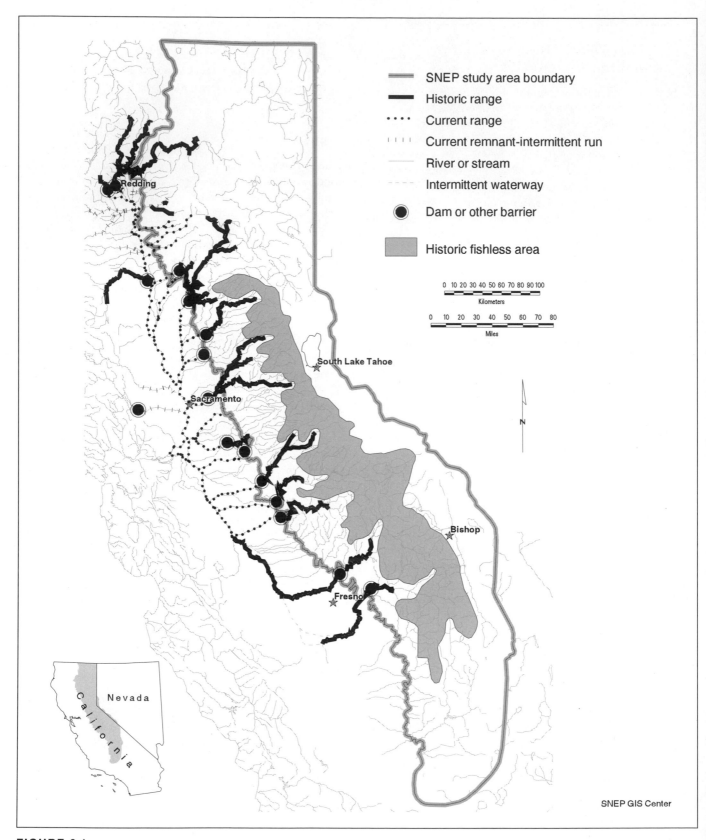

FIGURE 8.1

Two major changes in Sierra Nevada fish distribution. The shaded area shows streams and lakes that historically were without fish but that now mostly contain them. The dotted and heavy lines show current and historic distribution, respectively, of chinook salmon. (From volume II, chapter 33.)

outside the national parks are still regularly planted with trout to support recreational fisheries. This artificially maintained fishery provides substantial angler use, and fishing in the high-elevation lakes remains a major objective of those who visit these sites. Nevertheless, the predatory trout have greatly altered lake and stream ecosystems, resulting in local and rangewide changes in species assemblages of aquatic invertebrates. Introduced trout are also a factor contributing to the decline of some native amphibians, in particular the mountain yellow-legged frog, whose former distribution is almost perfectly coincident with the former fishless zone (figure 8.2).

Further, the widespread use of fish poison for fisheries management in Sierra streams and lakes for more than forty-five years has had undetermined impacts on nontargeted organisms.

Amphibians

Amphibians have suffered sharp declines in abundance, distribution, and diversity throughout the Sierra Nevada and elsewhere. Half of the twenty-nine native amphibian species are at risk of extinction because of declining populations or

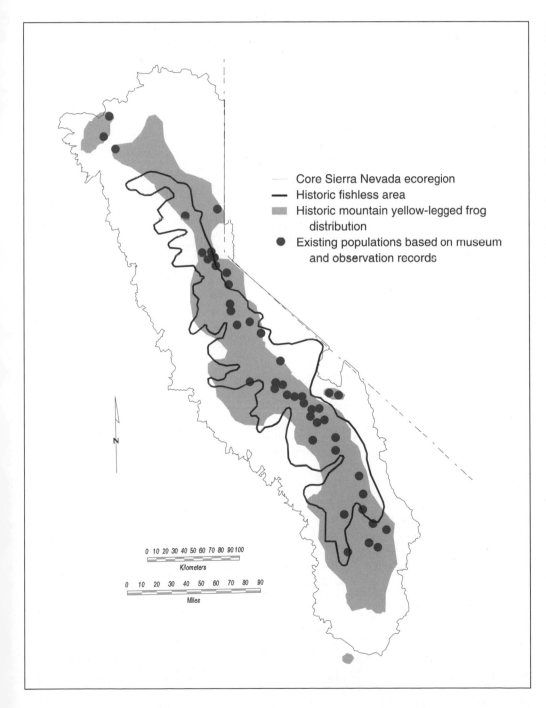

— Core Sierra Nevada ecoregion
— Historic fishless area
▨ Historic mountain yellow-legged frog distribution
● Existing populations based on museum and observation records

0 10 20 30 40 50 60 70 80 90 100
Kilometers

0 10 20 30 40 50 60 70 80 90
Miles

FIGURE 8.2

Decline of the mountain yellow-legged frog and its association with the historic fishless area in the Sierra Nevada. Current known populations of frog are shown as dots compared to the frog's former range, which closely coincided with the historic fishless area. Most lakes in the historic fishless area now contain populations of non-native fishes, which were introduced for sports fishing and are implicated in the decline of the mountain yellow-legged frog. (From volume II, chapter 32.)

❈ *Deer Creek Watershed Conservancy*

"Spring-run Chinook salmon and Steelhead once occurred in many streams throughout the Central Valley. Today these incredible fish occur in only a few Sacramento Valley streams, including Deer Creek. The important populations are monitored to ensure their continued existence. The survival of these fish has depended on the caring stewardship of property owners within the watershed and their future will rely upon continued responsible management of the land."

Deer Creek Watershed Conservancy
Vina, California

A stretch of Deer Creek on the Lassen National Forest. (Photo by Peter B. Moyle.)

very limited distributions. The Breckenridge Mountain slender salamander, absent in all recent searches, is already considered extinct. Species in danger include eight of the twenty salamanders and seven of the nine frogs and toads. Of the fourteen endemic amphibians in the Sierra, twelve are in danger of extinction. The decline of frogs is particularly alarming because they are now missing from a wide variety of habitats, ranging from alpine lakes to foothill streams. Populations of several frog species formerly stretched in a continuous band from north to south in a specific range of elevations for each species. There are also waters where native amphibians are still surviving. In the foothills, these tend to be small streams that have a dense riparian canopy, that are free of introduced species, and that have not been disturbed by grazing and other impacts. At high elevations, populations are found in clusters of fishless lakes and streams in remote areas. These observations show that populations of most amphibians, especially frogs, are no longer connected but exist as isolated groups that are highly vulnerable to extirpation. Current ecological theory strongly suggests that species such as these depend upon linkages among the populations that collectively span great distances or elevations. Fragmentation and extirpation without hope of recolonization may lead to

local, then regional, then Sierra-wide extinction of amphibian species if present trends continue.

Aquatic Habitats

The decline of native fishes and amphibians and changes in aquatic invertebrate assemblages in the Sierra Nevada largely reflect the deterioration of aquatic and riparian habitats. They have been altered by development of water and other resources. Of sixty-seven types of aquatic habitat categorized in the Sierra Nevada, almost two-thirds (64%) are declining in quality and abundance, and many are at risk of disappearing altogether. Factors contributing to this deterioration are many and cumulative. The health of any part of an aquatic system depends on all the influences of the channel network and watershed upstream of that point. In spite of better land-use practices, excessive sedimentation continues to be observed and documented in site-specific analyses, even though systematic, rangewide monitoring is lacking. Implementation of newer practices designed to prevent sedimentation (practices officially designated as best management practices under the federal Clean Water Act) may be too recent for positive results to be observed in some systems. But the close association between roads and sedimentation and the pervasive nature of roads within the streamside corridor mean that chronic problems may be persistent and difficult to overcome.

The land areas near water bodies (riparian areas, stream and lake management zones, etc.) are crucial as habitat for a large group of species. Approximately 17% of Sierran plant species, 21% of the vertebrate species, and almost 100% of aquatic invertebrate species in streams are closely associated with or dependent on riparian or wet areas. This area also yields essential inputs of food, nutrients, wood structure, and energy to the aquatic system and buffers the effects of land use. Thus, it provides several vital functions: special terrestrial habitat, aquatic structure, energy/food resources, and buffer. It is also the region to which historically it was easiest to gain access (roads), and it is fundamentally attractive to cattle grazing. Overgrazing and livestock concentration in riparian zones have altered stream morphology and vegeta-

tive composition in many areas throughout the Sierra Nevada. Intense grazing has been so widespread that few ungrazed reference sites exist for comparison. Riparian protection is recognized in current state and federal land-use management policies and has expanded in the past two decades; for example, clear-cut logging to a stream margin was practiced into the 1970s. Nevertheless, existing standards still do not adequately provide for sufficient land area or describe appropriate management for maintenance of all the vital functions. Small aquatic habitats (e.g., springs, intermittent streams) are more affected by adjacent land use than are larger streams and lakes, yet they generally fall under lower standards of protection. Wetlands and springs in the Sierra Nevada have been modified by water development, road construction and drainage, grazing, and residential development at large scales (e.g., Tahoe Keys) and on individual parcels. Foothill areas below about 3,300 feet appear to have the

❋ *Watershed Risk Assessment*

Potential for soil erosion was classified for watersheds in the Eldorado National Forest. Remote sensing and geographic information systems produced data on slope, vulnerability to soil erosion, and amount of bare ground. Threshold values were estimated for each factor. The resulting maps (e.g., figure 8.3), based on units of 0.22 acres, show those regions where no factor, one factor, two factors, or three factors exceeded the threshold and thus point to likely problem locations and to areas where mitigation or restoration projects would be most effective in reducing the cumulative effects of natural and human-induced watershed changes.

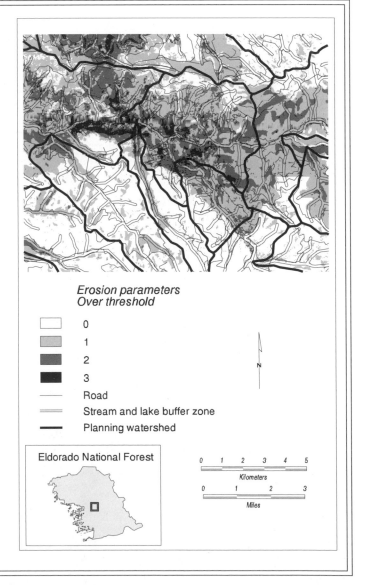

Erosion parameters
Over threshold

- 0
- 1
- 2
- 3
— Road
= Stream and lake buffer zone
— Planning watershed

Eldorado National Forest

Kilometers
0 1 2 3 4 5

Miles
0 1 2 3

FIGURE 8.3

A small portion of one watershed (tributaries to the South Fork of the American River near Kyburz) showing soil erosion potential. (From volume II, chapter 54.)

greatest loss of riparian vegetation of any region in the Sierra Nevada. In addition to land disturbance, creation of large reservoirs has submerged about 600 miles of riparian corridors along larger rivers, further fragmenting riparian habitat.

Direct modification of streams by dams, diversions, and channelization projects has had major, permanent impacts on larger streams and associated riparian zones where most of these projects have been built. Dams and water diversions of all sizes affect most watersheds in the Sierra Nevada (figure 8.4). Placer and hydraulic mining in the 1800s devastated streams and riparian zones, which are now partially recovered. But dredging operations were only the initial disturbance to which more recent impacts have been added. If population growth occurs as projected, new pressure is likely to be intense to extract local sources of stream gravel for roads and building.

Recovery and Restoration

Although few changes other than extinction are irreversible in an absolute sense, many environmental modifications can be considered to be effectively irreversible. Most structures, such as large dams, canals, residential developments, and highways, are permanent for practical purposes. However, impacts from permanent structures can often be reduced by changes in use of the structures or by creative mitigation. Other persistent impacts, such as unsurfaced forest roads and agricultural fields, can be removed or mitigated, and ecological functions of the site can be restored with sufficient investment. Cessation of chronic disturbances, such as grazing or trampling in riparian areas, seasonal water diversions, and stocking of nonreproducing fish, will allow natural recovery of different aspects of an ecosystem at varying rates. For example, wet meadows converted to dry terraces above an in-

FIGURE 8.4

Relative density of dams and diversions in planning watersheds *(a)* and reservoir capacity in watersheds of the SNEP study area *(b)*. (From volume II, chapter 36.)

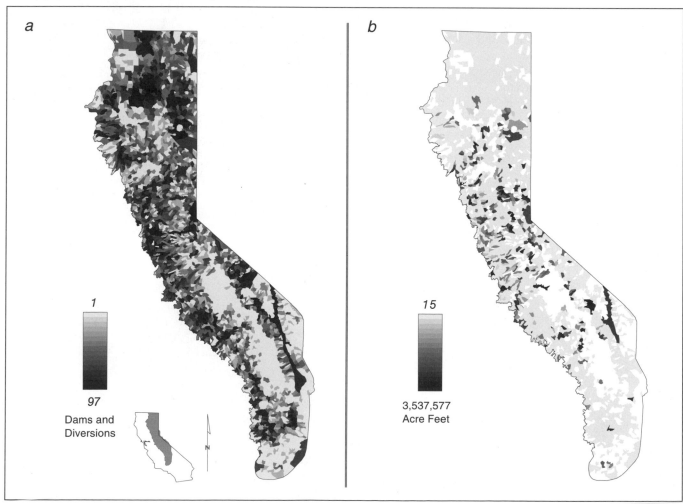

cised stream as a result of overgrazing may not recover even over a century without active restoration work. Riparian vegetation tends to become reestablished within a few years after chronic disturbance is eliminated, but readjustment of channel morphology to a natural shape may require decades. Although disturbances such as a single timber harvest or a fire can have severe short-term effects, natural recovery from them generally occurs at a much faster rate than recovery from chronic disturbances.

Knowledge Base

The knowledge base for improving water allocation and implementing sound watershed management in the Sierra Nevada is notably weak. Economic values of water in different uses are not well established. Information about water demand and historic water rights is not easily accessible. Records of water quality and sediment yield are available at very few sites throughout the mountain range. Rates of natural and accelerated erosion have not been measured at many locations in the Sierra Nevada. The impacts of various water and land-management practices are not quantified or even known in some cases. In the few cases where long-term, rangewide surveys exist, such as grazing transects in wet meadows on the national forests, data have not been summarized until now. The effectiveness of best management practices and restoration techniques are largely untested. In general, the basic data for sound decision making about improving water and watershed management are lacking. Specific habitat requirements of most riparian-dependent terrestrial vertebrate species are poorly documented, and general surveys of species distribution for most aquatic invertebrate species are missing. Adequate monitoring of natural processes, impacts, mitigation, and restoration could provide a much better basis for water resources planning and admin-

Upper-elevation reservoir on the Middle Fork Yuba River. Jackson Meadows Reservoir, Tahoe National Forest. (Photo by Richard Kattelmann.)

istration. Inadequate information is currently a major constraint on improvements in water and land management.

In summary, the aquatic/riparian systems are the most altered and impaired habitats of the Sierra. Species losses and changes in species assemblages have been accelerated in aquatic and aquatic-connected habitats. Frogs, in particular, have been declining at an alarming rate in recent years. Native fish and other assemblages have been fragmented by water projects. Many aquatic species are either listed as threatened or endangered or will be candidates for listing if present trends continue. The declines were especially severe during the first hundred years of water development, starting with hydraulic mining. Although declines have subsequently slowed in most cases, many continue and there is little evidence of long-term improvement in the status of aquatic organisms.

Restoration, better management, and research are needed to recover lost habitat, prevent further loss, and monitor efficacy of management. Suggested solutions are outlined in the strategies and in the individual assessments of volume II.

❄ *Mercury Contamination*

"Anthropogenic mercury is present in the aquatic biota throughout the historic Sierra Nevada gold region. Higher mercury regions include the highest densities of active dredging operations, which also correspond to the greatest historical mining. Bioavailable mercury shows amplification through the food chain. Although the absolute concentrations in rainbow trout presently are well below existing health standards, fish from some reservoirs in this region have markedly higher mercury than those in upstream rivers."

D. G. Slotton, S. M. Ayers, J. E. Reuter, and
C. R. Goldman, Technical Completion Report
(Davis: University of California Water
Resources Center, 1995)

STRATEGIES FOR IMPROVING WATERSHEDS AND AQUATIC BIODIVERSITY

Goals

Strategies for improving watersheds and aquatic biodiversity have two goals:

1. Improve the biotic integrity and sustainability of aquatic habitats and ecosystems in the Sierra Nevada. This goal implies that protection, management, and restoration of

watersheds is needed to maintain natural hydrologic and ecological processes.

2. Secure long-term social and economic benefits of a dependable supply of clean water from naturally functioning watersheds.

Possible Solutions

Conditions that lead to deterioration of aquatic and riparian ecosystems vary among different watersheds in the Sierra Nevada, but all river basins have been altered to some degree. Therefore, an optimal strategy for preventing further degradation includes all watersheds of the range but recognizes their differences. Such a strategy involves a mixture of approaches from protecting "the best of what is left" to restoring highly degraded systems. In addition to implementing long-term local and regional strategies, there is a need to prevent loss of species and habitats in the short term. There are also opportunities to reestablish chinook salmon and other native species of fish and amphibians in areas where they have been lost because of water development or introduction of exotics. Restoration of the functions of aquatic and riparian habitat where they are identified as impaired will support the recovery of imperiled species.

Watershed Focus

Problems and opportunities for solutions come from analysis on a watershed-by-watershed basis unless there are easier or

Functional riparian areas provide vital habitat for many terrestrial and aquatic organisms, bring large wood and food to a stream, and buffer land use. Sagehen Creek, Tahoe National Forest. (Photo by Jerry Morse.)

more effective ways of doing so. A watershed approach allows connections to be made between upstream actions and downstream consequences and benefits. Evaluation of the health of individual streams and their watersheds could identify particular problems and their causes. Reduction of the adverse impacts of land disturbance (e.g., erosion, streambank instability, loss of riparian habitat, loss of large woody debris and its recruitment) requires cooperation among citizens' groups, regulatory agencies, private landowners, and public land managers within a watershed. The Central Valley and Lahontan Regional Water Quality Control Boards may occupy the logical position to provide oversight and coordination of local watershed efforts. Alternatively, creation of regional boards with an ecosystem management focus might be considered to address problems that are connected across watersheds, such as restoration of native frog populations.

Restoration of Stream-Flow Pattern

In watersheds where water management activities degrade water quality and aquatic biodiversity, improvement may be possible by altering some aspects of reservoir or diversion operations. In general, restoring some semblance of a natural stream discharge regime (such as increasing minimum flows or peak flows) is beneficial to aquatic health. Voluntary adjustments in operations, greater use of conjunctive water-use practices, changes in timing and volume of releases from reservoirs during relicensing, and more stringent enforcement of the Fish and Game Code provide mechanisms for improving stream flows.

Reserve Systems and Management Practices

In watersheds where the principal problems are caused by land disturbance, there is a wide spectrum of possibilities, with different mixes being appropriate in different river basins. A reserve strategy of protected watersheds might be necessary to sustain and improve the few remaining areas of relatively natural flows or high biological integrity (e.g., Deer and Mill Creeks, Tehama County; Clavey River; North Fork Calaveras River; Middle and South Forks Kings River; North and South Forks Kern River). A system of protected areas could be maintained with variable mixes of public and private controls appropriate to each watershed, including economic incentives to landowners for protection of unique or unusual areas. In addition, it is critically important to apply locally adapted best management practices to all lands to minimize soil loss and impacts on aquatic systems.

Institutional Innovations

New policies and institutional mechanisms must be designed to recognize the ecological importance of riparian areas, minimize further disturbance and fragmentation, and provide incentives and funding for restoration activities. On public lands, a well-supported and financed effort is needed to relocate roads, campgrounds, and other incompatible uses out of riparian areas.

Improved riparian and in-stream protection can be achieved by designing variable-width buffers that recognize the dependent terrestrial community habitat requirements, energy and food supplies, and management-influence areas adjacent to aquatic systems. Existing data combined with GIS technology allows layout of such buffers as a first step until more refined information is obtained on-site. Continued efforts to rewater dry and near-dry channels below diversions could proceed through enforcement of existing laws and changes in in-stream flow requirements during relicensing of hydroelectric projects. Changes in road location and grazing management practices are needed to avoid further damage to mountain meadows and spring systems. Existing regulatory approaches to wetlands conservation require better coordination among agencies, local governments, and citizens' groups.

Restoration of Native Species

Runs of anadromous fish could be restored where feasible (e.g., to the San Joaquin River below Friant Dam and the Kings River below Pine Flat Dam) by maintaining adequate flows through altering reservoir release schedules, improving physical habitat, and improving water quality. There is also potential to restore salmon and steelhead above major dams wherever large expanses of suitable spawning habitat still exist (e.g., American River). Restoration of native species, especially amphibians, to some of their original range could be accomplished by controlling competing exotic species in carefully selected areas and avoiding new introductions. As a trade-off with recreational fishing, artificial stocking could cease in about a third of the high mountain lakes, where native frogs are under extreme threat from introduced fish, and the lakes could be allowed to revert to a fishless state.

Water-Use Payments

A possible funding source for expanded watershed and restoration activities is the beneficiaries of both the water-supply system and watershed management. A diversion tax on water is one possibility. Such a tax would be similar to severance taxes on minerals and yield taxes on timber, which have a long history in some jurisdictions. Taxes on diverted water as low as $1–$10 per acre-foot would generate from $20 million to $200 million for stable long-term funding. A trust fund or conservancy could then finance watershed improvements and monitoring throughout the Sierra Nevada.

Monitoring

A major long-term commitment to collecting, analyzing, and evaluating physical, chemical, and biological indicators of the status of aquatic systems is needed. The Central Valley and Lahontan Regional Water Quality Control Boards could be the coordinators of such a program. Cooperators could include the Department of Water Resources, U.S. Geological Survey, U.S. Natural Resources Conservation Service, National Biological Service, federal land-management agencies, the California Academy of Sciences, the University of California and other colleges and universities, local governments, water agencies, landowners, and citizens' groups. To provide adequate geographic coverage throughout the Sierra Nevada, dramatic improvements in efficiency over current data collection efforts would be necessary.

Implications

The economy of California largely depends on high-quality water originating in the Sierra Nevada and diverted to distant locations. Hydropower generated from falling water has been extensively developed throughout much of the mountain range. Watersheds with continuous vegetative cover and healthy riparian areas provide the highest-quality water, which requires little or no treatment for human uses. The connection between watershed condition and downstream quality is rarely recognized by water users. Almost none of the high economic value of water at its end use is returned to the source area. If maintaining and restoring the conditions contributing to water availability and quality become an objective, then some of the value of water would need to be reinvested in the source areas. Other institutional changes in water allocations could lead to more efficient water delivery to higher-valued uses at lower environmental costs.

Watershed management is an alternative means of organizing agencies and coordinating between those agencies and citizens' groups. Within each river basin, one existing management agency could assume leadership in organizing watershed efforts, or different organizations could cooperate in a mutually acceptable framework. The regulatory and adjudicative regional water quality control boards may be subdivided along watershed lines so as to facilitate such organization. In some cases, small changes in watershed management could create substantial improvements in aquatic systems at small cost to those who make the changes; in other cases, costly managerial changes may have little biotic effect. There is a need to identify when voluntary cooperation, compensation, and prescriptive enforcement are likely to work best.

The primary criteria for measuring success of improved water and land management are improvements in the status of imperiled species and in water quality, especially sediment. Maintenance of populations of aquatic and riparian species that are currently stable, and nondegradation of currently high water quality are other important criteria. The success of new institutional arrangements and funding mechanisms could be evaluated on an efficiency and equity basis, but the status of aquatic ecosystems should be the basis for assessing new programs.

CHAPTER 9

Air Quality

❋ CRITICAL FINDINGS

Sierra-wide Status In northern Sierra Nevada airsheds, and in most remote areas during the winter, air quality is some of the cleanest in the nation and even in the world. Southern airsheds on the west side are heavily impacted during spring, summer, and fall by ozone and small particles derived from Central Valley sources and have some of the poorest air quality in the nation.

Ozone Damage Extensive ozone damage occurs to sensitive tree species at low and middle elevations on the southwest and central-western slopes.

Ozone Standards The federal ozone standards for human health may be inadequate to protect biota from air-pollution damage.

Smoke Smoke from managed fires on the average contributes only modest amounts of small particles to human lungs compared with other Sierran sources; winter smoke from woodstoves creates much more severe local air-quality problems.

Visibility Visibility is severely degraded for much of the western slope of the Sierra Nevada each spring, summer, and fall by fine-particle sulfates, nitrates, and smoke transported from the Central Valley.

Dust Dust storms over the alkali and dry lakes of the eastern Sierra (Mono Lake and Owens [dry] Lake) create severe episodic health hazards to humans and presumably to plants and animals as well, when transported into the White and Inyo Mountains and the Sierra Nevada.

ASSESSMENT

Air quality in the Sierra Nevada is highly variable in quality—excellent much of the time and in many places, seriously degraded at other times and places. Many early writers extolled the quality of the air, and in the early twentieth century the Sierra Nevada was even the site of sanatoriums. Yet the Sierra Nevada was typically quite smoky in the summers as many small fires burned for months until the rains extinguished them each fall. There are two distinct aspects of air-quality issues in the Sierra. The first relates to state and federal ambient air quality standards (ozone, particulate mass, visibility reduction), which are periodically violated in the Sierra Nevada. The second relates to air-quality impacts not subject to ambient-air standards (acid deposition, transport of air toxics, eutrophication of Lake Tahoe), which have a more ecological than human health focus.

At present, the most important deleterious impacts are closely tied to the efficient wind transport of air pollutants from the Central Valley of California into the western slopes of the Sierra Nevada up to elevations of 6,000 feet or more. This transport is strong in summer, weak or absent in winter, severe in the southern reaches, and more modest north of Sacramento, where mountain slopes are more gentle. Of these pollutants, ozone has the best documented and most important effects, especially in its connection to serious injury to Jeffrey and ponderosa pines. Fine-particulate sulfates, nitrates, and smoke are also transported by the same winds, especially between April and October, and sharply reduce visibility. Other components of valley air, including nitrates, pesticides, and herbicides, are also efficiently transported into the mountains and deposited on vegetation and in watersheds, often with poorly understood but potentially significant effects. For example, the suggestion that valley air-quality changes may be a factor in the precipitous decline of some amphibians since the late 1960s needs further investigation.

Degradation of air quality is one of the difficult questions raised by proposals for increased use of prescribed fire both to control high levels of forest fuels and to restore the functional role of fire. There is good documentation on degradation of air quality in massive uncontrolled fires. There is much less data on the effect of prescribed fires on a rangewide basis, and smoke from such events is difficult to detect in the detailed fine particulate mass records since 1988. Most information comes from local measurements taken at such fires and the visual effect of smoke. While quantities of smoke from prescribed fires are usually much smaller than from wildfires, they can, under exceptionally unfavorable conditions, also approximate wildfire levels. However, only very rarely does either type of smoke exceed the federal 24-hour fine-particulate mass standard.

High-elevation towns of modest population can still generate very high levels of fine particles in winter smoke, with levels higher than are typically seen even in the largest urban areas of California. Rather surprisingly, there is a rough equality between the mass of fine particles seen in winter urbanized areas and that seen near downwind of massive forest fires. Both of these can greatly exceed state and even federal 24-hour particulate mass (PM-10) standards. Lake Tahoe has sharply reduced water clarity and increased algae, some of which is tied to local and/or transported atmospheric air pollutants such as nitrates. Other typically urban air pollutants, such as carbon monoxide, have been high enough to warrant creation of special air standards to protect human respiration at these high-altitude sites.

The rapid desiccation of eastern Sierra Nevada lakes, Mono

and Owens Lakes, has resulted in dust storms that in most years generate the highest 24-hour fine-dust levels in the United States. Much of this dust is transported into the Sierra Nevada and the White and Inyo Mountains, the latter being the home of the ancient bristlecone pines.

On the other hand, acid rain and snow are not as much a problem as in the eastern United States. No permanently acidified lakes or streams occur in the Sierra Nevada, although pulses of acidity can occur during spring snowmelt and during occasional summer thunderstorms in southern California deserts. In the winter, over much of the nonurbanized Sierra Nevada, levels of some human-origin pollutants such as sulfates are extremely low, mimicking even those of the high-altitude world baseline station on Mauna Loa in Hawaii.

In this section, we will examine a few of the most important topics concerning air quality in the Sierra Nevada, especially those aspects that may be improved or degraded by future human decisions.

Ozone Injury to the Forests

Summer ozone is transported very efficiently from the valley floor into the Sierra Nevada by the remarkably strong and stable terrain winds that move strongly upslope each day and weakly downslope each night. The resultant daytime ozone levels between 2,000 and 6,000 feet are essentially as severe as those on the valley floor. At night, while valley ozone levels rapidly decrease, ozone levels in the mountains stay high, with unknown impact in the morning when the stomata of plants open at first light. Figure 9.1 shows the relationship of elevation and summer ozone influence at sites in and near Sequoia National Park. The peak ozone level at Visalia, on the valley floor, is essentially the same as that at Ash Mountain (2,200 feet) or Giant Forest (6,000 feet). Only when elevation approaches 10,000 feet at Emerald Lake does the valley ozone influence seriously decrease.

These ozone levels lead then to ozone exposure, which is the product of the ozone concentration times the number of hours each concentration occurs. New relationships have been derived for this study that give precise damage measurements to forest trees, especially the economically important Jeffrey pine and also ponderosa pine. The trend of injury, calculated as the ozone injury index, decreases from south to north. Also shown is a measure of exposure, using 0.09 ppm as a cutoff. Exposure above this threshold, which also happens to be the California hourly standard (the federal standard is 0.12 ppm), matches very well with observed damage. Peak ozone hourly concentration does not match the damage indices nearly as well.

Poor Visibility

Visibility depends upon the concentration of fine particles, in fact the same particles that can penetrate deep into the lungs. Thus, to a good approximation, how far you can see is a mea-

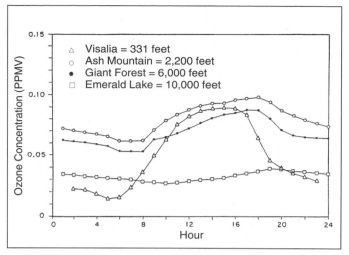

FIGURE 9.1

Daily ozone concentrations in parts per million in volume units (PPMV) at four different elevations in the southern Sierra. (From volume II, chapter 48.)

sure of what gets into your lungs. When measured at high altitudes in the national and state parks, the fine particles are very low in winter and high in summer. Levels are almost always higher at Sequoia National Park than Yosemite National Park or D. L. Bliss State Park at Lake Tahoe. Measurements at Lassen Volcanic National Park are about the same as those at Bliss State Park.

Particles may be either primary, such as dust, pollen, and smoke, or secondary, such as sulfates and nitrates. As with ozone, emissions of precursor sulfur and nitrogen gases that lead to the secondary particles largely originate from human activities that release sulfur dioxide (largely from Bay Area and southern San Joaquin sources) and nitrogen dioxide (mobile and stationary sources). Particle concentration of sulfates and nitrates roughly reflect the same north to south increase seen for ozone exposure. Figure 9.2 shows the annual concentrations of fine mass, sulfates, and nitrates for park and wilderness area sites. Smoke, an important component of fine-particle pollution in the summer, has a significant origin in biomass burning in the valley, including wheat and barley stubble, levee maintenance, and so on, but not including rice straw, which is burned later in the year.

Deposition of fine particles, especially sulfates and nitrates, on vegetation, soils, and bodies of water has unknown but potentially significant effects. The introduction of nitrates and sulfates into the Sierra Nevada hydrological cycle leads to the possibility of permanent or ephemeral acidification of lakes and streams, exacerbated by the generally low buffering capacity of high Sierra granite watersheds.

Although these same fine particles contribute to wet deposition in winter, levels of sulfates and nitrates are lower than in summer, especially north of Yosemite National Park. Again, the influence of upwind sites can be traced directly into the

FIGURE 9.2

Concentrations of fine aerosols, including fine mass, sulfates, and nitrates, along a south-to-north gradient (San Bernardino National Forest to Crater Lake National Park, Oregon) for 1992–93. Fine mass values are divided by 3 to fit on the graph. (From volume II, chapter 48.)

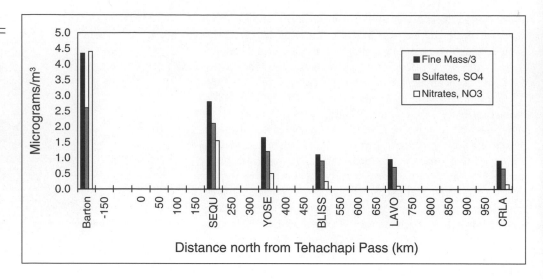

mountains. Sulfate and nitrate concentrations in snow have only a modest (about 50%) increase in concentration as one goes from north to south in the range.

Health and Ecological Effects of Urban Winter Smoke

Mountain valleys easily form atmospheric inversions, which are especially strong in winter. These trap local pollutants close to the ground, leading to extreme levels of fine particulate mass. Some of this mass may, however, be water trapped in smoke by wood combustion, so that the health effect of these winter episodes may not be commensurate with the apparent mass loading. Still, because the loading is so extreme, efforts to reduce fine particulate mass are well taken.

To put this problem into perspective, figure 9.3 shows typical winter smoke at Truckee, an area that forms a strong winter inversion, compared with the worst day of the catastrophic

Cleveland wildfire of 1992. The levels are essentially identical. However, the Truckee pollution extended only a very short distance from the town center in winter, since it is very local, while the concentrations in the Cleveland fire extended over perhaps a few hundred square miles. On the other hand, the winter smoke levels occur on a good fraction of all winter nights, while the Cleveland fire was an infrequent event that lasted only three days.

Smoke from Wildfire and Prescribed Fires

The increased fuel loading in the Sierra Nevada consequent to the suppression of burning in the twentieth century will almost certainly result in greater smoke concentrations in the future. The only questions appear to revolve around the nature of the fires, wild or prescribed, and the times and places under which they occur.

Prescribed fires may be human-initiated controlled burns

FIGURE 9.3

Comparison of large particulate matter (PM-10) levels at Truckee, California, for the peak day of the Cleveland wildfire, 9/30/92, and a typical winter day, 1/6/92. (From volume II, chapter 48.)

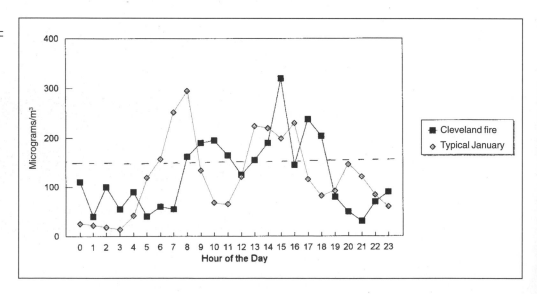

Visibility at Yosemite National Park. Several days each winter and spring are as good as or better than the left photo, but several days each summer are as bad as or worse than the right photo. Park air quality is the result of local smoke and nitrates, sulphates, and smoke transported from the Central Valley. (Photos courtesy of the National Park Service Air Quality Division.)

or lightning-started fires allowed to burn under certain conditions (prescribed natural fires). Air sampling sites in the Sierra Nevada have been able to detect such smoke on only a couple of occasions; though often very visible, smoke is generally only a minor contribution to fine particle mass loading. For example, a prescribed natural fire burned for a month near the Turtleback Dome air sampling site in Yosemite National Park. Mass concentrations for this event are shown in figure 9.4 along with the particle mass measurements due

mostly to campfires on the floor of Yosemite Valley. The prescribed natural fire generally resulted in an average of about 10 micrograms per cubic meter of mass, and only one measurement (85 µg/m^3) exceeded the state standard (50 µg/m^3).

An important contrast can now be seen between fine particles generated by wildfires and those from prescribed fires. As much or more acreage was burned per day in the Cleveland wildfire (7,000 acres per day) as is generally burned each year in prescribed fires in a typical national forest. The gen-

FIGURE 9.4

Concentrations of large particulate matter (PM-10) in Yosemite Village, Yosemite National Park, June through November 1994, as measured by the California Air Resources Board, and data from the IMPROVE sampler at Turtleback Dome high above the valley. (From volume II, chapter 48.)

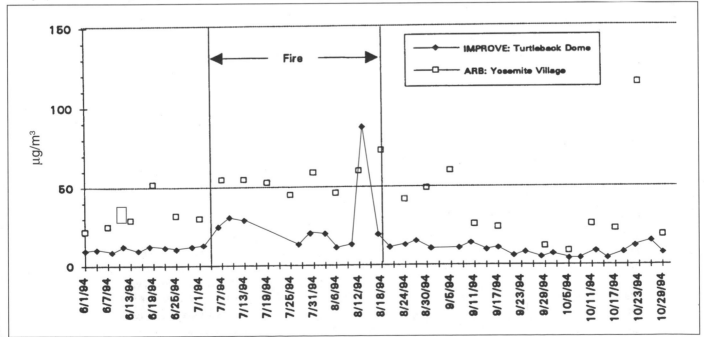

eral lack of obvious fine-particulate-mass impact from prescibed natural fire is due to the care taken in selecting favorable meteorology, burning conditions, and so on. Federal and state health standards for fine particulate mass would probably not be violated were the rate of prescribed fire accelerated by as much as a factor of five. There are, however, examples of prescibed fires that have failed to comply with air-quality standards because they did not pay close enough attention to meteorological factors or to the importance of dispersing burns in both time and space. One example involves prescribed fires near Sequoia National Park that burned on into an exceptionally dry fall (1995) as smoke dispersion became poorer. The effect was high smoke levels in downslope communities that roughly equaled the urban smoke present in high-altitude towns in winter.

Another point worthy of mention is the size of smoke particles. Whereas uncontrolled wildfires generate a considerable component of coarse mass, residential woodstoves and other slowly burning fires generate mostly fine particles. The U.S. Environmental Protection Agency is at this moment considering moving from a relatively coarse particle PM-10 standard (particles below 10 micrometers diameter, either 24-hour or annual concentration), to a finer particle standard (probably particles below 2.5 micrometers, annual average) more closely tied to health effects studies. While the finer particle standard will heavily impact smoke, an annual average standard would allow for a few days of higher concentrations if at other times the average concentration was low. This is the case at most Sierra Nevada sites, at least outside of cities.

In summary, one of the more unexpected results of the study was an approximate equality between maximum 24-hour PM-10 concentration in smoke from very different sources. All were above 100 $\mu g/m^3$, occasionally even exceeding the federal standard of 150 $\mu g/m^3$:

- The Cleveland wildfire west of Lake Tahoe, September 1992, burning at the rate of 7,000 acres per day, in hot, dry conditions, with good ventilation, towering smoke clouds covering hundreds of square miles, and burning for about three days.

- The fires near Sequoia National Park, fall 1995, started as prescribed fires, burning at a rate of about 300 acres per day, in dry, stable fall conditions with decreased ventilation, a low-elevation smoke cloud covering tens of square miles, with a duration of about thirty days.

- The typical winter smoke in towns like Truckee, largely from, at most, a few thousand domestic wood fires, in a strong winter inversion with poor ventilation, generating a shallow layer of smoke trapped in a valley that, for Truckee, probably did not cover even a few square miles.

The latter conditions are common for about one-third to one-half of all winter days in towns from Quincy to Mammoth Lakes.

This study and others also supported a relationship between smoke mass and visibility showing that at the federal standard one can see about two miles and at the state standard about six miles. The visibility problems of smoke can be major even at smoke levels that do not reach health-based standards on particulate mass.

The Degradation of Lake Tahoe

The Lake Tahoe air basin, especially the built-up areas at the south and north ends of the lake, experience seriously degraded air quality each winter. In addition to health and visibility effects, the ecological effect of air pollution on Lake Tahoe appears significant. Figure 9.5 shows transport of materials into the Lake Tahoe Basin as a function of time of year. The site at D. L. Bliss State Park, near Emerald Bay on the west shore, in effect, samples air equivalent to that in the Desolation Wilderness Area and the associated transports from upwind sources. The difference between the Bliss data and the South Lake Tahoe data thus represents the local contribution to fine particles. For sulfates, local sources are minor at all times. For other pollutants, such as organic matter and nitrates, there are massive winter enhancements at South Lake Tahoe, at which time transport from upwind sources is sharply decreased because of the trapping of pollutants in the Central Valley.

The low concentration of transported nitrates, and their small particulate size, must be contrasted with the high levels of local nitrates from the highways that ring the lake. The coarser winter nitrate particles are more likely to settle into Lake Tahoe than the fine particles transported from the Central Valley each summer, but the latter extend across the entire area of the lake. Direct nitrate deposition measurements are difficult to do, and the issue is still controversial. Fine particles are thus triply important at Lake Tahoe as they affect visibility, degradation of the lake, and human health concerns.

The Future of Air Quality

Air quality in the Sierra Nevada is at a critical point, with moderate to severe degradation becoming all too often accepted as the status quo. Ozone is in a holding pattern despite massive efforts to control primary transportation sources. Clearly, the Central Valley is not like California's urban areas, where ozone is in decline; this fact increases concerns for future Sierra Nevada air quality as valley and foothill populations grow. Except at Lake Tahoe, little effort is being made to address reduced visibility, which, to the average visitor, is the most evident sign of degraded air quality. Yet most of the haze seen today comes from the Central Valley, a change from the past. Very little is known about the effects of other substances, including herbicides and pesticides, that may be transported into the Sierra Nevada from sources such as the Central Valley. We also now know that there is an air-quality

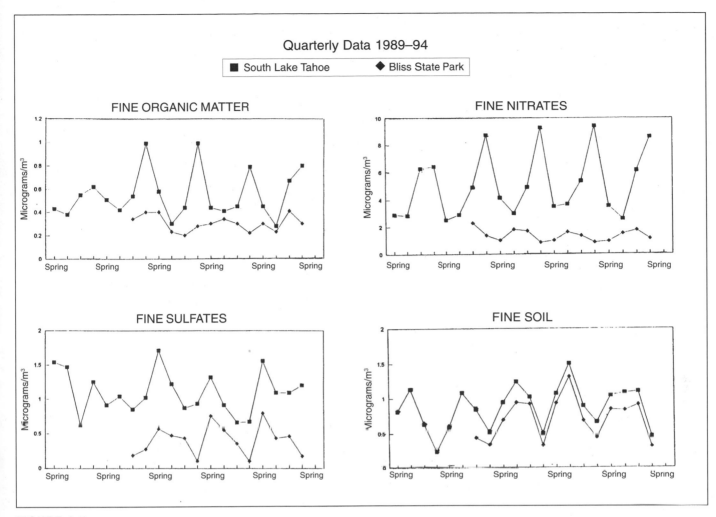

FIGURE 9.5

Concentrations of aerosols at two sites at Lake Tahoe (South Lake Tahoe and D. L. Bliss State Park) over the seasons, 1989–94. (From volume II, chapter 48.)

component, local and transported, in the decline in the clarity of Lake Tahoe's waters. The future will almost certainly bring more forest smoke, from either wildfires or prescribed burns, in response to the fuel buildup of the past ninety years.

There are areas within the Sierra Nevada for which air quality is improving. It was no accident that areas that were in rapid and demonstrable decline, first Lake Tahoe and then Mono Lake, also engendered the most effective scientific, legal, political, and regulatory responses. The dust problems at Mono Lake will soon decline as the lake's water level rises in response to recent legal and regulatory actions. Now urbanized enclaves in the mountains (Lake Tahoe, Mammoth Lakes) are also showing some progress, partly through improvement in vehicles, partly through controls on woodstoves and other sources.

Finally, there are factors of potential importance to air quality that are still quite uncertain; many of these are tied to

changes in the global climate. Scientists are confident that there has been a 25% increase in carbon dioxide and a doubling of methane in the past century, and an order of magnitude increase in chlorofluorocarbons in the past twenty years. Also, an overall small temperature rise and a small (less than 3%) increase in ultraviolet radiation are becoming apparent and may have influences yet to be determined. Less certain are predictions of increased climatic variability, an increase in summer rain, decrease in summer snow, and more frequent El Niño events, which can generate either drought or intense rainfall at different phases of the cycle. Model predictions for these and other potential air-quality influences are uncertain.

AN AIR-QUALITY STRATEGY

Goals

Three primary goals for an air-quality strategy for the Sierra Nevada are:

1. Reduce ozone levels and associated impacts.

2. Reduce fine-particle pollution and associated impacts.

3. Minimize smoke levels while maximizing the beneficial use of fire.

Possible Solutions

Ozone

Through rigid enforcement of the current California state standard of 0.09 ppm ozone, peak hourly rate, only modest damage would be expected for plant species known to be sensitive. Note that acceptance of the federal standard of 0.12 ppm, peak hourly rate, would not result in elimination of vegetation damage. New technology has been adopted and allows for identification of "grossly emitting" vehicles as they drive along the highway; removing these vehicles from service provides an effective means of significantly reducing emissions. In addition, reformulated gasolines now coming into use further reduce emissions of ozone precursors.

The dramatic decline of peak ozone concentrations that have been seen in recent years in areas like Los Angeles with high vehicular densities are not being seen in the Central Valley. Thus, it has become evident that confounding valley sources must exist. Most likely is the intense biological activity associated with agriculture and its accompanying emissions of hydrocarbon and ozone precursor gases. Also, regulatory controls have to date been somewhat less stringent in the Central Valley than in Los Angeles. The federal and particularly the state air-quality agencies are beginning to pursue ozone control measures associated with these apparent sources.

Fine-Particle Pollution

The Clean Air Act of 1977, extended by the amendments of 1990, mandates the mitigation of human sources of fine-particle pollution insofar as they degrade visibility in Class I areas such as Yosemite National Park. This can be accomplished by enforced limitations of upwind emissions of sulfur in the Bay Area and San Joaquin Valley, especially the oil refineries and chemical plants near the Carquinez Strait; continued efforts to control oxides of nitrogens, and tighter controls on or elimination of all agricultural burning during summer months. These measures would result in sharply improved visibility and the accompanying reduction of fine-particle deposition.

Smoke

Increasing by a factor of five the annual acreage of Sierra Nevada forests burned by surface-burning controlled burns and prescribed natural fire would reduce overall pollution from smoke. Burning would be concentrated in spring (mid-April through mid-June) and fall (mid-September through mid-November) to avoid coinciding with peak summer levels of smoke originating in the Central Valley. The increase in local and subregional smoke associated with prescribed burns must be traded off against the large regional smoke plumes of the wildfires that can be expected without increased prescribed burning.

Smoke originating from residential areas within the Sierra Nevada can be reduced by burn and no-burn days, highly efficient woodstoves, and changes in fuel from local pine to dried fruitwoods. Even more beneficial is an increasing transition from woodstoves of all kinds to natural gas, when available.

Implications

Meeting the air-quality goals has three principal implications:

1. Evidence indicates that if peak hourly ozone values remain below 0.09 ppm, injury to Jeffrey pine, ponderosa pine, and other sensitive species would be decreased.

2. The economic values associated with tourism would be enhanced by higher scenic visibility. Deposition of potentially harmful pollutants on vegetation, soils, and hydrologic systems would be reduced.

3. Comparing data from the 1992 Cleveland fire in the Eldorado National Forest with calculations for optimizing a fivefold increase in the annual controlled burn acreages for this same forest, indications are that there would be drastically lower levels of regional particle loading achieved by the application of human prescribed fire. Levels would be even less than the average daily winter levels typical for the woodstove smoke component at mountain communities like Truckee.

Although the particulate pollution levels from this strategy meet state and federal standards and would not greatly increase particulate smoke in towns downwind, it is not true that there would be no impacts. Fires, besides being unsightly, can carry allergens to susceptible human populations, with accompanying short-term respiratory impacts. This effect limits the amount of material that can be burned at any one time and place and should caution application of prescribed fire that would overlap with winter smoke problems already typical of some urban areas.

The proposed new federal fine-particulate standard, conceived as an annual average based upon a 2.5 micrometer cut point (PM-2.5), would put additional pressures on mountain urban communities to control winter smoke levels. The standard would actually favor this strategy, because the additional smoke from prescribed fires would not be exacerbating already elevated urban levels.

Spatial trends for air-quality concerns have been noted from the northern to the southern end of the Sierra Nevada. Trends for west to east transport of Central Valley and Bay Area pollutants are also clearly mapped, with many sources displaying clear signatures to the sophisticated monitoring apparatus already in place. Continued and enhanced monitoring will provide ample opportunity for gauging and interpreting the success of reducing Bay Area sources of fine particles, valley sources of biomass burning and ozone generation, and smoke from prescribed fire versus wildfire in the Sierra Nevada itself. A reversal of current trends would be obvious.

CHAPTER 10

Case Studies in Ecosystem Management

INTRODUCTION

To assess the various ways organizations and people come together to manage Sierran ecosystems, SNEP conducted four case studies to examine the efficacy of different institutional arrangements:

- The Mammoth-June case study examines how a single national forest is attempting to implement the new Forest Service policy for ecosystem analysis.

- The Lake Tahoe study investigates a set of institutional arrangements in which agencies and the public have worked jointly for over thirty years to restore and maintain the health of a watershed-lake ecosystem being threatened by urbanization.

- The study of the Mediated Settlement Agreement (MSA) examines a process designed to bring together diverse interests to map and manage the treasured giant sequoia forest type.

- The final case compares the mandates and organizational structures of four institutions, describing how they result in different approaches to land management: the Sequoia National Forest, the Sequoia and Kings Canyon National Parks, the Mountain Home State Demonstration Forest, and the Tule River Indian Reservation.

The summaries here explore the institutional lessons learned from local attempts to cope with the dynamics of ecological and socioeconomic change. The studies represent a modest effort to capture the complexity of issues affecting planning, current management practices, and the means for resolving conflict. They are incomplete in that they do not cover the full diversity of Sierra Nevada issues, but they do provide a reasonable sample of how institutions act and interact to affect ecosystems within the range.

THE MAMMOTH-JUNE CASE STUDY

The Mammoth-June Ecosystem Management Project (MJEMP) of the Inyo National Forest is one of the first attempts in the Sierra Nevada to follow the new Forest Service landscape-analysis policy for ecosystem management. This process is intended to guide national forests throughout California in analyzing capabilities and thresholds of moderate-sized landscapes (e.g., 20,000–50,000 acres) for long-term health and sustainability. A primary goal of these analyses is to develop a desired condition, or a "word-picture" of the landscape as it would ideally be in the future. This would serve to guide the nature and extent of management practices and other land-use activities that may occur into the future.

SNEP chose this project as a case study to review and analyze the potential for this new policy process, as exemplified in the MJEMP, to help achieve health and sustainability of ecosystems on Forest Service lands in the Sierra Nevada. SNEP's primary interest was in evaluating the concept of historic condition and historic variability, specifically, the usefulness and limitations of historical information in determining a desired condition. Further, SNEP critically reviewed the role of public participation in the new Forest Service landscape process. Insight about these and other issues from the MJEMP case study—framed as answers to questions that follow—helps clarify institutional potentials for and barriers to the integration of landscape analysis and ecosystem management into land management of the Sierra Nevada.

1. What is the history of interest in the Mammoth-June area that led to the current landscape analysis?

Lying between the resort towns of Mammoth Lakes and June Lake, Mono County, the 36,000 acres known as the Mammoth-June area (MJ area) have been the focus of use and public attention since the late 1800s. Dense red fir and lush mixed conifer forests blanket gently rolling topography and intermingle with several large flower- and wildlife-rich meadows against a backdrop of rugged cliffs and peaks that form the headwaters of the Owens River. Amid the otherwise steep, rocky, and semiarid landscapes of the eastern Sierra, the MJ area stands out for its abundance of forests, water, and wildlife. These scarce resources are the focus of continuing public controversy over developed versus undeveloped use in the area: grazing, timber harvest, geothermal development, alpine skiing, nordic skiing, wilderness appreciation, scientific study, and ecological reserves.

The Inyo National Forest, which administers nearly the entire area, has long tried to balance the shifting uses and competing public desires while maintaining what it perceived (also changing with the times) to be the integrity of the resources. The current MJEMP is only the latest in a line of formal planning processes and documents—dating back to 1950—that systematically outline and coordinate management objectives for the MJ area. Most recently, the 1988 Inyo National Forest Land Management Plan wrestled with competing desires for development of a large alpine ski area in the MJ area versus wilderness designation. The Land Management Plan left many of the issues unresolved, deferring decisions until a future cumulative-effects study and an environmental impact statement (EIS) analysis were prepared.

The EIS process began as the "Mammoth-to-June Integrated Resource Analysis" in 1990 but, with the release of the draft Forest Service *Regional Handbook on Ecosystem Management,* was changed in 1993 to the MJEMP.

Why was the Inyo among the first of the California national forests to embark on this new process? For several reasons the issues at the MJ area were becoming urgent enough in 1993 to demand imminent decision making. Because a cumulative-effects, or scientifically based, landscape analysis was called for by the Land Management Plan before any decisions could be made, the MJEMP (or something like it) was a prerequisite. Several key Inyo National Forest staff involved in planning, ecosystem management, and management of the MJ area had been deeply involved in developing and teaching the regional Forest Service ecosystem management process. They had the incentive, understanding, and peer and supervisor support to rapidly adopt its use on the Inyo National Forest. Promise of breaking the gridlock for decision making (e.g., over conflicts such as allocating the area for alpine ski development versus wilderness) in this area provided the essential priority at the forest level to fund the MJEMP.

2. *How was information on historical landscape condition used by the MJEMP to develop the "desired condition"? How does historical information and its use relate to ecological sustainability of the MJ area?*

The concept of historic condition of ecosystems has played a central if controversial role in conservation-biology discourse, especially in ecosystem management and ecological restoration. A central question is whether the condition of a landscape prior to significant human disruption (i.e., a historic condition) is one model, the best model, or the only model for long-term sustainability. Three dominant views in the debate suggest that a desired condition for long-term health and sustainability:

- mimics forest structure and composition of "pre-contact" time (e.g., 1850 or presettlement);

- lies within the natural range of variability, that is, the range of historic conditions that have occurred within a landscape over a relevant historic period;

- is unrelated to historic conditions.

The first two positions require that good historic data are available or can be obtained for analysis.

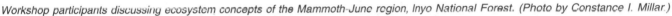

Workshop participants discussing ecosystem concepts of the Mammoth-June region, Inyo National Forest. (Photo by Constance I. Millar.)

The MJEMP demonstrated, within a landscape containing mixes of montane eastern Sierra forest types in conditions ranging from actively harvested to minimally disturbed old growth, the following key points regarding historic condition:

- Historic information, either about a specific time or about the range of conditions over a historic period, is extremely difficult to obtain or measure accurately within the budgets, time lines, and training of national forest staff. Most of the information obtained is highly inferential; mostly qualitative; localized, and extrapolated from point sources (pictures, a few locations); mostly short-range (as short as a five-year recent record); and mostly shallow in total time-depth. Quantitative data over long times were available on floristics from pollen cores in meadows and on fire frequency from fire-scarred trees and snags, but these provided frustratingly limited spatial resolution. Historic wildlife distributions were the most difficult to infer, being based on estimates of historic forest habitats and estimates of historic use of habitat.

- High-resolution historic information would require local, long-term research projects with interdisciplinary research teams and adequate budgets.

- Lack of detailed historic information, however, forced the MJEMP to proceed with the analysis in a way that may be best even if excellent measures were readily available: The MJEMP used inferences on historic information to guide the *direction* but not the *detail* of what a desired condition might be; that is, to guide the general pathway of change brought about by the interaction of desired ecosystem processes. In other words, the team took a fourth position in the debate over how historic condition relates to desired condition. The team chose not to try to mimic the detail of past structure or composition, nor to build the desired condition from a highly inferred, and perhaps erroneous, range of variability. Instead, the team sought to ensure that historic natural *processes* (e.g., fire, riparian function, water cycles, aquatic functions) would continue or be reintroduced into the MJ landscape and focused less on promoting exact structure or composition that resembled historic condition. The guiding philosophy of the desired condition was that processes in the future landscape were, for the most part, the same ones that operated under historic conditions. The challenge remained to infer or estimate the rates, forms, and magnitudes of these interacting processes.

- The team chose a desired condition that contradicted the historic condition for some resources. For example, the team felt that the continued reintroduction of Lahontan cutthroat trout (a native of east-side streams but not of those in the MJ landscape) was desired, although not historic. Further, the team described a desired future fuels condition that recognized the need to avoid catastrophic fire in the vicinity of the town of Mammoth Lakes. Such a condition would probably require active fuels treatment beyond the historic forest condition on the town side of the MJ landscape.

- The team's use of historic inference to inform and guide but not specifically determine the desired condition takes into account that the present and the future, despite human influence in the ecosystem, are different from the past. Climate change and disturbance due to fire, avalanche, and volcanic eruptions would have created different forest conditions in the present and into the future than the past regardless of what humans have or have not done. Returning an ecosystem to past structure and composition may be highly inappropriate ecologically, given current and future "natural" environmental conditions. A more useful approach, as is being taken in Sequoia National Park, is to try to determine (through models and inferences) what the forest would be like today if suppression and other management had not occurred. An appropriate condition is for ecosystems to be resilient and responsive to the natural change of the present and future. Although costly, historic data placed within the appropriate dynamic models can provide useful information on how to manage a forest for resilience and adaptiveness.

3. What role did "thresholds" play in developing the desired condition in the MJEMP?

The initial planning process for the MJ area, which followed the directions set out in the 1988 Land Management Plan for the Inyo National Forest, called for development of resource thresholds as well as analysis of cumulative effects. The reconstituted MJEMP retained this goal well into the study. As analysis proceeded, however, it became clear that thresholds were being interpreted in two incompatible ways. Eventually, because of the potential for misinterpretation and misuse, the team abandoned both their analysis and their use of thresholds.

One interpretation of thresholds was held by most of the MJEMP team members. These national forest staff are technical specialists trained as biologists, physical scientists, foresters, recreation specialists, or resource planners. They interpret thresholds conceptually as quantitative values that indicate when major and/or rapid changes of state (forest condition, wildlife viability, fish diversity and productivity, water abundance and quality, soil productivity, plant biodiversity) might occur. They maintain that resource thresholds are highly complex and vary with location in the MJ area, season, management activity, adjacent land use, condition of other resources, and changing weather and climate. The team felt that the data it was capable of collecting could not lead to estimation of quantitative thresholds with defensible accuracy.

Another interpretation of resource thresholds was voiced by decision makers on the Inyo National Forest, who viewed thresholds conceptually as management boundaries or limits. To these managers, thresholds represent the best scientific guess at allowable bounds on activities that could be permitted in an area: if a proposed project does not cause a threshold to be exceeded, then a management action or proposed activity could be considered. As interpreted, thresholds such as these are simple and static indicators that provide information to managers about resource capabilities in an area and define defensible decision space.

After much debate, the MJEMP analysis team rejected the notion that fixed and quantitative management thresholds could be determined or even exist for any resource condition in the MJ area. Team members willingly discussed the conceptual and qualitative nature of resource variation and extremes, and potential consequences of extending beyond these extremes, but they would not stand behind any numeric values that might be interpreted as thresholds. Many feared that such values would become management targets, and that areas might blindly be managed to threshold values. They emphasized instead an adaptive-management approach whereby ecosystem elements would be observed and interpreted as an ongoing process, monitoring intensity heightened if extreme values were approached, and case-by-case decisions made. Despite their inherent limitations, thresholds, or, more appropriately, management standards and limits, may be imperative in some situations. For instance, they may be useful where ecosystems are highly sensitive to minor disturbances, where trends in activities must be limited, where allowed activities are not "in sync" with natural changes, or as reference points upon which change is monitored. Many of these defensible uses of a reference point extend conceptually beyond what are interpreted as "ecological thresholds."

4. What was the role of public participation in the MJEMP? What are implications for public participation in the new Forest Service landscape analysis (ecosystem management) throughout Sierran national forests?

The role of social participation in landscape analysis, as suggested by regional and national Forest Service policy, is different from the conventional and now widely understood National Environmental Policy Act (NEPA) process. In the current Forest Service landscape analysis policy for the Pacific Southwest Region, public participation is encouraged at all steps of the process, although it is not required, and no specific approach is provided. In the case of Mammoth-June, the team organized a series of public meetings, initially to explain the process of analysis and to field questions, then to describe results, and finally to receive input for the desired condition. In all cases, the meetings were conducted interactively with the public, with team members present to show maps and explain data and opportunities made to record public input.

In the analysis leading to a desired condition, no formal appeal process aside from lawsuit is available for the public to challenge proceedings of a landscape analysis. The conclusion by Forest Service policy makers is that this kind of analysis is not a decision-making process; that a desired condition merely elaborates what has already been determined generally by a Forest Plan. The desired condition does not allocate

land, nor does it discuss specific management practices or land-use activities that would be permitted or prevented in an area. Rather, the desired condition describes, in ecological, physical, and social terms, the potential landscape conditions that could be met in the foreseeable future to achieve a sustainable landscape.

These assertions were challenged by one sector of the public during the MJEMP. In letters from the lawyer of Friends of the Inyo (FOI), the MJEMP was viewed as a decision-making process that should be subject to the NEPA process. In the MJEMP, the FOI argued, the public had inadequate opportunity to participate and contribute to the desired condition, and no appeal recourse was available to challenge the desired condition. This group felt that certain actions (such as designation of land as wilderness) would be precluded by the desired condition, and that other activities may be obviously promoted (such as mechanical thinning for fuel reduction in a roadless area). Part of this reaction might have been avoided by more public meetings held early in the MJEMP, which would have both clarified the process to the public and opened the team to public input. When more public participation in fact occurred late in the process, conflicts lessened somewhat between the Forest Service and the public. Public understanding heightened, forest staff incorporated public views and ideas, cooperation improved, and tensions decreased at least temporarily. The question about the decision-making authority of the new ecosystem management landscape-analysis policy, especially as described in a statement of desired condition, remains, nevertheless, a challenge for national forests throughout the Sierra Nevada and California.

5. Is investment in ecosystem management adequate to guide the Sierran national forests in maintaining sustainable ecosystems in areas such as Mammoth-June?

The activities needed to achieve ecosystem management are new and challenging, complex, long term, and expensive. Different kinds of knowledge must be brought to what has been taught traditionally to resource managers. Especially important is the need for critical scientific thinking. Necessary but missing from many landscape analyses such as MJEMP is a context of inquiry, experimentation, integrative thinking, and true interdisciplinary (rather than multidisciplinary) synthesis. Although specialists are skilled in conventional collection and interpretation of data, many do not have the critical understanding or experience to perform creative analyses that are needed to answer the new ecosystem questions they are asking. Thus, rather than advancing the understanding of system behavior, process, and interrelationship, they produce abundant new data about pieces of the ecosystem. Investments in intellectual capacity necessary to achieve complex analysis (e.g., formal education opportunities, work time for learning, freedom to train across disciplines, diverse work experiences) are essential but mostly not forthcoming.

Ecosystem management requires not only an experimental approach to analysis, but an experimental perspective in institutional behavior. Agencies are called to do things very differently today than in the past; this requires risk taking, making mistakes, and adaptive learning. Although the agencies give lip service to this spirit, in effect, it is mostly not felt by individuals and programs or reflected in budgets. The changing national political climate is reflected in rapid swings of policy and emphasis within the agencies. At ground level, these shifts translate into an "on-again, off-again" modus operandi, which is tremendously debilitating. Fears of doing things out of the ordinary, as well as uncertainty about how to conduct innovative analyses, result in the fall-back posture of adopting conventional methods veiled under new titles. All of this played itself out during the MJEMP. By contrast, when internal support was expressed and consistently maintained, the process blossomed.

Forest Service funding that would allow managers in general to adequately plan, assess, implement, and monitor ecosystem management has dropped precipitously just as the need is increasing. Moneys traditionally available for regeneration, restoration, habitat improvement, and resource monitoring came primarily from timber harvest (per the Knudsen-Vanderburg Act); these funds have nearly evaporated on the Inyo National Forest, as in other Sierran regions, as logging activities have decreased. Allocated agency funds for ecosystem management are meager, short term, and inconsistent; many hands reach into a small pot. In some cases, cost-share support from local communities has been successfully leveraged to complete projects. Together, the lack of funding, priority, training, and risk taking make the likelihood of successful ecosystem management low.

6. What difficulties face a single-institution (Forest Service) technical team in achieving multiple-stakeholder goals of a landscape analysis?

Several conditions of the MJEMP suggested at first that the landscape analysis might logically be done internally as a Forest Service staff effort. The lands under analysis in the MJ area were within the administration of the Inyo National Forest, technical agency staff representing the major areas under study were available, funding was primarily internal, no land allocations or management prescriptions were to be made, and no environmental analysis (NEPA) was involved. As conceived nationally by the Forest Service and described regionally by the California handbook on ecosystem management, landscape analysis is a technical exercise intended to identify resource capacities, limits, trends, and future conditions. Public participation is encouraged, but no formal process is outlined or required. Projects and treatments, should they be proposed, would come later in an independent process within traditional NEPA scope.

Under closer scrutiny, the MJEMP actually had several components, some of which might not be appropriately confined to analysis by a single-agency technical team. The MJ area has a large and diverse constituency, both of people interested in the area itself and of those concerned about implica-

tions for adjacent lands and communities. Further, the role of the MJEMP as a flagship ecosystem management project of the Inyo National Forest meant that it received attention as a pilot process, beyond the implications to a particular area. Public understanding of what ecosystem management actually entails, or how it will be implemented locally, was poor. The relationship of the Land Management Plan to the MJEMP, and especially to land allocations or decisions about the future of the landscape, was unclear. Suspicion of the new process was high.

The challenge to the agency in such a situation is how to coordinate an interactive, adaptive-management process with stakeholders prior to, and concomitant with, the technical team's analysis. Information needs to be brought out early, among the agency staff and constituents and among the different interest groups themselves, about changes in intent since the Land Management Plan, about elements of ecosystem management, and about how and why a landscape analysis would be conducted. The full range of public views and suggestions regarding the current and future condition of the area need to be heard early in the process so that they can be brought into the technical team's work.

The actual scientific work of the technical team belongs to specialists and resource professionals. This too, however, is best conducted as an open process with vigorous input and review from experts outside the team and outside the agency. Because the analysis and interpretation of historic variability are not straightforward, significantly more scientific involvement is needed than if a routine resource inventory were being done. Opportunities for the public to learn from the specialists about technical findings in meetings and workshops, as the MJEMP team held occasionally, are important throughout the process.

The most effective role for the various stakeholders in developing a future condition is less clear. If sustainability were a property robustly described with high confidence and little variability by specialists, then the technical team would properly be the primary author. As it is, however, in situations like the MJ analysis, there is such limited understanding of what conditions (averages, ranges, and temporal variabilities) result in long-term ecological sustainability, such disparity in fact about what is socially implied by sustainability, and such low accuracy in quantitative estimates, that the process extends beyond science and beyond data collection. More appropriately, during the development of a desired condition, the technical team would prepare technical information and analyses, including its best interpretations of long-term capacities and sustainability. The final development of a desired condition, however, is best handled as a mutually interactive, iterative, discursive process among agency staff (decision makers, planners, and specialists) and diverse constituencies (scientists, interest groups, other agencies). This process will challenge all involved to new forms of open communication and will require conscious commitment to a continuing dialogue.

THE LAKE TAHOE CASE STUDY

With a long, science-based history of environmental assessment, property acquisition, restoration. and management, the Lake Tahoe Basin (LTB) provides much information on the role of adaptive management policies in an altered ecosystem. Though it is not a strict parallel for other parts of the Sierra, the knowledge and experience of ecosystem governance may be greater in the LTB than at any other locale in the Sierra or the United States. The experience shows promise largely because decisions are based on the best available ecosystem information and because a broad spectrum of public and private entities have participated.

1. How does this case study demonstrate an approach to defining and understanding an ecosystem?

Ecosystems are complex, difficult to define, and have unclear boundaries. Thus, it is difficult to focus on interrelationships between elements and management needs. Efforts to understand and define the ecosystem of the LTB have been fueled by concentrating on a valued attribute of the ecosystem—the exceptional clarity of the waters of Lake Tahoe. That it is a relatively small watershed and that the boundaries of the ecosystem and basin are the same aided the effort. Although external influences (e.g., air quality) impact the basin, the small scale of the ecosystem aided in understanding the structure and function of its constituent parts. It was also made possible by the availability of three decades of water-quality data—one of the most significant data sets of its kind in the world.

The initial focus on water clarity has motivated efforts to broaden the understanding of the relationship to water quality of wetlands, soils and vegetation, and deposition of nutrients from the air. Water and nutrient flows off the watershed into the lake were understood, early on, to cause decreased lake clarity. A system to classify the land's capability to withstand disturbance was developed in the 1960s. Recently, research has been undertaken to identify the role of atmospheric deposition of nutrients and the biotic structure of organisms within the lake. Wildlife considerations have also been integrated into this system of evaluation.

Recently, there has been increasing focus on the health of the forests in the ecosystem. Between 25% and 40% of the trees in the LTB are dead or dying. This focus is being spurred on by the threat of catastrophic fire and degradation of scenic values in the region. This effort will result in a better sense of terrestrial vegetative and hydrologic processes.

Ideally, our approach to ecosystem management should be based on an overview understanding of the structure and function of all parts of the ecosystem. However, this type of effort will require the commitment of a substantial amount of resources over a long period of time. The Lake Tahoe experience shows how this endeavor can be sustained by focusing on a valued attribute that, in turn, will at least partially illuminate, or provide the basis for dealing with, the structure and function of the ecosystem as a whole. The key to "valuing" the ecosystem is educating one another on the values that exist to some degree in all ecosystems.

2. What role does long-term information play in understanding and managing this ecosystem?

Knowing the rate of LTB ecosystem change places the problem in temporal perspective and assigns the issue an appropriate level of importance. For example, a scientist working with the Tahoe Research Group recently stated (verbally, to the SNEP assessment team) that, in the absence of humans and nutrient introduction from large volcanoes, Lake Tahoe would have taken approximately 400,000 years (from the end of the Pleistocene) to progress to the level of diminished clarity currently found. Thus, the 10,000 years of human occupation have seen the lake progress to a state that normally would have taken roughly forty times longer. (If only the last 150 years of human occupation are considered, the ratio is even more striking.) Though this is an estimate based on a general, but quite substantial, knowledge of lake eutrophication, it places the magnitude of the problem in perspective, assigning a high level of importance to investment in restoration and management.

The past thirty-five years have seen the establishment of an unprecedented water-quality database. Water clarity and related indicators have been monitored by the Tahoe Research Group, creating a continuous record of data that is unparalleled in the Sierra. In addition to its value as a record of water quality, the database enables researchers to evaluate other variables with respect to a single, widely accepted indicator. Thus, issues as diverse as construction, forest management, and erosion control practices may be evaluated, in part, with respect to their impact on water quality. The long term of the database helps establish a relatively high degree of accuracy.

Certain types of historical information, such as water quality and fire interval data, have provided specific guidance about managing the LTB ecosystem. Other types of data may not provide specific guidance but help achieve the understanding of changing ecosystem structure and function that forms the basis for long-term policy and target standards. Historical information also helps isolate the roles of nature and humans, distinguishing between what is under our control and what is not.

Is historical knowledge adequate for ecosystem management of the Lake Tahoe Basin? Clearly there is a need for additional data. For example, more data are needed to develop a comprehensive nutrient budget for Lake Tahoe. Little is known about the basin's forest prior to the arrival of Native American peoples. Similarly, the incidence of fire in prehistoric times is not well understood. Nevertheless, the existing, widely acknowledged record, particularly that of the past thirty-five years, provides a basis for ecosystem management that is scientifically based.

3. What role do ecosystem performance standards play in guiding the basin ecosystem to a desirable future condition?

Pursuant to a bi-state compact, the Tahoe Regional Planning Agency (TRPA) is required to adopt environmental threshold carrying capacities that are necessary to maintain a significant scenic, recreational, educational, scientific, or natural value of the region. The TRPA's Regional Plan must be designed to achieve the thresholds.

Nine standards are evaluated every five years by TRPA (the standards are called "thresholds" in the LTB). In the most recently completed evaluation (1991), only one standard was in compliance. Standards are viewed more as targets to achieve over many years; accordingly, there is an effort not to change the standards, so that a continuous picture of ecosystem performance, and change, can become clear. If a standard is not met over time, the governing institutions can infer that the standards may have been set at unrealistic levels for this ecosystem operating at this juncture in its evolution under this set of human modifications or that restoration and mitigation techniques are inadequate to bring the ecosystem into compliance with the standards. Identifying the standards and setting reasonable levels of performance, based on available concepts and data at the time, are important tools of adaptive management.

Standards also establish a consistent form of accountability for land-use managers and regulatory agencies, as well as an important framework for additional research and monitoring activities. Adopted standards can focus people and institutions on specific parameters, a process that helps to build consensus. Places with great fluxes of tourists often have difficulty achieving and sustaining a sense of community that fosters sustained discourse about goals. At Tahoe, the process of institution building and the setting of performance standards has been responsible, in part, for creating a sense of place and community that is based on an understanding of how the ecosystem works and to what ends it should be managed. Thus community capacity for intelligent and effective stewardship has been forced from private, local, state, regional, and federal components, each of which sees it to its own advantage to participate and cooperate (e.g., casinos and ski areas know the lake and basin attributes are an important part of their marketing advantage).

4. Is the coalition of individuals and institutions able to engage in adaptive ecosystem management?

Adaptive ecosystem management is the ability to use the best available knowledge for manipulation (restoration, management, use, etc.) of the ecosystem; to monitor the effects of that manipulation; to judge whether the effects are contributing to a healthy, sustainable system; and to make appropriate adjustments and adaptations in management and knowledge. This process includes adapting human behavior and knowledge to the sequence of ecosystem states over time. Episodic changes in ecosystem and function—brought about by na-

ture or humans—often produce significant gains in knowledge. This is true of the action to export all sewage from the basin. This action was based on the best technical understanding of the ecosystem at the time, an understanding that said lake productivity (algal growth) was critically linked to the amount of nitrogen moving to the lake from, primarily, septic tanks. A system to export sewage from the basin was constructed, but follow-up monitoring showed the lake still diminishing in clarity. Further research indicated that the disturbance of watersheds released nutrients. This information led to policies that limited land coverage (e.g., impervious surface) in the basin. More recent research motivated by this continuing trend produced the conclusion that the lake was now in a phase in which clarity was limited by phosphorus now that nitrogen loading was diminished. This information was an important reason for increased emphasis on soil erosion control and watershed restoration. In each case, institutional learning and adaptation of behavior occurred.

The use of performance standards, the general sense of the basin's history, and the cooperative interlocking of multiple-level institutions give members of the Tahoe community the capability to monitor and share with one another their perception of changes in the environmental and socioeconomic components of the system. What is more important, the availability of funding has given local agencies and nonprofit organizations the ability to develop and implement projects that address their needs and those of the ecosystem.

Our evaluation suggests that a relatively sophisticated form of adaptive management is occurring in the LTB. Individuals and institutions have established the need for scientific information, have sought the resources for acquiring it, and are prepared to use it as a basis for land-use policies for restoration activities and resource management practices. To date, the courts have consistently upheld the validity of this scientific information, and related concepts, as a rational basis for adaptive ecosystem policy.

The process of adaptive management would be enhanced not only by more coordination of information gathering and interpretation but also by strong advocacy for critical research funding. These tasks could be accomplished by an active science advisory board for the LTB.

5. Is investment adequate to sustain the valued attributes of the Lake Tahoe Basin ecosystem?

Varying degrees of investment will be required in the Sierra Nevada. In some areas, the investment may involve only monitoring and passive management. In others, substantial investments may be needed to restore ecosystems.

At Lake Tahoe, there has been a mixed pattern of private and public uses for more than 130 years. The initial uses were predominantly private (timber, grazing, recreation). Over the past 90 years, more than 85% of the basin has been acquired by public agencies. Nevertheless, urbanization has left its indelible mark—the creation of more than 49,000 subdivided lots and 29,000 acres of developed area. The urbanization of

Turn-of-the-century logging in the Truckee River basin around Lake Tahoe used animals, narrow gauge railroads, and water flumes to haul out logs. Extensive areas in this region of mixed conifer forest had most of the tree cover removed. (Courtesy of Searles Historical Library/ J. Morse.)

the LTB and past resource management practices have fragmented the ecosystem in such a manner that an extraordinary investment is needed to stabilize the system.

During the past fifteen years alone, more than $300 million has been invested in acquisition and restoration activities. A greater investment is still needed to fund soil erosion and watershed restoration projects identified in the region's water-quality plan. These kinds of activities are essential to achieving TRPA's thresholds. The goal of these programs is to reduce almost 50% of the sediment entering the lake.

Investment in knowledge is a subject of both concern and opportunity. It is of concern because the task of managing the Lake Tahoe Basin ecosystem is becoming more difficult as both natural and human processes evolve and intertwine. There are powerful scientific and technical participants in the basin that have demonstrated over the last thirty years that good knowledge is mandatory for guiding ecosystems. LTB science

and research have been critical to court decisions supporting management and restoration programs; however, if investment in research continues to diminish, the need to understand and manage will exceed the generation of knowledge. An adaptation to this situation is under discussion as Tahoe organizations seek new combinations of skills to fill the growing knowledge gap. For example, the Forest Service's ecosystem management policy is attempting to bring scientists and managers into more efficient cooperation even as funding for management and research is reduced significantly.

The positive side of our assessment of knowledge investment derives from the unique opportunity at Lake Tahoe to learn from restoration and management projects. The opportunity can be realized if the results of the large investment in institutional formation and cooperation, land-use regulation, environmental restoration, and ecosystem science can be made available, with interpretation, to the constituents of this and other ecosystems living at some distance from Tahoe. The state's bioregional information center concept, which links the Tahoe experience with worldwide telecommunications networks, leads in this direction, as does the Tahoe–Lake Baikal cooperative education program. The assessment team's judgment is that the three decades of Tahoe experience, if communicated effectively, can be of immense value for all types of ecosystem management projects internationally. The educational potential is far from being realized at present.

There is also a need to increase management funding. Such funding is needed to take the major steps to reduce fire hazard and nutrient flux to the lake while restructuring the forest so as to sustain an efficient stewardship program.

The current level of public investment is inadequate. Federal funding for both acquisitions and control of soil erosion has dropped sharply. There is a decrease in federal investment for management of more than 70% of the basin's land base. State investment has remained stable but far below needed levels. For example, the TRPA "208" Plan anticipates an annual investment of $9 million from state sources for soil erosion control alone; currently, only a portion of this total is being made available.

The magnitude of the need is extraordinarily large. During these difficult fiscal times, the prospects of long-term funding are unknown. It is clear that both public (e.g., bond acts, budgetary appropriations) and private investments (e.g., redevelopment programs) will be needed, because neither sector can afford to do these activities alone. Additionally, market mechanisms such as mitigation banks and transfers of development rights should be more fully developed to generate revenues.

The amount of investment will depend upon the value—economic and otherwise—placed on this resource. The LTB economy ($2 billion visitor-serving economy involving 20,000 jobs) is inextricably linked to the health of Lake Tahoe and its surrounding forests. For the rest of the Sierra Nevada, it is very important to understand the problem of investment distribution; it costs many times more to restore an ecosystem than to prevent degradation.

6. How was ecosystem management institutionalized in the LTB?

The institutionalization of the LTB resource management process began in the early 1950s with the efforts of small organizations, foundations, and individuals, and led, within a decade, to task forces sponsored by both state and federal governments. During this period, federal leadership (reflecting federal legislative mandates), advocacy organizations, and elected federal and state officials played a prominent role in developing approaches for ecosystem management at Lake Tahoe. Understandably, local governments were concerned about losing their jurisdiction over land-use matters. Since 1969, a number of public and private institutions have been formed to assist in the management of this ecosystem. Due to the nature of resource degradation, they reflected a need to

sustain ecosystem management activities within this ecosystem over a long period. Specifically, institutions were created to implement long-term monitoring and research; a regional planning approach was developed that matches ecological boundaries and transcends existing political boundaries; and resource management agencies were designed to acquire, restore, and manage land for ecosystem purposes.

First, the process of ecosystem management at Lake Tahoe required developing or adapting organizational structures and approaches to ecosystem activities. For example, TRPA, a bi-state agency, was created to develop and enforce land-use standards. The Lake Tahoe Basin Management Unit, carved out of three national forests, was established to manage all U.S. Forest Service lands within the LTB. The state of California created the Tahoe Conservancy to administer resource protection programs. In the private sector, nonprofit organizations were created to support ecosystem efforts.

Second, the ecosystem process places a premium on cooperation: sharing of data, cooperative project planning and implementation, and the provision of funds.

Third, there is an emphasis on public-private collaborative efforts such as the Tahoe Truckee Regional Economic Coalition and the Tahoe Coalition of Recreation Providers. These organizations recognize the interdependency of economic and environmental concerns and the need for both public and private sectors to combine resources.

Last, there is a growing recognition of participatory and consensus processes for moving initiatives forward—a byproduct realizing that both sides may lose more than they gain through litigation. Certainly the overall approach is controversial in some quarters. There are still concerns about infringement of property rights and about litigation. There are concerns that the environment is emphasized to the detriment of the economy. However, the current form and processes of ecosystem management at Lake Tahoe provide some optimism that institutions may be able to deal with the uncertainty, complexity, and cost and time requirements involved in this approach.

THE MEDIATED SETTLEMENT CASE STUDY

Giant sequoia (*Sequoiadendron giganteum*) is known worldwide as an awe-inspiring species of immense size, longevity, and attractive form. Because of the extraordinary range of values and adaptability of the species, giant sequoia has been successfully planted beyond its native range in northern and southern California, Oregon, New Zealand, and Europe. Limited in natural distribution to approximately seventy distinct groves concentrated in the southwestern part of the Sierra Nevada (figure 10.1), giant sequoias are widely recognized for their social, economic, and scientific importance. Since the

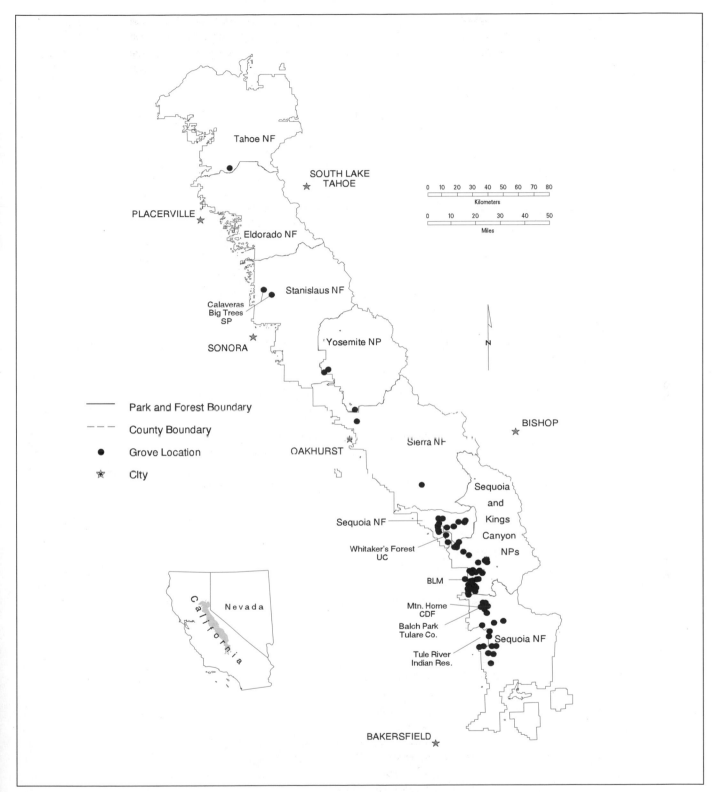

FIGURE 10.1

Locations of giant sequoia groves in the Sierra Nevada. (From volume II, chapter 55.)

late 1800s giant sequoias have been a focus of local, national, and worldwide attention. Giant sequoia trees have provided wood products, served as scientific resources (tree-ring and fire scar records), major tourist attractions, and a source of spiritual renewal. Increasingly, giant sequoias have been protected in various public ownerships (national parks, national forests, a state and county park, a state demonstration forest, and a university forest).

In February 1988, the Sequoia National Forest published the Land and Resource Management Plan (LMP) and Record of Decision documenting land allocation and management decisions for the forest. The LMP was administratively appealed to the chief of the U.S. Forest Service by twenty-one appellants. Giant sequoia management was only one of many appeal issues. Four appellants interested in wild and scenic rivers and the California Department of Fish and Game resolved their issues through the appeal process. One appeal was dismissed, leaving fifteen appellant groups, including intervenors, with substantial issues on appeal. The claims and issues of these remaining parties were so disparate that the Forest Service elected to use formal mediation and hired a professional mediator. The resulting 1990 Mediated Settlement Agreement (MSA) specified terms of agreement on, among other issues, grove mapping and the future management of giant sequoia on the Sequoia National Forest.

1. Why does the SNEP report contain a special section relating to giant sequoia and the Mediated Settlement Agreement?

In 1992 the United States Congress considered two bills (H.R. 5503 and H.R. 6013) relating to an ecosystem study of the Sierra Nevada. H.R. 5503 was passed, authorizing the study. The Sierra Nevada Ecosystem Project Steering Committee's charge to the project scientists called for "an examination of the Mediated Settlement Agreement, Section B, Sequoia Groves, and recommendations for scientifically based mapping and management of sequoia groves." We reviewed the Mediated Settlement Agreement documents and the mapping of the groves and addressed giant sequoia management and sustainability issues.

2. How did the mediation process work?

A professional mediator was hired and gained the acceptance of all parties for beginning a negotiation process. The process began in February 1989 and ended in July 1990 with a Mediated Settlement Agreement. The purpose of the negotiations was "to resolve issues and concerns raised in the appeals of the Sequoia Forest Plan through mediated settlement involving appellants, intervenors and the Forest Service to the mutual satisfaction of all the participants" (Exhibit C, page 1, MSA). Protocols for the negotiation process were established with detailed expansion for each section; purpose and goals, structure for the negotiation process and the decision-making process, among other protocols, were detailed at the beginning.

Most of the appellants participated in the mediation, although not all of them completed the process. Much of the agreement deals with various issues of the forest LMP. Our review focused on Section II B of the MSA, Giant Sequoia Groves. The agreement terminates with formal revision of the forest LMP.

3. Was the Mediated Settlement Agreement an effective tool for resolving conflicts?

The MSA was a means for resolving an otherwise irreconcilable conflict among the Forest Service, environmental, recreation and commodity interests. The agreement applied only to the Sequoia National Forest; however, in 1992 uniform policies for giant sequoia were extended to all of the national forests with naturally occurring giant sequoia groves (Sierra, Sequoia, and Tahoe National Forests) through Regional Forester Ronald Stewart's direction and a subsequent 1992 proclamation by President George Bush. The goal "shall be to protect, preserve, and restore the Groves for the benefit and enjoyment of present and future generations." The MSA specifies a process for the identification of grove administrative zone and grove influence zone boundaries. Grove-specific management plans are required. Permitted activities within the groves and grove influence zones are listed.

The mediation process appears to have been a practical approach to resolving the giant sequoia conflict of 1988. Mediation allowed for (1) participation and sharing of information by the key players; (2) agreement on objectives; and (3) agreement on a process for resolution of key issues. The process was accepted by virtually all concerned parties as a compromise that would allow forest management to proceed in "full view" of the appellants while more difficult questions were being considered. It addressed the most obvious and immediate threats to the groves (e.g., logging of associated whitewoods, fuel hazard reduction). Means of achieving long-term preservation were left for later resolution through participation by interested parties and planning in accordance with NFMA (National Forest Management Act) and NEPA (National Environmental Policy Act).

4. Are there substantial deficiencies in the MSA that interfere with necessary protection, including management activities?

Implementation of the MSA process was hampered by the language of the agreement, which requires concurrence from all parties for any amendment to the MSA. As unanticipated issues arose, some of the signatories were not responsive, thus frustrating MSA's specified amendment process. The MSA lacks provisions for handling basic issues of public safety, maintenance of existing easements, and other uses in the groves. The Forest Service has since worked out an administrative process for handling the maintenance issues satisfactory to the active MSA signatories but not specifically provided for in the agreement. It is important to anticipate the whole range of issues during the negotiation process.

The MSA is a combination of precise directions (e.g., grove administrative boundaries are defined as 300 or 500 feet outward from the tree-to-tree perimeter line) and general language stating management objectives without specific direction (e.g., "The objective of fuel load reduction plans shall be to preserve, protect, restore and regenerate the Giant Sequoia Groves without unnecessary damage to any old growth tree in the Grove"). Specifically, there were no definitions of such terms as *protect*, *preserve*, *restore*, or *original condition* or direction on how they were to be accomplished, thereby giving the Forest Service considerable flexibility, as long as commercial logging was kept out of the groves. Success in accomplishing agreed-on objectives will require a strong participatory process and trust building.

Mediation provided a way of negotiating resolution of disagreement, not necessarily of sharing or implementing the best science. Despite these problems, the parties, including the Forest Service, have generally been able to work within the agreement. Annual reports document steady, slow progress in accomplishing the tasks specified in the agreement and confirm agency commitment, improved communications, and strong participation by some of the signatories.

MSA Summary Conclusions

- Despite operational problems in implementing the giant sequoia section of the MSA, we conclude that the mediated settlement approach is a reasonable means of conflict resolution for controversial resource management issues. This negotiation identified the importance and difficulty of resolving conflicts among values, process, and science.

- The MSA recognized the need for research, which perhaps gave impetus to the formation of an interagency research group. The Giant Sequoia Ecology Cooperative has been formed by the Forest Service, National Park Service, National Biological Service, and California Department of Forestry and Fire Protection and is waiting for University of California signature. This group has the potential of becoming the scientific core for developing specifics for an adaptive management approach to protect, preserve, and restore the groves.

- Unless the Giant Sequoia Ecology Cooperative can be strengthened and funding ensured, there is little likelihood an adaptive management program will be developed and carried forward that will ensure the protection, preservation, and restoration of the groves. Members must be commited to work together in a continuous collaborative effort of research, planning, execution of management activities, and evaluation of results. Alternative funding sources to augment limited federal and state funds should be explored.

- The MSA work has proceeded slowly, at times testing the workability of the agreement. The active participants have found practical solutions to overcome the few MSA struc-

tural deficiencies; mapping is completed; work on grove management plans and a cooperative prescribed fire are planned for 1996. Other MSA work needs to be accelerated.

- The agreement has provided an opportunity for the signatories to fully participate with the agency as plans are developed. Through the MSA they have an increased role in the activities from planning to execution. The issue of requiring unanimity of signatories for formal amendments is yet to be resolved. Not all signatories remain active in the process.

- Interested parties not participating in or not affiliated with MSA participants were not accommodated in agreement provisions. The Forest Service has responded to this potential problem by keeping all interested parties informed of grove management activities.

- The agreement seems to provide the flexibility necessary to develop a scientifically supportable plan for giant sequoia management in spite of the lack of a comprehensive scientific basis in developing the MSA. Of equal importance, it has provided a structure for communication among otherwise adversarial parties and provided a mechanism for increasing stakeholder involvement in key discussions and decisions.

- The MSA has helped to restore trust between the active participants and the Forest Service. This cooperation has probably been facilitated by their realizing that the only alternative may be statutory direction or more litigation.

- The MSA provided rationale and impetus for establishing a Giant Sequoia Management Program for the Sequoia National Forest where none had previously existed.

- The MSA must be recognized as only a beginning step in developing a comprehensive strategic plan for each grove. The interested parties, the agencies, and the Giant Sequoia Ecology Cooperative must move quickly toward this planning goal, incorporating the best appropriate science, even in the face of declining budgets.

Grove Mapping

Mapping of giant sequoia groves may appear to be a simple task but in fact is enormously complicated by irregular patterns of naturally occurring giant sequoia trees, rugged topography, and the importance of identifying the full area of ecosystem influences for each grove. The entire influence area must be considered for long-term giant sequoia sustainability.

1. How were the groves mapped?

Grove mapping within the Sequoia National Forest began in 1992 and was completed by the Forest Service in 1995. MSA procedures were followed. The mapping of the boundaries employed a three-step approach; a perimeter line was established joining all the outermost trees of a grove; next, a buffer of either 300 or 500 feet (specified in the MSA for each grove) was added to the perimeter line. This combined area became the grove administrative boundary. An additional 300 to 500 feet (MSA-specified) were added to the administrative boundary to define the grove influence zone. Field review of all grove boundaries by the MSA boundary team is still in progress.

The project used special aerial photos with expert photo interpretation followed by field verification. Final grove administrative boundaries were posted and traversed using a global positioning receiver. Grove influence zones were derived in the GIS by adding the MSA-prescribed distance to the administrative boundary, except when otherwise provided in the MSA. Final maps were produced from the digital database.

2. Is the mapping adequate for grove-specific plans?

Our examination of the mapping process raised questions with respect to the grove buffers and influence zones. The assignment of a buffer of either 500 or 300 feet beyond existing giant sequoias appears to be arbitrary rather than science-based. The MSA provides no justification or basis for specified buffer widths. We can only conclude that the mediation process did not allow for resolution of this issue using ecologically based criteria.

Although the giant sequoia grove mapping has been completed, we believe ecologically based influence zones incorporating hydrology, fuels, and other landscape-scale considerations should be a high priority in the preparation of individual grove management plans. Incorporation of available ecological knowledge is critical and should be supplemented with new understanding in defining the influence zone necessary to ensure the long-term health of the groves. This issue should be addressed by the Giant Sequoia Ecology Cooperative.

Mapping Summary Conclusions

- The mapping as specified in the MSA has been completed; there remains some field verification by the MSA grove mapping team. The mapping included appropriate technology to produce accurate maps and provide permanent boundary reference. Mapping took longer than anticipated and produced some unexpected results: (1) several of the groves are more extensive than previously thought; (2) one new grove, not previously described, was identified; (3) two groves previously named do not exist; (4) groupings of isolated trees suggest recognition of four additional groves.

- The MSA mapping that established grove influence zones should be considered an interim step until ecologically based grove influence zones can be established for each grove.

- The Giant Sequoia Ecology Cooperative should be assigned the task of developing specific, science-based criteria for defining grove influence zones.

Management and Long-Term Sustainability of Giant Sequoia Ecosystems

Early logging activities proved to be largely uneconomic and were followed by protection of the sequoia groves for the better part of a century. Protection was accomplished through suppression of potentially destructive fires and public acquisition of both logged and unlogged groves. The late 1960s brought recognition of the importance of periodic disturbance to giant sequoia ecosystems. Experimental, and later operational, burning was accompanied by a variety of research projects that documented the importance of fire (including locally hot fires) to sequoia regeneration, forest structure, nutrient cycling, and fuel reduction. Other research documented the historic role and frequency of fire as well as the effects of nearly a century of fire suppression on forest structure and fuel accumulations.

1. Is the long-term sustainability of giant sequoia ecosystems dependent upon public acquisition of additional groves?

There is no compelling evidence to conclude that the long-term sustainability of giant sequoia ecosystems, as a whole, depends on acquisition of the groves now in private ownership. However, public acquisition from willing private owners might be desirable to provide additional public recreation opportunities, preserve specific ecological features unique to particular groves, and increase the public agencies' ability to manage grove areas already in public ownership. The National Park Service and Forest Service collectively manage more than three-fourths of all grove area. In addition the California Department of Parks and Recreation, University of California, California Department of Forestry and Fire Protection, Bureau of Land Management, Tulare County, and Tule River Indian Reservation manage a total of 14%, leaving about 10% of grove area in private ownership.

2. What are the greatest threats to long-term sustainability of giant sequoias and their ecosystems?

There is evidence suggesting that inaction is currently the most significant threat to giant sequoias, the groves, and their ecosystems. Historically unprecedented fuel loads in most of the groves increases the chances of catastrophic wildfire. High-intensity wildfire is increasingly likely to preempt future management options.

In August 1987, a lightning-ignited wildfire swept into the Redwood Mountain Grove (Sequoia National Forest and Kings Canyon National Park). The fire intensity caused scorching or burning of the crowns of large pines, firs, and even monarch giant sequoias, killing the trees. The fire was successfully contained when it burned into an area where fuel reduction by prescribed burning had been completed.

Many other agents may affect the groves. Annosus root rot can weaken giant sequoia resistance to windthrow. Air pollution (ozone) effects on giant sequoia seedlings and ponderosa and Jeffrey pines are of increasing concern, especially in the southern part of the range. More sugar pine trees are succumbing to white pine blister rust, thus changing the mix of associated species in giant sequoia groves.

The strong public interest must be nurtured by all interested parties through sharing of information, issues, and management plans affecting the groves. Public understanding and support are an essential part of future management strategies for the groves.

3. Is there a sufficient research base to support an adaptive management approach leading to long-term sustainability?

In recent decades much has been learned about the history, ecology, and genetics of giant sequoia ecosystems and the effects of various management practices on them. Tree-ring records have provided detailed understanding of the paleohistory of climate, fire, and forest dynamics for selected groves. Ecological studies have improved understanding of the effects of fire and fire suppression on regeneration, forest succession, and nutrient dynamics. Studies of associated fauna, pathogens and disease, and the effects of human impacts (trampling, air pollution, and fire suppression) have provided insight into the functioning and sensitivity of giant sequoia forests.

At the same time, the various agencies and entities charged with managing giant sequoia have implemented an assortment of management strategies from which there is much more to be learned. Nevertheless, there remains considerable uncertainty regarding the long-term consequences of alternative future management scenarios. For example, we are uncertain what the long-term effects of various treatments such as prescribed burning or silvicultural prescriptions (alone or in combination) would be on the sustainability of the forest. This uncertainty, together with the great emotional value placed on these magnificent forests, has focused attention on the appropriateness of recent management activities. As the agencies develop future restoration and preservation programs, utilization of all available sources of information, including identification of successes, failures, and findings of past actions will be essential. The research base is sufficient to prepare grove management plans and begin some management activities (e.g., fuel reduction), but scientific resources are presently inadequate to provide the monitoring and develop the additional understanding necessary for a comprehensive adaptive program leading to long-term sustainability.

4. What is meant by adaptive management?

Our present knowledge of grove restoration and conservation is imperfect, meaning that grove managers must have the flexibility to change their practices as knowledge increases. The variety of lands, conditions, and policies represented by the various giant sequoia management agencies provide op-portunities for utilizing varying combinations of fire and silviculture. Because we do not fully understand the long-term effects of differing fire regimes or silvicultural practices (and combinations thereof) on these forests, we must learn as we go. The concept of adaptive management, by which careful monitoring of the effects of management actions improve the understanding of those actions and thus improve the management program, should be an integral part of future management strategies. Continuation of management actions (including no action) without documentation of and learning from those experiences is simply unacceptable.

5. What should the future strategy for long-term sustainability include?

The lack of detail in the MSA regarding specific actions to ensure the long-term protection and preservation of giant sequoia is a major concern. The new knowledge needed to guide giant sequoia management will grow rapidly if the various land management agencies cooperate in management planning and research and compare the results of their various management practices. The recent establishment of a giant sequoia specialist position on the Sequoia National Forest and of the Giant Sequoia Ecology Cooperative are good beginnings. They need to be strengthened and institutionalized. There is increasing concern that the combined resources of all involved agencies, interest groups, and individuals may be inadequate for the task, especially with declining agency budgets for both research and management. Alternative funding mechanisms must be found, and agencies must commit a continuing level of research and management resources adequate for a viable program. We judged both commitment and resources adequate to support development of a strategic management plan for the groves but woefully short for the interagency-university cooperation so necessary for meaningful progress in grove management.

That the MSA was written specifically for the Sequoia National Forest does not lessen the importance of the giant sequoia groves on other agency lands or the need to include all giant sequoia lands in designing future management strategies. Similarly, because of the wide differences in ecological, institutional, and social conditions represented by the groves, it must be recognized that there is no universally correct strategy, or "right answer." The need to address these differences and to test management concepts justifies multiple strategies and approaches.

ECOSYSTEMS UNDER FOUR DIFFERENT INSTITUTIONS

Certain attributes of institutions greatly influence land management. The purpose of this case study is to compare four public institutions in the southern Sierra Nevada to understand the degree to which two attributes—the institution's original mandate and its organizational structure—influence their patterns of ecosystem management. The institutions are a national forest (Sequoia National Forest), a state forest (Mountain Home State Demonstration Forest), a national park (Sequoia and Kings Canyon National Parks, two parks but managed as one administratively), and an Indian reservation (Tule River Indian Reservation). Although these four institutions manage comparable ecosystems, their unique organizational characteristics, histories, and operating rules, in combination with their different mandates, have produced different patterns on the landscape, different mixes of benefit flows, and different levels of conflict. We suggest that the present landscape pattern associated with each institution, and the probable direction of these landscape patterns, can be best accounted for by the interaction between internal organizational characteristics and institutional mandates, rather than by biophysical endowments or scientific principles of land, timber, forest, or ecosystem management. The degree of organizational centralization, the linkages between resource science and resource management, the criteria used for budget allocations, the means for ensuring public accountability, and the degree of planning and management flexibility are key factors that influence the different social and ecological effects of these four institutions.

The challenges of maintaining ecosystem integrity are compounded by the recognition that resource management and stewardship efforts based on the "island-in-time" self-contained reserve model are inadequate to ensure resource preservation or conservation, because significant impacts on areas within a reserve arise from outside it and management regimes within a reserve affect those aspects of an ecosystem that lie outside it. Examples of such "porosity" include air pollution, fire, visitor use, and in some cases sedimentation and changes in hydrologic regimes resulting from upstream management activities. Accordingly, the case study also examines factors that contribute to the ability of public land management institutions to respond to increasingly complex and interdependent social, political, and ecological environments while simultaneously maintaining their legitimacy and the integrity of the ecosystems within their jurisdiction. Tight feedback loops between responsible research and resource management, high levels of institutional legitimacy and public trust, and active interorganizational coordination positively affect institutional performance under the increasingly porous and complex conditions faced by all public forest owners in the Sierra Nevada.

1. What are the origins of the four institutions, and what ecosystems fall within their jurisdictions?

The Mountain Home State Demonstration Forest was purchased by the state of California in 1946 from the Michigan Trust Company. It is administered by the California Department of Forestry and Fire Protection (CDF). The Fresno-Visalia community organization Native Sons and Daughters of the

Golden West was instrumental in lobbying the California legislature to purchase the tract to preserve the giant sequoia (*Sequoiadendron giganteum*) groves it contains. Giant sequoia preservation was also one of the reasons for creating the Sierra Forest Reserve in 1893, from which the Sequoia National Forest was formed in 1908, and for reserving in 1890 the two sections and four townships that formed the nucleus of Sequoia and Kings Canyon National Parks. The Tule River Indian Reservation, established in 1873, is located in southern Tulare County. More than nine Californian tribes speaking different languages were relocated here from a much larger region; consequently, only a few of the culturally significant areas for the tribes are located within the reservation.

The jurisdictions of these four institutions have similar ecological characteristics. The Sequoia National Forest and Sequoia and Kings Canyon National Parks encompass lower-elevation oak and grass woodlands, mixed conifer and true fir belts, and substantial areas above the timberline. The Tule River Indian Reservation extends from oak and grass woodlands up through the mixed conifer and true fir belt. The Mountain Home State Demonstration Forest is restricted to the mixed conifer belt. Giant sequoia groves are located within the boundaries of all four institutions. This study focuses primarily on resource management strategies and issues related to the mixed conifer belt.

2. What are the mandates of the four institutions?

Although the jurisdictions of the four institutions encompass relatively similar ecosystems, their legislative mandates differ significantly. The Mountain Home State Demonstration Forest is a "multiple use forest, primarily for public hunting, fishing and recreation" (section 4426, chapter 1496 of the *Statutes of the State of California*). The noncommodity focus of this multiple-use mandate differs from the multiple-use mandate of Sequoia National Forest, which gives equal weight to commodity and noncommodity values. The original purpose of the Sequoia and other forest reserves, as described in the 1897 Organic Act, was to "preserve and protect the . . . reservation," to secure "favorable conditions of water flow," and "to furnish a continuous supply of timber." The 1960 Multiple Use Sustained Yield Act expanded the commodity-oriented mandate of the Forest Service to include outdoor recreation, range, wildlife, and fish, in addition to those purposes set forth in the 1897 legislation.

The initial legislation establishing Sequoia National Park called for protection of the natural features within its boundaries. Consequently, military troops were used to protect the park from illegal activities such as grazing, logging, and trapping, while, in the Sierra Forest Reserve, mining, grazing, and logging were allowed to continue. In contrast to the commodity and multiple-use orientation of the Forest Service, the 1916 legislation establishing the National Park Service states that the Park Service's purpose is "to conserve the scenery and the natural and historic objects and the wildlife therein and to provide for the enjoyment of same in such manner and by such means as will leave them unimpaired for the enjoyment of future generations." Unlike the other three institutions, the Tule River Indian Reservation emphasizes the sovereignty of those living within its boundaries. Its mandate specifies no particular resource management objective.

3. How has the organizational structure of the Mountain Home State Demonstration Forest affected the interpretation of its mandate, the landscape, benefit flows, and conflict levels?

The management of the Mountain Home State Demonstration Forest is characterized by a relatively small staff, for the land area managed. The staff has been in place long enough to possess localized site-specific knowledge, and this, combined with decentralized decision making, enables them to experiment with, monitor, and evaluate different forest management techniques and to engage with non-CDF researchers to conduct research. The decentralized organization of the forest administration promotes an active research program consistent with the purpose of a demonstration forest.

Unlike the national forests, where incompatible uses such as timber production and recreation can be practiced on widely separated areas, at the Mountain Home State Demonstration Forest all multiple-use objectives must be met from a relatively small land area. Consequently, the giant sequoia groves and camping facilities constitute a preserve/recreational forest, while the adjacent and surrounding non-sequoia forest is managed as an uneven-aged production forest. Grazing permits are not issued because of incompatibility with recreation and to allow historically overgrazed areas to regenerate. Timber harvests are planned to minimize visual impacts by using only single-tree and small-group selection harvests. Clear-cutting is not practiced for aesthetic reasons, and harvest intervals have been increased from 15–20 to 30 years to minimize harvest-related forest damage. Annual recreational use of the demonstration forest has increased from 3,000 visitors in 1963 to close to 40,000 in recent years. A combination of tempered harvesting practices, outreach and education efforts, and the short two-week public comment period required under the Timber Harvest Plan limit public controversy and conflict to low or negligible levels.

Preservation of old-growth giant sequoia groves, the demonstration forest's mandated emphasis on recreation, and sustained yield production forestry in non-sequoia areas have produced a mosaic of differently managed and used patches within a relatively constrained geographical area. The forest is extensively roaded; there are no large intact landscape units. Riparian areas and meadows are in better condition than they would be otherwise due to the ban on stock grazing. The decentralized organization of the forest administration has provided the local decision-making autonomy necessary for establishing and maintaining feedback loops between resource science and resource management. Although the forest administration staff do not have the capacity to conduct research themselves, they successfully compensate for this by contracting with other agencies and universities.

4. How has the organizational structure of the Sequoia National Forest affected the interpretation of its mandate, the landscape, benefit flows, and conflict levels?

The Sequoia National Forest is part of a strongly hierarchical organization. The forest staff follow centrally mandated and externally legislated standardized planning procedures that leave relatively limited opportunity for local-level planning innovation and provide few incentives for intensive monitoring and evaluation of the impacts of resource management plans other than to ensure that legal stipulations are fulfilled. Staff members of the Sequoia National Forest are more frequently transferred than those of the other institutions in this study. At the forest level, administrators and staff have minimal control over funding for research or generation of research questions. With the exception of management-oriented administrative studies, forest staff do not conduct scientific research, although they do participate with Forest Service Research (a separate branch of the agency, with a broad mission beyond resource management and the bounds of national forest lands) when research projects occur on the forest. Relative to Sequoia and Kings Canyon National Parks and Mountain Home State Demonstration Forest, there has been less opportunity to integrate research on local conditions with resource management. Except for fire protection, the majority of funding for forest management activities is tied to commodity production targets (including recreation). Although mechanisms exist to enable fire managers to plan and conduct prescribed burns to promote noncommodity ecosystem values, they are generally not well funded. Commodity orientation of fire programs and funding priorities has constrained the ability of forest managers to effectively use fire as a resource management tool to achieve non-commodity-driven resource values and conditions. The ecological effects of fire on other resources is increasingly emphasized at the national level in the agency, and its effects are gradually being felt locally.

These landscape effects of the multiple-use mandate reflect the influence of the agency's strongly centralized organization, which results in a relatively lower degree of local decision making, reduced opportunities to integrate local research and resource management, and stronger linkages between funding and commodity production. Until the 1950s the primary uses of the Sequoia National Forest were extensive watershed protection, wilderness study and classification, grazing, low levels of hydroelectric development and mining, some logging on the western slopes of the forest, and recreational use. In the 1950s the Forest Service began an extensive timber harvesting program that focused on sustained-yield timber production in some areas and in other areas sought to integrate timber production with other multiple-use land-management objectives. By the late 1970s some stands had become understocked. In response to these forest conditions and to other external pressures, management of the forest shifted to extensive clear-cutting and a shortened cutting cycle (from 150 to 70 years). This accelerated short-rotation timber harvesting program continued through the mid-1980s. During this same period, the Forest Service, aware of the ecological importance of giant sequoia groves, acquired adjacent groves, excluded groves from timber management goals, and established a four-class grove classification system with acceptable management activities for each class. Although the shift to short-rotation clear-cutting was silviculturally sound, inadequate investment in postharvest site preparation and reforestation as well as harsh site conditions created other problems. By the mid-1980s public concern about clear-cutting and other environmental consequences of the timber harvesting program and the threat that harvesting in and adjacent to giant sequoia groves posed to that species, led to twenty-two administrative review appeals challenging the 1988 Forest Land Management Plan and the supporting environmental impact statement. The Forest Service's response to the appeals led to a series of mediated negotiations that culminated in the Mediated Settlement Agreement (see the Mediated Settlement Agreement case study in this chapter for discussion and analysis of this agreement and related giant sequoia management issues).

Grazing on Sequoia National Forest is regulated by annual permits for specific allotments. The Forest Service is now under pressure to revise its grazing policies due to concern about possible range deterioration, the adequacy of existing efforts to monitor range condition, and the timing of grazing permits.

More people visit Sequoia National Forest than the adjacent Sequoia and Kings Canyon National Parks. In order to accommodate the growing recreation activity within the forest, campground management and other recreational activities are contracted to private firms through special-use permits.

The Sequoia National Forest is also involved in formal and informal interagency coordination. Recently, the Sequoia National Forest administration was instrumental in organizing the Giant Sequoia Ecology Cooperative. The cooperative, formed soon after the 1992 symposium Giant Sequoias: Their Place in the Ecosystem and Society, held in Visalia, California, is an interagency response to public controversy over management and regeneration of large giant sequoias and common agency recognition of the sparse scientific basis for giant sequoia management. The cooperative facilitates the coordination and sharing of research related to giant sequoias among the member institutions. Ideally it will combine the strengths of each member institution in a manner that strengthens the linkage between resource scientists and resource managers and improves public accountability of the participating agencies vis-à-vis sequoia management.

In summary, the management of Sequoia National Forest has been characterized by fire and watershed protection, intensive and extensive timber harvesting and associated road construction, continued grazing, and high levels of recreational use. This reflects the multiple-use mandate of the For-est Service embodied in the 1960 Multiple Use Sustained Yield Act. However, the landscape effects of the Forest Service's mandate have also been shaped by the strongly centralized organization of the service, the budget priority given to commodity resource production activities, the lack of adequate reinvestment in reforestation and other non-commodity-resource values, and the lack of effective integration of research with resource management. Together these factors make it difficult to use innovation in forest management and grazing policy, have restricted the use of fire as a means to restore ecosystem structure and function, and have made it difficult to sustain a feedback loop based on intensive monitoring and evaluation between resource science and resource management.

5. How has the organizational structure of the Sequoia and Kings Canyon National Parks (SEKI) affected the interpretation of its mandate, the landscape, benefit flows, and conflict levels?

SEKI is also part of a strongly centralized and hierarchical organization, although in practice, SEKI represents a midrange alternative to the less-centralized Mountain Home State Demonstration Forest and the strongly centralized Sequoia National Forest. Unlike either the national forest or the state forest, SEKI has a regular on-site research presence (although a separate unit from park administration) and hence potential to link research with resource management. Like the Sequoia National Forest, it must satisfy NEPA planning requirements. But in other respects, such as relative freedom from externally defined target output quotas, relative ability to fund its own research and direct its own research agenda, and a budget-setting process that is not based on commodity outputs but politically directed to individual park units, it has more local-level decision-making autonomy than the national forest. Consequently SEKI has relatively more authority and resources to improve the scientific basis and reduce the unanticipated consequences of its resource management plans. While this model of agency research dedicated to specific parks makes integration of research and resource management more likely, it also has limitations. Financial constraints and political and constituency pressures often challenge the ability of park resource managers to implement the management plans developed in consultation with park resource scientists. Under conditions of fiscal retrenchment, competition for funding often emerges between resource managers and research scientists. The creation of the National Biological Service (NBS) and subsequent transfer of all the research scientists from SEKI to the NBS is the most recent threat to SEKI's research capability.

Whereas on the Sequoia National Forest public support to fulfill its mission increased in the 1970s due to legislation requiring public involvement in resource planning, the early superintendents of SEKI had long depended on a measure of "visitor days" to legitimize the park's purpose and budget and to help justify its expansion. The low number of visitors to the park during the first thirty years of its existence led to concerns among park administrators that, without adequate public support, it and the National Park Service might not survive. To generate more public support, radio and magazine publicity was encouraged, and a campfire program and guided nature walks for park visitors were initiated that have become the hallmark of the National Park Service's on-site interpretive program. Early superintendents of SEKI depended heavily on public support to fulfill its mission, obtain budget support, and help justify expansion. Both the National Park Service and the Forest Service were provided guidance by NEPA legislation to strengthen disclosure of planned activities and provide for public involvement in all significant management activities. The Sequoia National Forest received additional formal public involvement direction through the National Forest Management Act of 1976.

Consistent with its legislative mandate, and in contrast to the multiple-use mandates of Mountain Home State Demonstration Forest and Sequoia National Forest, SEKI has followed a preservationist and recreation strategy of land management in combination with efforts, initially, to encourage visitors and then, when their increasing numbers threatened the natural features the park was mandated to protect, to control and restrict visitor impacts. SEKI's current ecological landscape is a product of the historical institutionalization of total fire suppression; the park's preservation mandate, which limits commercial uses of the park's natural resources; the historically high visitation rates and concentration of visitors in some areas; and the commitment among park administrators to block proposed highways into the park's backcountry and across the Sierra crest to Owens Valley. The absence of commercial timber harvesting (significant numbers of trees have been removed to reduce hazards), mining, and grazing, combined with a commitment to minimize road construction, has preserved the integrity of larger landscape blocks than on the other agency jurisdictions in this study. Although reintroduction of fire has begun, fire suppression has interrupted ecological processes, transformed the forest structure, and halted the regeneration of some conifer species, notably giant sequoia.

6. How has the organizational structure of the Tule River Indian Reservation affected the interpretation of its mandate, the landscape, benefit flows, and conflict levels?

The objectives and policy that govern resource management on the Tule River Reservation are set by the nine elected members of the Tribal Council. In addition to the elected council, the traditional elders council also provides considerable leadership. Together the Tribal Council and elders council provide multiple informal avenues for conflict resolution and monitoring and sanctioning of individuals' resource management practices. The federal Bureau of Indian Affairs (BIA) has formal authority on the reservation but currently does not play an active role in natural resource management. The reservation's Natural Resource Department implements resource management programs with assistance provided by a resource management consulting firm.

The resource management philosophy of the reservation closely approximates Mountain Home State Demonstration Forest's multiple-use mandate, with the exception that the public owners live on the reservation. As on the demonstration forest, timber sales have historically been a primary source of locally generated revenue. Since the reservation assumed direct control of its natural resources from the BIA, its timber management program has sought to balance the economic value of timber with recreational and aesthetic values and the sociocultural benefits the forests provide the reservation's inhabitants. Unlike the federal and state institutions in this study, the reservation has a social review process that does not involve complex reporting and legal analysis.

In addition to timber harvesting, grazing and firewood cutting are important consumptive uses of the reservation's resource base. Firewood cutting is important for both local use and off-reservation sale. Rules restricting cutting areas are difficult to enforce. The resource management staff apparently feels that the social conflict that strict enforcement would generate does not warrant the slight improvement in resource management it would provide. Grazing on the reservation follows 1983 guidelines established to promote long-term range productivity and reduce some localized overgrazing problems. Stocking levels have decreased as some tribal members no longer graze stock and others have not increased their herd sizes. The physical impacts of relatively lax policies toward both firewood harvesting and grazing are visible to both the resource management staff and interested tribal members. Stronger responses could be developed and implemented if needed, but the staff clearly weighs this against the conflict among tribal members that would ensue.

The Tule River Indian Reservation's approach to resource management exemplifies the key tenets of a multiple-use management philosophy that balances commodity and noncommodity resource values. Timber harvest levels are planned to be compatible with noncommodity uses of the forest. In a manner analogous to the Mountain Home State Demonstration Forest, timber harvest receipts cross-subsidize other resource management activities and still produce a financial surplus. Most of the beneficiaries live on the parcel, unlike the beneficiaries of the other public institutions. Daily contact between stakeholders holding a range of goals and the resource managers who report to the Tribal Council provides numerous opportunities to discuss resource management and resolve conflicts without the formal reporting procedures used in most state and federal systems.

7. What are key organizational factors that influence how an institution interprets its mandate and with what ecological and social effects?

The case study descriptions suggest that the degree of organizational centralization, the extent of linkage between resource science and resource management, whether or not funding is tied to commodity resource outputs, the mechanisms for ensuring public accountability, and the degree of local-level planning and management autonomy shape how institutions interpret their mandates and the consequent effects on the landscape, benefit flows, and conflict levels. Two paired examples illustrate this: the Sequoia National Forest and the Mountain Home State Demonstration Forest, and Mountain Home State Demonstration Forest and the Tule River Indian Reservation. On paper, the mandates of the Sequoia National Forest and the Mountain Home State Demonstration Forest both emphasize "multiple use," but they give different weights to the importance of those multiple uses. Based only on knowledge of their respective mandates, we would expect the Sequoia National Forest to resemble a multiple-use forest and the state demonstration forest to be primarily oriented toward preserving giant sequoia and providing recreational opportunities. On the contrary, we have shown not only that both forests are managed as multiple-use forests but also that the ways in which conflicting patterns of resource use are reconciled, the integrity of the feedback loop between research and resource management, and the degree of controversy over resource management activities differ significantly. These differences can be accounted for by examining the differences in relative degree of centralization, constituency relations, and funding structure between the national forest and the state demonstration forest.

The Mountain Home State Demonstration Forest emphasizes timber production to cross-subsidize the administration and management of the rest of the forest. However, due to its decentralized organization and local planning autonomy, Mountain Home forest managers can practice intensive forest management in small patches of mixed conifer forest while simultaneously enhancing recreational opportunities and preserving giant sequoia groves in adjacent areas. Freedom from the need to maximize commodity output enables the forest managers to temper timber harvesting to reduce potential conflict with recreation use by using single-tree or small-group selection harvest methods and by decreasing the entry frequency by 50%. These same organizational and funding characteristics enable forest managers to experiment with, and monitor and evaluate, alternative timber management and fire regimes.

The Sequoia National Forest, by contrast, also manages for multiple use but through quite different organizational, planning, and funding structures. The strongly centralized organization of the forest administration, the tendency for funding to be linked with commodity outputs, and the lack of dedicated local research capacity limit the ability of the forest managers to develop innovative timber management plans. More flexible funding arrangements that do not prioritize commodity over noncommodity resource management, a more complete feedback loop between research and resource management, and a more vigorous set of outreach and inter-

pretive programs may have resulted in less-controversial resource management plans.

The Mountain Home State Demonstration Forest and the Tule River Indian Reservation illustrate an example in which the high constituency accountability of the latter and the mandate of the former produced roughly comparable landscape outcomes. Both these institutions follow intensive resource management programs that nevertheless are able to balance commodity and noncommodity resource values in ways that satisfy the diverse needs of the public(s) to whom they are accountable. The Tule River Indian Reservation is not mandated to follow any specific resource management approach. Its culturally attuned multiple-use management regime developed because of the high levels of accountability reinforced through a number of political and cultural channels. The Mountain Home State Demonstration Forest also provides a mix of commodity and noncommodity resources, but not because of formal public accountability procedures. In contrast to the complex public input procedures used on both the national park and the national forest, public input for these two smaller parcels is more informal and less structured. Nevertheless, both the Tule River Indian Reservation and the demonstration forest have a strong record of being responsive to local concerns.

8. What factors influence an institution's effectiveness under increasingly complex and contested conditions?

The case study descriptions suggest that the ability to maintain institutional legitimacy and public trust, the ability to obtain and integrate local research with resource management, and interagency coordination influence an institution's effectiveness under conditions of porous boundaries and complex social and political environments.

Maintaining institutional legitimacy and the public's trust is increasingly difficult as social and political environments become increasingly complex and the tensions inherent in satisfying diverse and sometimes conflicting values grow stronger. Formal and informal procedures for public involvement can together preserve institutional legitimacy and contain conflict within acceptable bounds. A public agency is more likely to retain its institutional legitimacy and the trust of the public owners of the resources it manages by following a proactive strategy of public outreach, on- and off-site interpretive programs, and extension work that involves all of the various concerned interest groups. Accomplishing this probably requires a minimal degree of local-level autonomy, a widening of the envelope of acceptable planning outcomes in the interests of fostering substantive public involvement, leadership support and organizational incentives for personnel to invest time and energy in outreach efforts, and a nondefensive attitude that allows errors to be acknowledged and transformed into learning opportunities.

On-site research capacity, either "in-house" as at Sequoia and Kings Canyon National Parks, or contracted out, as at the Mountain Home State Demonstration Forest, provided the monitoring and evaluation capacity necessary for minimizing the unanticipated effects of management plans and, when combined with local-level planning autonomy, an information base for developing micro-scale management plans. A "hybrid" research organization that combines elements of the separate Forest Service Research branch and the localized Park Service research program might provide local autonomy for effective feedback between research and resource management while simultaneously providing organizational resources and insulation from short-term administrative imperatives necessary for sustained research. Although independence is important, effective integration of research with resource management will occur only when research is organized at the local level, either through "in-house" administrative studies or through cooperative studies involving university researchers or scientists in other state and federal natural resource agencies.

Interagency coordination emerges when the benefits outweigh the costs of coordination. Cooperative interagency research capitalizes on the comparative advantages of different resource management agencies as well as the expertise of university researchers. Interagency associations such as the Giant Sequoia Ecology Cooperative can function as clearinghouses for sharing recent research and provide local-level arenas for resolving potential conflicts among agencies and between them and local communities and local governments. All forms of interagency coordination help bring policy and managerial coherence to ecosystems driven by jurisdictional boundaries.

The organizational structure of public resource management institutions affects the social and ecological outcomes they create as well as their ability to manage complex environments and porous boundaries. This comparative case study has identified potential organizational policy levers that influence the ability of public institutions to handle complexity and porosity. The range of levers includes shifts in the funding and organization of research to create new research relationships, relaxing of links between commodity outputs and budget levels, local-level flexibility, means and incentives necessary for maintaining institutional accountability and

legitimacy, and formal and informal modes of interagency coordination at all levels. Policies that operate in these nonlegislative arenas are often process- rather than target-oriented; instead of legislating outcomes, they attempt to create institutional mechanisms for resolving conflict that incorporate scientific research and maintain institutional accountability.

CONCLUDING NOTES ON THE CASE STUDIES

It is self-evident to conclude that institutions must cooperate to manage ecosystems. This chapter illustrates different forms of cooperation with an understanding that most progress toward stewardship and sustainability involves a good deal of conflict. There are, in the Sierra, different scales of interest. Ecosystems like Lake Tahoe, the Mammoth-June region, and the giant sequoia region have a national and international constituency, yet the commitment of local institutions is required before progress toward sustainability can be made.

There is much to be said for local control over management, as illustrated by the efficiency of Mountain Home State Demonstration Forest. But at Lake Tahoe, Mammoth-June, and the giant sequoia region, the national interest expressed through federal agencies in those places has been critical to a long-term and comprehensive approach to planning and management. In Lake Tahoe and the giant sequoia region, state institutions have shown leadership and intelligent restoration and ecosystem management. These case studies have confirmed the importance of balance among local, state, and national interests.

The chapter has emphasized institutional arrangements. Yet the SNEP assessment team fully recognizes that where there are successes, there are committed individuals who have remained in an area long enough to develop sophisticated knowledge of the ecosystem and credibility throughout the community of institutions.

CHAPTER 11

Institutional Integration

INTRODUCTION

The strategies examined by SNEP represent responses to problems identified in the Sierra Nevada through the SNEP assessments. The strategies are not fully analyzed alternative management schemes, nor does any one strategy address all aspects of the ecosystem. Rather, they are potential components of regional or rangewide alternatives yet to be formulated. As these strategies are taken together, common properties emerge that SNEP suggests will characterize successful approaches to sustainable management of the Sierra Nevada.

WHOLE SYSTEMS

The strategies collectively consider the Sierra Nevada to be a whole system. Although individual SNEP strategies are incomplete, they show how actual solutions must address not just parts of the system but also the ways in which parts interact to create the whole. The full scope of those interactions brings together things hitherto considered separate: core forest areas and matrix, people and nature, regions within and regions outside the Sierra.

The strategies emphasize sustainable management over the entire landscape. For example, the areas of late successional emphasis (ALSE) strategy incorporates management of the lands between core areas of late successional emphasis (i.e., the matrix) and management of core areas themselves. Similarly, the biodiversity management area (BMA) strategy depends largely on the contribution of lands outside the BMAs. The distributed forest conditions strategy proposes that sustainability of late successional forests emerge as a property of an entire landscape, not small reserved portions thereof. Reserves, when discussed, are viewed as part of a larger conservation strategy. Managing the entire landscape for ecosystem sustainability requires that public and private resources and lands be considered together, along with the suite of institutions and rights associated with them.

The diversity of the strategies indicates that addressing whole systems means confronting the full range of system components: physical, biological, and social. The system consists not just of biological structures, such as old-growth stands, but also of ecological functions and human communities—both communities of place within the Sierra and communities of interest elsewhere in the state and nation. SNEP strategies illustrate these components and scales and demonstrate how components could be linked in practice.

The strategies also reveal different scales within the larger Sierran ecosystem. Some strategies respond to regional issues: for example, air quality in the southern Sierra, distributed forest conditions in the eastern Sierra, county buildout on the west slope. Others address truly rangewide concerns: for example the BMAs, ALSEs, and aquatic strategies. The aquatic and air-quality strategies suggest a scale that extends far beyond the range itself.

Finally, the whole system is not static but rather changes over time. The fire strategy addresses a significant source of change in the Sierra and also emphasizes our uncertainty about the historic scope of fire and the risks associated with its purposeful application. Social dimensions of the mountain range change as well. These dynamics are addressed by the county buildout and community well-being strategies. The nature of change requires that management approaches be flexible enough to learn from and adapt to changing ecological and social conditions.

The view of the Sierra as a whole system, or a web of biological and social influences stretching over and beyond the range and evolving over time, suggests that no easy policy or technical "fix" can be implemented in the Sierra Nevada. Many institutions will absorb, elaborate, and recast SNEP strategies to find solutions. Congressional involvement is essential to recasting policy in the Sierra. Existing federal laws constitute part of the web of influences that have served to bring parties together in search of new solutions. The rest of the web is composed of important state and local institutions and their associated laws and policies, as well as affected parties and stakeholders wherever they live. Considerations of cost, local variation in landscape attributes and their conditions, different patterns of land ownership and human communities, as well as other varying factors argue for flexible program design and implementation.

COLLABORATION

Collaboration among various agencies, private interests, and the public at large in the Sierra is the most significant principle that emerges from SNEP strategies. As they collaborate, agencies, private landowners, and the public begin to function as interacting parts of a whole system, and the number of ways to balance use and environmental quality increases exponentially. Collaboration may also encourage private landowners to innovate and to develop creative approaches that will accomplish broad ecological goals in advance of regulations. The mix of lands and resources in the Sierra, including intermingled private and public land, required SNEP to assess ecological conditions at appropriate scales and develop strategies at similar scales. For example, accounting for cumulative watershed effects required that solutions be addressed by all watershed stakeholders. These examples suggest that actual strategies must also extend across property or jurisdictional boundaries.

Successful collaboration requires a mix of expertise and considerable institutional support. Mobilization of people and resources and coordination of activities may require collaboration at a local scale, but as activities engage more technical, financial, or legal issues, specialized expertise usually found in state or federal agencies will be required. Collaboration will succeed to the extent that it receives ongoing support from top management and feeds directly into existing budgets, business processes, and agency missions.

Collaboration springs out of perceived mutual interest. State and federal agencies and other interests have experience in collaborating, especially in response to disasters and threats to life and property. A potential for improvements in service and structure of incentives may also lead to collaboration. In the absence of other threats, avoiding potential regulation remains one of the most powerful incentives to collaborating. Decentralizing control and restructuring agencies to focus on clients may greatly enhance effective collaboration.

Careful restructuring of natural resource laws could encourage participation, thereby reducing the temptation to withdraw and increasing the effectiveness of collaboration. The incentive for collaboration diminishes if alternatives provide apparently quicker, albeit incomplete, resolution for individual participants. Bilateral negotiation rather than full collaboration, for example, probably will lead to only partial solutions, perceptions of bad-faith bargaining, and a retreat to adjudication.

Collaboration will collapse if any of the parties attempts to dominate. Like any negotiation, successful collaboration is based on mutual respect for the rights and equity of all participants. This concept is particularly clear in the case of private landowners, for whom equity is generally expressed in terms of land values. It applies as well to public agencies and takes the form of legal authority, budgets, and scope of action. For members of the public, the form it takes is less established but no less important.

GOAL SETTING

The development of goals is fundamentally a social and political process rather than a technical one. SNEP's contribution lies in defining important dimensions of goals—for instance, old growth, aquatic biodiversity, community well-being—rather than the goals themselves. Identification of specific goals requires active participation of all stakeholders. Although the need for goals to organize human activity may appear self-evident, the barriers to convening and managing the development of ecosystem goals are enormous. Convening such a process requires common acceptance of the whole ecological and social system, joint understanding of how the system works, and a shared sense of the importance of the values at stake. Lake Tahoe is a good example in that its value is tangible. to people, it is related to its watershed through water and sediment flows, and it has loss of clarity as the preeminent problem. Other issues that have a central ecological role and impact on economic value, such as the erosion of biodiversity and fire, may also bring stakeholders together.

Public agencies can incorporate collaborative goal setting into their land-management mission. They are already able to contribute technical, legal, and financial expertise to the goal-setting process, and they are also capable of representing and interpreting rangewide and national perspectives. They can also help to convene the full range of stakeholders needed to address issues, ownerships, and jurisdictional and even cultural boundaries. This process may involve trades and negotiations among participants. In so doing, agencies would not direct the goal-setting activities but rather, within legal and practical limits, participate in a manner that allows stakeholders to achieve common understanding and agreement.

FUNDING MANAGEMENT AND RESTORATION

The SNEP strategies focus primarily on technical or planning aspects of management and restoration. Generally they do not attempt to specify cost or funding source. The fire and ALSE strategies propose some harvest of timber and biomass. These activities will produce income but may not cover the full cost of the strategies. None of the strategies are likely to succeed unless they look beyond nearby commodity outputs to identify the full range of beneficiaries of their actions and to devise mechanisms to recover a portion of that benefit. For instance, for those activities in the fire strategy that seek to reduce the likelihood of large, severe wildfire, specific beneficiaries that should be included are local property owners, distant metropolitan water consumers, regional air-quality boards, fire-control agencies, and national disaster relief agencies, among others. Successful projects depend on equitable allocation of costs to appropriate beneficiaries and use of appropriate mechanisms to recover those costs.

Arrangements for funding and cost recovery associated with implementation of the strategies will require innovative approaches that might include establishing fees or markets or allocating rights to be traded. Enabling these mechanisms may require legislative involvement even while retaining local flexibility. Equally, legislative proposals to permit local or regional cost allocation and recovery should provide opportunities for site-specific experimentation and further modification as these arrangements mature or as the local and regional conditions and objectives change.

REGIONAL CONTEXT

Translation of SNEP strategies into actual policy may proceed more easily through development of regional policies for the different regions of the Sierra. These regions differ in population levels, density, and growth, and in the manner in which they incorporate costs of resource use and environmental risk, governmental coordination, and activism. The pattern of employment, commodity production, and services directly dependent on the Sierra Nevada ecosystem varies greatly across the range; economic linkages clearly define distinct regions within the Sierra. SNEP strategies emphasize different issues in different regions. For instance, the air-quality strategy is important in the southern Sierra, the fire strategy emphasizes the west-central Sierra, and the grazing strategy focuses on the Modoc country and eastern rangelands. Consequently, agencies and other institutions that are critical to the resolution of ecosystem management problems in one region may be much less important in others. Similarly, funding arrangements are likely to vary significantly from region to region. It is, therefore, unlikely that a single model or policy would apply equally well across all regions, except perhaps one that encouraged widespread institutional innovation toward ecosystem stewardship.

MONITORING AND ADAPTING

To determine if the strategies achieve ecosystem sustainability, someone must monitor. To do this requires a commitment to design, finance, and adapt over the long term.

The most effective monitoring programs would generate information on effects at several spatial scales. For instance, the distributed forest conditions strategy attempts to achieve a desired regional condition by implementing treatments incrementally at the watershed level. Monitoring only within watersheds where treatment has proceeded will not answer how well the strategy is achieving the regional condition.

Monitoring a strategy's results relative to its goals is a necessary part of adaptive management. An open process is necessary to build trust; without it, monitoring can fuel conflict rather than reduce it. In many instances, no single agency or group is available that will be considered impartial by all stakeholders, in part, because values influence interpretation as well

as methods. Building trust in monitoring processes requires agreement on the choice of methods and multi-stakeholder (or multi-party) involvement. With particularly sensitive issues, all-party participation in monitoring may also be required.

Decision processes must incorporate specific mechanisms for changing the direction of the policy or project. Monitoring data that highlight inadequacies is of little use without a concomitant process for shifting strategies or reallocating resources. The need for institutional flexibility is particularly important. For example, in addressing issues related to the fire ecosystems of the Sierra, unexpected catastrophic fires may quickly change the context of ecosystem management by reducing old growth, degrading watershed condition, or creating new options for fuel management.

The importance of monitoring argues for the establishment of a broadly based convenor to facilitate range- and region-wide coordination. Organization of such a group—whether it arises at the local, regional, or Sierra-wide level—must be structured to fit the need. However construed, it ought to be collaborative in nature, to be authoritative in charge, and to focus on monitoring local conditions for achievement of rangewide goals and strategies. Such a group, for example, could help to assemble information in the year 2000 to examine improvements or changes in the following:

- Quantity and distribution of Sierran old-growth forests
- Status of conditions of concern:
  - ozone levels, local air-quality problems
  - amphibians
  - riparian quality
  - vertebrates at risk
  - community well-being
  - restoration of fire and treatment of fuel conditions
  - trends of native grasses and alien weeds on rangelands
  - foothill habitats
- Other emerging issues

Also inherent in the strategies is a need for a central caretaker of information to develop and maintain data pertinent to rangewide monitoring and planning. A manager would have responsibility for organizing and synthesizing local databases as part of rangewide systems and would ensure coordination of distributed databases. Decentralized input of information, as well as access to existing data sets, could be obtained through the Internet, with public access available on-line or through public terminals at libraries and other public locations. Decentralized information also would facilitate a system whereby public agencies and others could provide appropriate tools and expertise, together with training on how to employ these technologies, that would enable local governments, other public agencies, and individual citizens to use these sources of information in ecosystem planning and monitoring.

OPTIMISM FOR THE FUTURE

SNEP assessments reveal a great wealth of knowledge, expertise, and involvement in the ecological integrity of the Sierra. The concern of many individuals and groups for the region's future is of long standing and well known. Less publicized is that, in some areas, people with strong ties to the region have already joined together to assess environmental conditions and to create dynamic regional strategies for resource management and environmental stewardship. In the process, diverse communities are being engaged in the search for solutions. As dialogues about collaboration begin to occur across ownerships and jurisdictions, one can anticipate the development of further solutions to issues that are best observed and addressed at the landscape or watershed scale.

After many years of attempting unsuccessfully to "declare" various natural resources policies, agencies now realize that no single optimal policy can be delineated, much less imple-

mented. Local and regional approaches to problem solving, however, are complementary to central planning and can make positive contributions to ecosystem conservation. Regional and subregional delineation, as it occurs, will further involve shared responsibility, power, and leadership by individuals and groups who are quite capable of working with public resource agencies to develop solutions to many resource management problems. Agencies can learn from people while not abdicating responsibility for ensuring that the public interest is protected. Public enthusiasm can make an enormous difference. If the energy and optimism now present in the region and in the larger Sierra community can be embraced, society will gain a great opportunity to move resource policy forward in the Sierra. On the other hand, if public concern and awareness are not channeled into current efforts to address the environmental issues in the Sierra, many institutions and individuals who now willingly give their time and energy to this cause may become discouraged and turn away from collaborative efforts.

SNEP's research, assessments, and strategies offer confidence that a change in approach to management of natural resources and ecosystems is possible, desirable, and indeed already under way in parts of the Sierra. The next phase in improving environmental quality in many areas of the Sierra involves less focus on redrawing jurisdictional boundaries or enacting more stringent mandates and more focus on building coalitions and stronger communities.

CHAPTER 12

The Future

This study, like other major ecosystem assessments, raises our understanding to a new level. In the process, many new questions and uncertainties are revealed. Weaknesses in how existing knowledge has been used become apparent. The need to know and to use knowledge wisely is unending. The need to refine the delicate relationship between how we use and extract resources from the Sierra Nevada and how we live in the mountain range will continue. The Sierra Nevada is also a treasure for those who live around the nation and the world. Its future condition involves this wider interest.

With the end of this project a new process begins. The people must examine the ideas and test them against their own sense of validity and need for change. Several major themes are present in this report.

First, we have identified problem areas and offered some alternatives for addressing them. In some cases, problems have emerged because of unintended outcomes of use of resources and, in others, because of a change in social values. Left unresolved is the question of whether our society has the will and the capability to correct such problems. Implementation of new approaches or possible solutions is the responsibility of the public and its institutions. The beginning is to acknowledge that problems exist: willing minds and able hands can find solutions.

Second, most of the problems of the Sierra can be solved, although the timescale and degree of solution will differ depending on the problem. For example, economic conditions, wildlife habitat, forest structure, and community well-being are restorable. Reduction of damaging air pollution could occur in a matter of days, but restoration of complex forest structure might take a century and recovery of degraded river channels, even longer.

One problem that is irreversible is loss of species and loss of distinct populations of species. There is a well-known parable about wisdom: does the wise person eat the seed corn or plant the seed corn? Plant, of course, for the future. But if one is already starving, the outcome will be the same regardless of the choice. Options exist now for charting the course toward restoration. Failure to use these options increases the chance of irreversible loss and reduces the range of options over time.

Third, because our understanding of complex human communities and ecological systems is never perfect, all strategies for improvement are in some ways experiments. Learning as we go and adjusting as necessary work best when we give as much care and planning to measuring the response to new management strategies as we do to implementing them. Changes in our agencies and institutions will be necessary to adjust this balance between measuring outcomes and implementing new management. Monitoring designs that compare different approaches among agencies and private landowners could have the added value of collaborative efforts, sharing of resources and expertise, and more efficient testing of alternatives. The blessings of abundant resources may have allowed us to temporarily avoid the questions of sustainability and to establish highly independent resource agencies. The future may not allow the luxury of either.

Appendixes

APPENDIX 1

Contents of Volumes II and III

APPENDIX 2

SNEP Science Team, Contributors, and Staff

STEERING COMMITTEE

Chair: Jim Space, Director, U.S. Forest Service, Pacific Southwest Research Station, Albany, CA

Former Chair: Barbara C. Weber, U.S. Forest Service, Forest Service Research, Washington, DC

George Bartholomew, University of California, Los Angeles, CA

Dennis Breedlove, California Academy of Sciences, San Francisco, CA

Bruce M. Kilgore, Pacific West Field Area, National Park Service, San Francisco, CA

Jeffrey Romm, University of California, Berkeley, CA

Jerry A. Sesco, U.S. Forest Service, Forest Service Research, Washington, DC

Former Member: Don C. Erman, University of California, Davis, CA

SCIENCE TEAM

Don C. Erman, Team Leader, University of California, Davis, CA

Michael Barbour, University of California, Davis, CA

Norman Christensen, Duke University, Durham, NC

Frank W. Davis, University of California, Santa Barbara, CA

Harrison Dunning, University of California, Davis, CA

Deborah L. Elliott-Fisk, University of California, Oakland, CA (former team leader)

Jerry F. Franklin, University of Washington, Seattle, WA

David Graber, National Biological Service, Three Rivers, CA

K. Norman Johnson, Oregon State University, Corvallis, OR

John W. Menke, University of California, Davis, CA

Constance I. Millar, U.S. Forest Service, Pacific Southwest Research Station, Albany, CA

Janet H. Momsen, University of California, Davis, CA

Peter B. Moyle, University of California, Davis, CA

David J. Parsons, U.S. Forest Service, Aldo Leopold Wilderness Research Institute, Missoula, MT

Rowan A. Rowntree, U.S. Forest Service, Northeastern Forest Experiment Station, Albany, CA

John Sessions, Oregon State University, Corvallis, OR

John C. Tappeiner, National Biological Service, Corvallis, OR

Susan L. Ustin, University of California, Davis, CA

SPECIAL CONSULTANTS

Philip S. Aune, U.S. Forest Service, Pacific Southwest Research Station, Redding, CA

Joan Brenchley-Jackson, University of California, Davis, CA

Tom Cahill, University of California, Davis, CA

Gary Darling, State of California Resources Agency, Sacramento, CA

Michael F. Diggles, U.S. Geological Survey, Menlo Park, CA

Timothy P. Duane, University of California, Berkeley, CA

Robert Ewing, Weyerhaeuser Corporation, Tacoma, WA

Gregory Greenwood, California Department of Forestry and Fire Protection, Sacramento, CA

Richard Kattelmann, University of California, Santa Barbara, Mammoth Lakes, CA

Jon Kennedy, U.S. Forest Service, Sacramento, CA

Jonathan Kusel, Forest Community Research and University of California, Westwood, CA

Douglas Leisz, Placerville, CA

Dennis Machida, California Tahoe Conservancy, South Lake Tahoe, CA

Kevin S. McKelvey, U.S. Forest Service, Pacific Southwest Research Station, Arcata, CA

Larry Ruth, University of California, Berkeley, CA

James R. Shevock, U.S. Forest Service, Regional Office, San Francisco, CA

Carl N. Skinner, U.S. Forest Service, Pacific Southwest Research Station, Redding, CA

William Stewart, Pacific Institute, Oakland, CA

C. Phillip Weatherspoon, U.S. Forest Service, Pacific Southwest Research Station, Redding, CA

SNEP ASSOCIATES AND ADDITIONAL CONTRIBUTORS

M. Kat Anderson, University of California, Los Angeles, CA

Roger P. Ashley, U.S. Geological Survey, Menlo Park, CA

John A. Aubert, University of California, Davis, CA

Berni Bahro, U.S. Forest Service, Eldorado National Forest, Placerville, CA

Mark Baker, University of California, Berkeley, CA

Steve Beckwitt, Sierra Biodiversity Institute, Nevada City, CA

David Beesley, Sierra College, Rocklin, CA

Peter Beesley, University of California, Davis, CA

Neil H. Berg, U.S. Forest Service, Pacific Southwest Research Station, Albany, CA

Kelly K. Busse, U.S. Forest Service, Redwood Sciences Laboratory, Arcata, CA

Dave Campbell, University of California, Davis, CA

Susan Carpenter, Carpenter and Associates, Riverside, CA

John J. Carroll, University of California, Davis, CA

Chi-ru Chang, Duke University, Durham, NC

Larry Costick, University of California, Davis, CA

Paul Cousar, University of California, Davis, CA

Dennis P. Cox, U.S. Geological Survey, Menlo Park, CA

Catherine Davis, University of California, Davis, CA

Larry Davis, University of California, Berkeley, CA

Maureen L. Davis, U.S. Forest Service, Pacific Southwest Research Station, Albany, CA

Sam C. Doak, Doak and Associates, Portland, OR

Michael Embury, University of California, Santa Barbara, Mammoth Lakes, CA

Nancy A. Erman, University of California, Davis, CA

George T. Ferrell, U.S. Forest Service, Pacific Southwest Research Station, Redding, CA

Frank W. Fisher, California Department of Fish and Game, Red Bluff, CA

Jo Ann Fites-Kaufmann, U.S. Forest Service, El Dorado National Forest, Placerville, CA

Louise Fortmann, University of California, Berkeley, CA

Barry Garrison, California Department of Fish and Game, Sacramento, CA

Eric R. Gerstung, California Department of Fish and Game, Sacramento, CA

Charles R. Goldman, University of California, Davis, CA

Robert Harris, U.S. Forest Service, Lake Tahoe Basin Management Unit, South Lake Tahoe, CA

Robert Hawkins, U.S. Forest Service, Inyo National Forest, Bishop, CA

John A. Helms, University of California, Berkeley, CA

C. Thomas Hillman, U.S. Bureau of Mines, Spokane, WA

Sandra Hoffman, University of California, Berkeley, CA

Susan J. Husari, U.S. Forest Service, Regional Office, San Francisco, CA

James Jenkinson, U.S. Forest Service, Pacific Southwest Research Station, Albany, CA

Mark R. Jennings, Davis, CA

Dale Johnson, U.S. Forest Service, Inyo National Forest, Bishop, CA

Russell Jones, University of California, Davis, CA

Lynn S. Kimsey, University of California, Davis, CA

William C. Kinney, Davis, CA

Julia Klein, University of California, Berkeley, CA

Sue Kloss, University of California, Berkeley, CA

Roland A. Knapp, University of California, Santa Barbara, Mammoth Lakes, CA

G. Mathias Kondolf, University of California, Berkeley, CA

Robert J. Laacke, U.S. Forest Service, Pacific Southwest Research Station, Redding, CA

Ray Lacy, California Tahoe Conservancy, South Lake Tahoe, CA

Michael Landram, U.S. Forest Service, Regional Office, San Francisco, CA

Philip G. Langley, Forest Data Corporation, Walnut Creek, CA

David J. Larson, California State University, Hayward, CA

Susan Lindstrom, Truckee, CA

Rene Lobato, University of California, Davis, CA

Jonathan London, Environmental Science, Policy, and Management, Berkeley, CA

Steve Luddington, U.S. Geological Survey, Menlo Park, CA

Kelly E. Lyons, University of California, Davis, CA

Scott N. Martens, University of California, Davis, CA

Sarah Marvin, University of California, Berkeley, CA

Joe R. McBride, University of California, Berkeley, CA

Philip M. McDonald, U.S. Forest Service, Pacific Southwest Research Station, Redding, CA

Bruce J. McGurk, U.S. Forest Service, Pacific Southwest Research Station, Albany, CA

Kurt Menning, University of California, Berkeley, CA

Carol Miller, Colorado State University, Fort Collins, CO

Paul R. Miller, U.S. Forest Service, Pacific Southwest Research Station, Riverside, CA

Robert J. Miller, U.S. Geological Survey, Menlo Park, CA

Michael J. Moratto, Applied Earthworks, Inc., Fresno, CA

Barry C. Moring, U.S. Geological Survey, Menlo Park, CA

Dana Murphy, University of California, Oakland, CA

William W. Oliver, U.S. Forest Service, Pacific Southwest Research Station, Redding, CA

Craig M. Olson, University of California, Berkeley, CA

William J. Pickthorn, Isochem Company, Palo Alto, CA

Jorge Pinzon, University of California, Davis, CA

Roger J. Poff, R. J. Poff and Associates, Nevada City, CA

Daniel J. Porter, University of California, Davis, CA

John Randall, The Nature Conservancy, Davis, CA

Paul J. Randall, California Department of Fish and Game, Sacramento, CA

Linda A. Reynolds, U.S. Forest Service, Inyo National Forest, Bishop, CA

Rebecca T. Richards, University of Montana, Missoula, MT

Ken B. Roby, U.S. Forest Service, Plumas National Forest, Quincy, CA

Deborah L. Rogers, U.S. Forest Service, Pacific Southwest Research Station, Albany, CA

Penny Rucks, U.S. Forest Service, Lake Tahoe Basin Management Unit, South Lake Tahoe, CA

William Russell, University of California, Berkeley, CA

James R. Rytuba, U.S. Geological Survey, Menlo Park, CA

David Sapsis, California Department of Forestry and Fire Protection, Sacramento, CA

Joy Schaber, University of California, Davis, CA

Mark W. Schwartz, University of California, Davis, CA

Arthur Shapiro, University of California, Davis, CA

Debra A. Sharkey, University of California, Davis, CA

James Spero, California Department of Forestry and Fire Protection, Sacramento, CA

Thomas A. Spies, U.S. Forest Service, Pacific Northwest Research Station, Corvallis, OR

Richard B. Standiford, University of California, Berkeley, CA

Paul F. Starrs, University of Nevada, Reno, NV

Scott Stephens, University of California, Berkeley, CA

Nate Stephenson, National Biological Service, Three Rivers, CA

Scott Stine, California State University, Hayward, CA

David M. Stoms, University of California, Santa Barbara, CA

Victoria E. Sturtevant, Southern Oregon State College, Ashland, OR

Dale A. Thornburgh, California State University, Humboldt, Arcata, CA

Dean Urban, Duke University, Durham, NC

Wesley W. Wallender, University of California, Davis, CA

Robert D. Westfall, U.S. Forest Service, Pacific Southwest Research Station, Albany, CA

Leah Wills, Plumas Corporation, Quincy, CA

Wallace B. Woolfenden, U.S. Forest Service, Inyo National Forest, Lee Vining, CA

Chester T. Wrucke, U.S. Geological Survey, Menlo Park, CA

Qing Fu Xiao, University of California, Davis, CA

Ronald M. Yoshiyama, University of California, Davis, CA

David S. Ziegler, Carson City, NV

Robert Zomer, University of California, Davis, CA

SNEP GIS CENTER

Steve Beckwitt
Mary B. Cunha
Lian Duan
John T. Gabriel
Karen Gabriel

Kay Gibbs
Steve Greco
Bob Haxo
Brian Hill
Russell Jones

SNEP STAFF

Karen Beardsley
Deanne DiPietro
Erin Fleming
Jennifer Lucas

Lisa Morse
Michael Oliver
Cindy Seaman
Minghua Zhang

CENTERS FOR WATER AND WILDLAND RESOURCES STAFF

Ginny Cyphers
Sue Enos
Gina Farrell
Elizabeth Frey

Brenda Nakamoto
Michelle Watanabe
Jeff Woled

U.S. FOREST SERVICE, REGION 5, REMOTE SENSING LAB

Kevin Casey
Gabe Garcia
Kama Kennedy
Lisa Levien

Deborah Nicolls
Jeff Milliken
Ralph Warbington

CALIFORNIA DEPARTMENT OF FORESTRY AND FIRE PROTECTION STAFF

Clay Brandow
Patti Cox
Cindy Gangler
Greg Greenwood
Russ Henly
Paul Knott
Robin Marose

Andy Richardson
Mark Rosenberg
Jim Spero
Eric Spry
Marge Steele
Sarah Turan

UNIVERSITY OF CALIFORNIA NATURAL RESERVE SYSTEM STAFF

Madeline Drake
Elaine Miller

Eric Rainbolt
Susan Rumsey

STUDENT ASSISTANTS

Anyarat Chin
Roland Hui
Chinh Lam

Sarah Yarnell
Elaine Yau

SNEP REPORT PRODUCTION

Sarah Boone
Desne Border
Zipporah W. Collins
Kelly Crabtree
Donna Eades
Amy Einsohn
Barbara Fuller
Ken Grassell
Joei Heart
Beverly McGuire

Joan Olson
Rebecca Pepper
Tina Reynolds
Virginia Rich
Robert Robinson
B. Shimon Schwarzschild
Chris Sparks
Karen Stough
Lisa Wolters

PACIFIC SOUTHWEST RESEARCH STATION STAFF

Cynthia Jacobs

KEY CONTACTS

Randy Abbott
Jeanne Adams
Michael Albrecht
Laurel Ames
Arthur Baggett
Robert Barnes
Jane Baxter
Dan Beard
Jerry Belson
Rebecca Bendick
Rex Bloomfield
Linda Blum
Louis Blumberg
Barbara Boyle
James Brannum
Ray Butler
Bernard Carlson
Carolyn Clark
Katherine Clement
Rose Comstock

James Craine
William Dart
Martha Davis
Noel Day
Michael De Lasaux
James Eaton
Sally Fairfax
Douglas Ferrier
Robert Flewelling
Charles Goldman
Terry Gorton
Robert Gracey
Jack Hanson
Stan Hanson
Robert Harris
Lance Hastings
Robert Heald
Marc Hite
John Hoffman
Frannie Hoover

Tom Infusino
Hazel Jackson
Patricia Kelly
Don Klusman
David Knowles
Bill Krauss
Lowell Landowski
Andrea Lawrence
Roy Leidy
Donna Lindquist
Richard Luchesi
Kathryn Lynch
Tom Martens
Lillian McRay
Michael McRay
Robert Meacher
Joel Medlin
Sally Miller
John Mills
Ron Monk
Mario Moratorio
Betty J. Morris
Rochelle Nason
John Norby
Ray Nutting
Robert C. Nuzum

Johanne Owens
Mark Palmer
Joan Reiss
John E. Reuter
Bob Roberts
Carl Rountree
John Schramel
Mary Schroeder
Walt Schultz
Jeff Shellito
Christine Sproul
Alberta Steele
Dwight Steele
Ron Stockman
Daniel J. Tomascheski
G. B. Tucker
Robert H. Twiss
Van U'rens
Michael Vasey
Roland Westergard
Jim Wilcox
John Williams
Richard Wilson
J. Steven Worthley
Sami Yassa

Digital Geographic Data for the Sierra Nevada Region

SNEP compiled a large amount of existing geographic data and information pertaining to the Sierra Nevada ecosystem. This material ranged from digital maps and images that spanned the entire region to analog maps and data tables for local areas, and also included original data, maps, and model outputs generated by SNEP scientists and consultants. A technical support staff was hired to integrate this information into a coherent, well-documented database and to assist the Science Team with data compilation, data quality assessment, analysis, and product generation. The staff was located in Sacramento, where it deployed a moderate-sized local network of workstation computers linked to the Internet. This appendix provides a tabular summary of the digital data compiled by SNEP and an overview of data cataloguing and archiving activities.

DATABASE DESCRIPTION

The two general objectives of SNEP's database activities were the following:

1. Compile and provide existing data and information to support assessment and modeling activities of the SNEP Science Team and consultants.

2. Contribute to the development of a Sierra Nevada Information System accessible at local, state, and federal levels.

In meeting the first objective, the SNEP GIS staff acquired and integrated a large amount of geographic data on cultural, ecological, and physical environmental themes (table A3.1). To deal with the various restrictions on data distribution, SNEP classified every data set obtained or produced during the study into one of six access categories:

1. Unrestricted (public)

2. Unrestricted, but permission should be obtained from source agency

3. Accessible to Science Team and consultants, no special permission required

4. Accessible to Science Team and consultants only after signing of a waiver agreeing not to redistribute the data to anyone else

5. SNEP GIS staff only

6. File owner only

Only the first three categories of data are included in the SNEP archive. Products developed by SNEP are generally treated as unrestricted. Interim and draft versions were not generally distributed and are not part of the archival database.

A large fraction of the data was provided by the U.S. Forest Service from its Forestland and Resource Database (FRDB), in particular, the GIS ARC/INFO database developed at Pacific Meridian Resources in Emeryville, California. This database includes information on administrative boundaries, land planning units, biological resources, and physical conditions. The data are integrated vertically for each national forest. That is, maps of many different themes for each national forest have been co-registered in the GIS so that they can be overlaid and jointly analyzed. SNEP horizontally integrated selected themes across all of the national forests in order to conduct regionwide analyses. However, because the data for individual forests undergo frequent revision, the FRDB data were catalogued and archived by individual national forest (table A3.1).

Another important data source was the State of California's Teale Data Center, which maintains statewide coverages of political boundaries, land ownership, roads, and urban areas. These data must be purchased from Teale Data Center and have been catalogued but not included in the SNEP database. Similarly, recent satellite imagery used by SNEP to map vegetation and for regional hydrologic modeling is copyrighted and must be obtained from private vendors.

Several important regional maps and databases that were produced by SNEP are available in the data archive. These include hydroelectric plants, roadless regions derived from the Forest Service and Teale Data Center, road coverages, SNEP study region and subregion boundaries, late successional forests, plant communities and dominant species, and significant areas. These data sets are documented extensively in SNEP reports as well as through associated data dictionaries.

Table A3.1 lists only geospatial data in the SNEP archive and does not include other kinds of digital information produced by SNEP such as reports, graphics, and modeling software. Eventually it is our intent to incorporate much of this information into the SNEP archive.

PLANS FOR DATA DISTRIBUTION VIA THE INTERNET

To assist in the development of an accessible Sierra Nevada Information System, SNEP staff worked with staff in the Resource Agency's California Environmental Resource Evaluation System (CERES/University of California, Santa Barbara [UCSB]) program and the Alexandria Digital Library (ADL) project to define protocols for data documentation, cataloguing, and on-line storage. CERES is an information system developed by the California Resources Agency to facilitate access to a variety of electronic environmental data pertaining to California. Project Alexandria is a research project at UCSB whose primary goal is to design, implement, and deploy a digital library for spatially indexed information.

An important component of SNEP's data cataloguing effort has been preparation of metadata for project GIS coverages. Metadata are "data about data" that describe the content, quality, condition, and other characteristics of data. Spatial data pose special problems of documentation that have been addressed by the Federal Geographic Data Committee (FGDC), CERES, Alexandria, and many other organizations. These groups have been developing standard, structured descriptors of spatial data so that the data can be located and accessed across a network using computerized database management tools. SNEP has employed CERES and FGDC metadata standards to catalogue the database in order to make the data accessible through Project Alexandria's digital spatial library facility at UCSB. The ADL will provide a framework for putting these collections on-line, providing search and access to these collections to broad classes of users, and allowing both collections and users to be distributed throughout the Internet.

During 1995 the Alexandria Project completed the design and implementation of a successful "rapid prototype" system (RPS). The RPS is a "stand-alone" digital library that includes interface, catalogue, storage, and ingest components and is running in the Map and Imagery Library at UCSB. The Alexandria Project is now extending the RPS to a system supporting multiple users over the Internet. In line with its basic strategy, the second version of ADL will be connected to the World Wide Web.

SNEP GIS METADATA SUMMARY

SNEP metadata were catalogued by two methods for inclusion in the Alexandria Digital Library. The first method catalogued data sets originating with the U.S. Forest Service and the National Park Service. These data sets were catalogued using the CERES metadata schema. Details of that cataloguing effort can be found in a metadata summary by Quinn Hart of CERES. The second method catalogued data sets created by SNEP and is described by this summary. Priority was given to those data sets that are unique and not available from other sources. This metadata cataloguing work was the combined effort of SNEP, CERES, and Alexandria personnel.

Files

Three unique data sets were catalogued, the coverages and databases compiled for the SNEP late successional old-growth forest and significant natural areas projects and the tree seed zones of California. There were fifty-seven metadata entries, fifty-two ARC/INFO coverages, three data dictionaries, and two ARC/INFO databases. All of the coverages are geographically associated with national parks or national forests except the tree seed zones, which extend over the entire SNEP study area.

Metadata Entry Form and Elements

In cooperation with the Alexandria project, SNEP selected a subset of the FGDC metadata elements, based on applicability to the SNEP data sets and compliance with Alexandria's metadata standards.

The metadata entry form was created in Microsoft Access by Alexandria personnel. This was the Alexandria project's first attempt to distribute a metadata entry form. The form consists of a subset of FGDC elements chosen by SNEP with additional USMARC elements required by Alexandria.

Geographic Coordinates, Transfer Size, and Format

The geographic coordinates and transfer size for each layer were derived by use of an ARC/INFO Arc Macro Language (AML). The AML projects the individual SNEP coverages to latitude and longitude coordinates and provides the size of each file in ARC/INFO export format.

Resource Description

The name of the file as it is known to SNEP GIS staff is used.

Beginning Date and Ending Date

The data sets catalogued did not require that a range of dates and times be described. For both beginning and ending dates, the year the data were captured is used for the late successional old-growth forest and significant natural areas projects, and the date of the source map is used for the tree seed zones.

Local Call Number

A local call number is a metadata element mainly applicable to bibliographic information, but it is used here to refer to the file address (often referred to as the file "path") on the computer used by SNEP GIS. This element refers to a particular metadata system, in this case, the American National Standard for Bibliographic Information Interchange.

Originator

The Sierra Nevada Ecosystem Project is listed as the originator on all coverages except the tree seed zones. For the tree seed zones the source from the original map is used.

Publication Information

The date of publication of the SNEP data is 1996, and the publisher is Centers for Water and Wildland Resources, University of California, Davis, California 95616.

Contact Information

The University of California, Santa Barbara, Biogeography Laboratory is listed for all of the contact information. Contact information is listed four times under the headings Metadata Contact Information, Holdings, Distribution Information, and Processing Steps.

Maintenance and Update Frequency

Maintenance and update frequency are entered as unknown at this time.

Map Projection Name and Direct Spatial Reference Method

All of the SNEP data are in Albers Conical Equal Area, and all of the data sets catalogued are in vector format.

Metadata Elements Not Utilized

There are several metadata elements that are not utilized. This was due to the type of data catalogued and the information available. SNEP catalogued only data sets in vector format so those metadata elements strictly for raster data were not needed. Unutilized metadata elements include: row count, column count, indirect spatial reference method, horizontal positional accuracy value, latitude resolution, longitude resolution, geographic coordinate units, and supplemental information.

Narrative Fields

Each data set catalogued has entries for the fields Attribute Accuracy Report, Abstract, Entity, and Attribute Overview. However, the Alexandria metadata form allowed only a very limited number of characters (255) per field, so entries are extremely concise. Reference is given to the data dictionary for more detailed information.

Theme Keywords

Alexandria uses the Library of Congress subject headings. Theme keywords used for the late successional/old-growth forest data set are "late successional forests" and "old-growth forests." For place keywords, "Sierra Nevada," "national forest," and the county and state names are used. For the Significant Natural Areas data set, theme keywords used include "ecological significant areas," "geological significant areas," and "cultural significant areas." Place keywords for Significant Natural Areas include "Sierra Nevada," "national forest," and state names.

Source Citation

All SNEP data sets catalogued are based on national forest visitor maps, U.S. Geological Survey (USGS) 7.5 minute quadrangles, orthophotoquads, and USGS national park maps. Source citation information was gathered from these hard-copy sources. For the tree seed zones coverage, source citation information from the hard-copy tree seed zones map was used.

Browse Graphic Files (BGF)

In a CERES/SNEP cooperative effort a combined AML and script was written to create the browse graphic files (BGF). This program will create a BGF in graphics interchange format (GIF), the size required by Alexandria for all coverages in a specified directory. SNEP created BGFs for all of the coverages catalogued.

GIS directory.

Type	Theme	USA	California	Nevada	Sierra Nevada	BLM	State Parks	Lassen Volcanic NP	SEKI NP	Yosemite NP	Modoc NF	Lassen NF	Plumas NF	Tahoe NF	Lake Tahoe Basin	Eldorado NF	Stanislaus NF	Sierra NF	Sequoia NF	Toiyabe NF	Inyo NF	Source	Scale	Data Type
Cultural	Administrative boundary, NF proclaimed										×	×	×	×	×	×	×	×	×	×	×	USFS	1:24K	V
Cultural	Administrative boundary, national forest										×	×	×	×	×	×	×	×	×	×	×	USFS	1:24K	V
Cultural	Administrative boundary/ownership		×	×																		ArcUSA	1:2M	V
Cultural	Administrative boundary/ownership				×																	Teale	1:100K	V
Cultural	Administrative/special-use sites										×	×	×	×		×	×	×	×		×	USFS	1:24K	V
Cultural	Calowl Plan A										×	×	×	×		×	×	×	×			USFS,	1:24K	V
Cultural	Census Geography 1990–92				×																	USBOC, Teale	1:100K	V
Cultural	Cities		×	×																		ArcUSA	1:2M	V
Cultural	Cities				×																	Teale	1:100K	V
Cultural	County boundary		×	×																		ArcUSA	1:2M	V
Cultural	County boundary				×																	Teale	1:100K	V
Cultural	County boundary														×							TEGIS	1:24K	V
Cultural	County boundary										×	×	×	×	×	×	×	×	×		×	USFS	1:24K	V
Cultural	Developed recreation sites										×	×	×	×	×	×	×	×	×		×	USFS	1:24K	V
Cultural	Farmland 88		×																			DOC-FMMP	1:100K	V
Cultural	Farmland 92				×																	DOC-FMMP	1:100K	V
Cultural	Geographic names, places		×	×																		ArcUSA	1:2M	P
Cultural	Giant sequoia management																		×			USFS	1:24K	V
Cultural	Hydroelectric power plants				×																	SNEP	1:600K	P
Cultural	L&RMP land suitability class										×	×	×	×	×	×	×	×	×		×	USFS	1:24K	P
Cultural	LMP management area											×		×	×						×	USFS	1:24K	P
Cultural	LULC 1970				×																	USGS, UCSB	1:24K	V
Cultural	Managed areas				×																	Teale, UCSB	1:100K	V
Cultural	Near natural/backcountry										×	×	×	×		×	×	×	×		×	USFS	1:24K	V
Cultural	Parcel, LTB, DG														×							TEGIS	1:24K	V
Cultural	Parcel, LTB, El Dorado County														×							TEGIS	1:24K	V
Cultural	Parcel, LTB, PL														×							TEGIS	1:24K	V
Cultural	Parcel, LTB, WA														×							TEGIS	1:24K	V
Cultural	PLSS, LTB														×							USGS, TEGIS	1:24K	V

Acronyms

BLM	Bureau of Land Management	LMP	Land Management Planning
CDF&FP	California Department of Forestry and Fire Protection	LTB	Lake Tahoe Basin
DFG	California Department of Fish and Game	LULC	Land Use Land Cover
DG	Douglas County	LWQCB	Lahontan Water Quality Control Board
DMA	Defense Mapping Agency	m	Meter
DOC	Department of Conservation	M	Million
ESRI	Environmental Systems Research Institute	NF	National Forest
FIA	Forest Inventory Analysis	NP	National Park
FMMP	Farmland Mapping and Monitoring Program	NWS	National Weather Service
GAP	Gap Analysis Project	P	Point
K	Thousand	PL	Placer County
L&RMP	Land and Resource Management Planning	PLSS	Public Land Survey System
Lasnp	Lassen Volcanic National Park	R	Raster

SBI	Sierra Biodiversity Institute
SCS	Soil Conservation Service
SEKI	Sequoia and Kings Canyon National Parks
SNEP	Sierra Nevada Ecosystem Project
Teale	Stephen P. Teale Data Center
TEGIS	Tahoe Environmental Geographic Information System
UCSB	University of California, Santa Barbara
USBOC	United States Bureau of Census
USBR	United States Bureau of Reclamation
USFS	United States Forest Service
USGS	United States Geological Survey
V	Vector
WA	Washoe County

Type	Theme	USA	California	Nevada	Sierra Nevada	BLM	State Parks	Lassen Volcanic NP	SEKI NP	Yosemite NP	Modoc NF	Lassen NF	Plumas NF	Tahoe NF	Lake Tahoe Basin	Eldorado NF	Stanislaus NF	Sierra NF	Sequoia NF	Toiyabe NF	Inyo NF	Source	Scale	Data Type
Cultural	Rangeland emphasis										x			x								USFS	1:24K	V
Cultural	Ranger districts and compartment										x			x			x	x	x			USFS	1:24K	V
Cultural	Recreation emphasis (adopted ROS)															x	x	x	x			USFS	1:24K	V
Cultural	Regions, CA Department of Fish and Game		x																			DFG	1:1M	V
Cultural	Regions, Jepson		x																			UCSB		V
Cultural	Research natural areas (rnas)										x	x	x	x	x	x	x	x	x		x	USFS	1:24K	V
Cultural	Resource units, BLM				x																	BLM		V
Cultural	Roadless regions (draft)				x																	SNEP	1:24K, 1:100K	R
Cultural	Roads		x	x																		ArcUSA	1:2M	V
Cultural	Roads			x																		USBR	1:100K	V
Cultural	Roads				x																	Teale MPGIS	1:100K	V
Cultural	Roads										x	x	x	x		x	x	x	x		x	USFS	1:24K	V
Cultural	Roads, LTB														x							USGS, TEGIS	1:24K	V
Cultural	SNEP ecoregion (core)				x																	SNEP	varies	V
Cultural	SNEP study area				x																	SNEP	varies	V
Cultural	SNEP subregions				x																	SNEP, UCSB	1:24K	V
Cultural	Special area not withdrawn mediated																x		x			USFS	1:24K	V
Cultural	Special area not withdrawn plan																x		x			USFS	1:24K	V
Cultural	Special areas											x	x	x		x	x	x	x		x	USFS	1:24K	V
Cultural	Special interest areas										x	x	x	x		x	x	x	x		x	USFS	1:24K	V
Cultural	USGS 7.5 minute quadrangles				x											x						ArcUSA	1:24K	V
Cultural	USGS 7.5 minute quadrangles										x	x	x	x	x	x	x	x	x		x	USFS	1:24K	V
Cultural	Visual quality zone										x	x	x	x	x	x	x	x	x		x	USFS	1:24K	V
Cultural	Wild and scenic rivers										x	x	x	x	x	x	x	x	x		x	USFS	1:24K	V
Cultural	Wilderness, Lassen Volcanic NP							x														NPS, SNEP		V
Cultural	Wilderness, NF										x	x	x	x	x	x	x	x	x	x	x	USFS	1:24K	V
Cultural	Wilderness, Sequoia & Kings Canyon NPs								x													NPS		V
Cultural	Wilderness, Yosemite NP									x												NPS		V
Ecological	CALVEG		x																			USFS, CDF&FP	1:250K	V

continued

Acronyms

BLM	Bureau of Land Management	LMP	Land Management Planning
CDF&FP	California Department of Forestry and Fire Protection	LTB	Lake Tahoe Basin
DFG	California Department of Fish and Game	LULC	Land Use Land Cover
DG	Douglas County	LWQCB	Lahontan Water Cuality Ccntrol Board
DMA	Defense Mapping Agency	m	Meter
DOC	Department of Conservation	M	Million
ESRI	Environmental Systems Research Institute	NF	National Forest
FIA	Forest Inventory Analysis	NP	National Park
FMMP	Farmland Mapping and Monitoring Program	NWS	National Weather Service
GAP	Gap Analysis Project	P	Point
K	Thousand	PL	Placer County
L&RMP	Land and Resource Management Planning	PLSS	Public Land Survey System
Lasnp	Lassen Volcanic National Park	R	Raster

SBI	Sierra Biodiversity Institute
SCS	Soil Conservation Service
SEKI	Sequoia and Kings Canyon National Parks
SNEP	Sierra Nevada Ecosystem Project
Teale	Stephen P. Teale Data Center
TEGIS	Tahoe Environmental Geographic Information System
UCSB	University of California, Santa Barbara
USBOC	United States Bureau of Census
USBR	United States Bureau of Reclamation
USFS	United States Forest Service
USGS	United States Geological Survey
V	Vector
WA	Washoe County

TABLE A3.1 (continued)

Type	Theme	USA	California	Nevada	Sierra Nevada	BLM	State Parks	Lassen Volcanic NP	SEKI NP	Yosemite NP	Modoc NF	Lassen NF	Plumas NF	Tahoe NF	Lake Tahoe Basin	Eldorado NF	Stanislaus NF	Sierra NF	Sequoia NF	Toiyabe NF	Inyo NF	Source	Scale	Data Type
Ecological	Deer emphasis areas													×		×		×	×		×	USFS	1:24K	V
Ecological	Ecological unit inventory														×	×						USFS	1:24K	V
Ecological	Emergency Activity Reporting System (EARS: 1989–93)				×																	CDF&FP	NA	DB
Ecological	FIA grid inventory plots										×				×	×					×	USFS	1:24K	V
Ecological	Fire history, USFS										×	×	×		×	×	×	×	×		×	USFS	variable	V
Ecological	Fire management analysis zones (FMAZ)																	×				CDF&FP	1:100K	R/V
Ecological	Fire, 1921–93, Sequoia & Kings Canyon NPs								×													NPS	1:24K	R
Ecological	Fire, 1931–93, Yosemite NP									×												NPS	1:126	V
Ecological	Fuel breaks												×			×				×		USFS, SNEP	1:24K	V
Ecological	Furbearer habitat				×						×	×										USFS	1:24K	V
Ecological	Giant sequoia grove point locations				×												×	×				various	varies	P
Ecological	Giant sequoia, Mountain Home																					CDF&FP	1:24K	V
Ecological	Giant sequoia, national park groves								×										×			SEKI	1:24K	V
Ecological	Giant sequoia, north of Kings River									×							×	×				various	1:24K	V
Ecological	Giant sequoia, Sequoia NF																		×			Sequoia NF	1:24K	V
Ecological	Giant sequoia, SNEP compilation				×																	various, SNEP	variable	V
Ecological	Hardwood		×																			CDF&FP	1:24K	V
Ecological	Historic and current chinook spawning area				×																	SNEP	1:114	V
Ecological	Historic fishless area				×																	SNEP	1:500K	V
Ecological	Historical fire report database (EARS HIST: 1981–88)				×																	CDF&FP	NA	DB
Ecological	Integrated inventory plots										×	×	×		×	×	×					USFS	1:24K	P
Ecological	Land capability, Bailey														×	×						SCS, Bailey, TEGIS	1:24K	V
Ecological	Low site timberland										×	×	×		×	×	×		×			USFS	1:24K	V
Ecological	LSOG plot locations										×	×	×	×	×	×						UCSB, SNEP	1:24K	P
Ecological	Meadow management zone												×	×		×	×		×			USFS	1:24K	V
Ecological	Modified yield timber type											×	×	×		×	×		×		×	USFS	1:24K	V

Acronyms

BLM	Bureau of Land Management	LMP	Land Management Planning
CDF&FP	California Department of Forestry and Fire Protection	LTB	Lake Tahoe Basin
DFG	California Department of Fish and Game	LULC	Land Use Land Cover
DG	Douglas County	LWQCB	Lahontan Water Quality Control Board
DMA	Defense Mapping Agency	m	Meter
DOC	Department of Conservation	M	Million
ESRI	Environmental Systems Research Institute	NF	National Forest
FIA	Forest Inventory Analysis	NP	National Park
FMMP	Farmland Mapping and Monitoring Program	NWS	National Weather Service
GAP	Gap Analysis Project	P	Point
K	Thousand	PL	Placer County
L&RMP	Land and Resource Management Planning	PLSS	Public Land Survey System
Lasnp	Lassen Volcanic National Park	R	Raster
SBI	Sierra Biodiversity Institute		
SCS	Soil Conservation Service		
SEKI	Sequoia and Kings Canyon National Parks		
SNEP	Sierra Nevada Ecosystem Project		
Teale	Stephen P. Teale Data Center		
TEGIS	Tahoe Environmental Geographic Information System		
UCSB	University of California, Santa Barbara		
USBOC	United States Bureau of Census		
USBR	United States Bureau of Reclamation		
USFS	United States Forest Service		
USGS	United States Geological Survey		
V	Vector		
WA	Washoe County		

TABLE A3.1 (continued)

Type	Theme	USA	California	Nevada	Sierra Nevada	BLM	State Parks	Lassen Volcanic NP	SEKI NP	Yosemite NP	Modoc NF	Lassen NF	Plumas NF	Tahoe NF	Lake Tahoe Basin	Eldorado NF	Stanislaus NF	Sierra NF	Sequoia NF	Toiyabe NF	Inyo NF	Source	Scale	Data Type
Ecological	Monitoring sites														x							LWQCB, USFS, USGS, SCS	1:24K	P
Ecological	National Interagency Fire Management Integrated Database				x																	USFS	NA	DB
Ecological	Old growth																			x		USFS	1:24K	V
Ecological	Old growth/stand structure inventory plots																		x			USFS	1:24K	P
Ecological	Plantation inventory plots																	x	x		x	USFS	1:24K	V
Ecological	Rainfall										x						x				x	USGS	1:100K	V
Ecological	Range allotments, NF (draft)		x									x	x	x		x	x	x	x		x	UCSB	varies	V
Ecological	Riparian conditions				x																	SNEP	NA	DB
Ecological	SBI old growth				x																	SBI		V/R
Ecological	SNEP Aquatic Diversity Management Areas				x																	Calwater, SNEP	varies	V
Ecological	SNEP Index of Biological Integrity watersheds				x																	Calwater, SNEP		V
Ecological	SNEP late successional				x		x	x	x	x	x	x		x	x	x	x	x	x	x	x	SNEP	varies	V
Ecological	SNEP significant areas—cultural				x	x			x	x		x	x	x	x	x	x	x	x	x	x	SNEP	1:1267	V
Ecological	SNEP significant areas—ecological				x	x			x	x		x	x	x	x	x	x	x	x	x	x	SNEP	1:1267	V
Ecological	SNEP significant areas—geological				x				x	x		x	x	x	x	x	x	x	x	x	x	SNEP	1:12672	V
Ecological	Soils								x													NPS, SCS	20m	R
Ecological	Soils, LTB														x							TEGIS	1:24K	V
Ecological	Soils, order 2 and 3 composite												x		x	x						USFS	1:24K	V
Ecological	Soils, order 3														x	x						USFS	1:24K	V
Ecological	Soils, STATSGO		x																x			SCS	1:250K	V
Ecological	Spotted owl habitat—SOHAS										x	x	x	x	x	x	x	x	x			USFS	1:24K	V
Ecological	Spotted owl habitat PACS and BASE																	x	x	x		USFS	1:24K	V
Ecological	Stream channel conditions																		x			Sequoia NF		V
Ecological	Streamside/riparian management: zone										x	x		x	x	x	x	x	x		x	USFS	1:24K	V
Ecological	Timber																			x		USFS	1:24K	V
Ecological	Timber type														x					x		USFS, TEGIS	1:24K	V

Acronyms

BLM	Bureau of Land Management
CDF&FP	California Department of Forestry and Fire Protection
DFG	California Department of Fish and Game
DG	Douglas County
DMA	Defense Mapping Agency
DOC	Department of Conservation
ESRI	Environmental Systems Research Institute
FIA	Forest Inventory Analysis
FMMP	Farmland Mapping and Monitoring Program
GAP	Gap Analysis Project
K	Thousand
L&RMP	Land and Resource Management Planning
Lasnp	Lassen Volcanic National Park
LMP	Land Management Planning
LTB	Lake Tahoe Basin
LULC	Land Use Land Cover
LWQCB	Lahontan Water Quality Control Board
m	Meter
M	Million
NF	National Forest
NP	National Park
NWS	National Weather Service
P	Point
PL	Placer County
PLSS	Public Land Survey System
R	Raster
SBI	Sierra Biodiversity Institute
SCS	Soil Conservation Service
SEKI	Sequoia and Kings Canyon National Parks
SNEP	Sierra Nevada Ecosystem Project
Teale	Stephen P. Teale Data Center
TEGIS	Tahoe Environmental Geographic Information System
UCSB	University of California, Santa Barbara
USBOC	United States Bureau of Census
USBR	United States Bureau of Reclamation
USFS	United States Forest Service
USGS	United States Geological Survey
V	Vector
WA	Washoe County

TABLE A3.1 (continued)

Type	Theme	USA	California	Nevada	Sierra Nevada	BLM	State Parks	Lassen Volcanic NP	SEKI NP	Yosemite NP	Modoc NF	Lassen NF	Plumas NF	Tahoe NF	Lake Tahoe Basin	Eldorado NF	Stanislaus NF	Sierra NF	Sequoia NF	Toiyabe NF	Inyo NF	Source	Scale	Data Type
Ecological	Tree seed zones				x																	USFS, SNEP	1:1M	V
Ecological	Unsuitable forestland										x	x	x	x		x	x	x	x	x	x	USFS	1:24K	V
Ecological	Vegetation, national parks							x	x	x												NPS	1:24K	V
Ecological	Vegetation, Camp Creek															x						USFS	1:100K	V
Ecological	Vegetation, GAP		x		x																	UCSB	1:1M	V
Ecological	Vegetation, Kuchler		x																			ESRI, BLM	1:845K	V
Ecological	Vegetation, Leiberg, 1902												x	x								SNEP	1:845K	V
Ecological	Vegetation, NF (eveg)										x	x	x	x		x	x	x	x	x	x	USFS	1:24K	V
Ecological	Vegetation, plot data, national park								x												x	NPS	1:24K	P
Ecological	Vegetation, riparian														x							USFS, TEGIS	1:24K	V
Ecological	Vegetation, State Board of Forestry, 1888													x		x						SNEP	NA	V
Physical	Basin boundary, Lake Tahoe													x	x							TEGIS	1:24K	V
Physical	Dams and diversions, nonjurisdictional				x																	Teale	NA	P
Physical	Dams, jurisdictional				x																	DWR, DFG	1:250K	P
Physical	Digital elevation model				x																	DMA, ESRI, SBI	100m	R
Physical	Digital elevation model							x	x	x	x	x	x	x		x	x	x	x	x	x	USGS, USFS	30m	R
Physical	Geology														x	x						various, TEGIS	variable	V
Physical	Geology, California		x																			DMG, 1977	1:750K	V
Physical	Hydrobasin, Calwater		x																			CDF&FP	1:24K	V
Physical	Lake Tahoe shoreline														x							TEGIS	1:24K	V
Physical	Lakes	x																				ArcUSA	1:2M	V
Physical	Lakes										x	x	x	x		x	x	x	x	x	x	USFS	1:24K	V
Physical	Lakes		x																			USGS	1:100K	V
Physical	Lakes, other than Lake Tahoe														x							USGS, CDF&FP, TEGIS	1:24K	V

Acronyms

BLM	Bureau of Land Management
CDF&FP	California Department of Forestry and Fire Protection
DFG	California Department of Fish and Game
DG	Douglas County
DMA	Defense Mapping Agency
DOC	Department of Conservation
ESRI	Environmental Systems Research Institute
FIA	Forest Inventory Analysis
FMMP	Farmland Mapping and Monitoring Program
GAP	Gap Analysis Project
K	Thousand
L&RMP	Land and Resource Management Planning
Lasnp	Lassen Volcanic National Park
LMP	Land Management Planning
LTB	Lake Tahoe Basin
LULC	Land Use Land Cover
LWQCB	Lahontan Water Quality Control Board
m	Meter
M	Million
NF	National Forest
NP	National Park
NWS	National Weather Service
P	Point
PL	Placer County
PLSS	Public Land Survey System
R	Raster
SBI	Sierra Biodiversity Institute
SCS	Soil Conservation Service
SEKI	Sequoia and Kings Canyon National Parks
SNEP	Sierra Nevada Ecosystem Project
Teale	Stephen P. Teale Data Center
TEGIS	Tahoe Environmental Geographic Information System
UCSB	University of California, Santa Barbara
USBOC	United States Bureau of Census
USBR	United States Bureau of Reclamation
USFS	United States Forest Service
USGS	United States Geological Survey
V	Vector
WA	Washoe County

TABLE A3.1 (continued)

Type	Theme	USA	California	Nevada	Sierra Nevada	BLM	State Parks	Lassen Volcanic NP	SEKI NP	Yosemite NP	Modoc NF	Lassen NF	Plumas NF	Tahoe NF	Lake Tahoe Basin	Eldorado NF	Stanislaus NF	Sierra NF	Sequoia NF	Toiyabe NF	Inyo NF	Source	Scale	Data Type
Physical	Rivers				×																	ArcUSA	1:2M	V
Physical	Rivers				×																	Teale	1:100K	V
Physical	Slope, LTB														×							USGS, TEGIS	1:24K	R
Physical	Streams										×	×	×	×	×	×	×	×	×			USFS	1:24K	V
Physical	Streams, LTB													×	×		×				×	USGS, TEGIS	1:24K	V
Physical	Watersheds, LTB														×							USGS, TEGIS	1:24K	V
Physical	Weather zones				×																	NWS, CDF&FP	1:100K	V

Acronyms

BLM	Bureau of Land Management
CDF&FP	California Department of Forestry and Fire Protection
DFG	California Department of Fish and Game
DG	Douglas County
DMA	Defense Mapping Agency
DOC	Department of Conservation
ESRI	Environmental Systems Research Institute
FIA	Forest Inventory Analysis
FMMP	Farmland Mapping and Monitoring Program
GAP	Gap Analysis Project
K	Thousand
L&RMP	Land and Resource Management Planning
Lasnp	Lassen Volcanic National Park
LMP	Land Management Planning
LTB	Lake Tahoe Basin
LULC	Land Use Land Cover
LWQCB	Lahontan Water Quality Control Board
m	Meter
M	Million
NF	National Forest
NP	National Park
NWS	National Weather Service
P	Point
PL	Placer County
PLSS	Public Land Survey System
R	Raster
SBI	Sierra Biodiversity Institute
SCS	Soil Conservation Service
SEKI	Sequoia and Kings Canyon National Parks
SNEP	Sierra Nevada Ecosystem Project
Teale	Stephen P. Teale Data Center
TEGIS	Tahoe Environmental Geographic Information System
UCSB	University of California, Santa Barbara
USBOC	United States Bureau of Census
USBR	United States Bureau of Reclamation
USFS	United States Forest Service
USGS	United States Geological Survey
V	Vector
WA	Washoe County

APPENDIX 4

The SNEP Process in Detail

This appendix outlines, in greater detail than presented in the body of volume I, the key steps SNEP took to conduct its study. The goal is to present a candid overview, rendering the process as it actually unfolded, rather than presenting a *fait accompli.* This is not intended as critical review—that will come later—but to aid the reader in understanding the human, technical, and societal context in which SNEP worked. Our hope is that by understanding this context, those who use our products will recognize the power as well as the limitations of our conclusions and in so doing more effectively translate this new information into action.

SNEP ASSIGNMENT

One of the difficulties SNEP faced initially was in interpreting the several charges it received. The different sources of SNEP assignments resulted in debate over authority, priority of issues, scope, and type of analysis. The request from Congress that gave rise to the Sierra Nevada Ecosystem Project came in two forms. The 1993 Department of Interior and Related Agencies Appropriation Act, as authorized by H.R. 5503 (1992 Congress), allocated $150,000 for an old-growth forest assessment of the Sierra Nevada. The House Committee on Agriculture also approved H.R. 6013 (Sierra Nevada Forest Ecosystems Study Act of 1992), which called for a comprehensive ecosystem assessment of the entire Sierra Nevada. The intent of H.R. 6013 was read into the record, but it fell victim to adjournment so was never formally approved. Because both bills eventually strongly guided SNEP, as explained later, their content is summarized here.

H.R. 5503

The Conference Report for Interior and Related Agencies 1993 Appropriations Act authorized funds for a "scientific review of the remaining old-growth in the national forests of the Sierra Nevada in California, and for a study of the entire Sierra Nevada ecosystem by an independent panel of scientists, with expertise in diverse areas related to this issue."

In a letter to the chief of the Forest Service explaining the intent of the appropriation language, the chair of the Committee on Natural Resources, Agriculture, Merchant Marine, and Fisheries, along with the chair of the Appropriations Subcommittee on Interior and Related Agencies and other interested legislators, reiterated the call for a scientific review of the remaining late successional old growth in the national forests of the Sierra Nevada and a study of the entire Sierra Nevada ecosystem. The letter further stated that the review's immediate objective should be to produce maps identifying the old-growth forest ecosystems and key watersheds on national forest lands in the Sierra Nevada range and the plant and animal species associated with those ecosystems.

According to the letter, the study should also evaluate different alternatives for protecting the old-growth Sierra Nevada forests and key watersheds, in terms of risks to the ecosystem and associated species and effects on timber harvest levels and other management activities, and should determine whether reserves are needed to protect old-growth and watershed values. Recommendations for management of forest and rangelands within and outside such reserves were requested as well.

H.R. 6013

The Sierra Nevada Ecosystem Study Act of 1992 called for the establishment of a scientific committee to accomplish six tasks:

1. Delineate the various ecosystems of the Sierra Nevada forests.

2. Inventory the resources of these ecosystems, including watersheds and late successional forests, and the species associated with them.

3. Evaluate the health conditions and trends of these ecosystems.

4. Identify the processes, activities, and other factors that affect the health conditions and trends of these ecosystems, including drought, fire and fire suppression, timber harvest and forest practices, disease infestations, livestock grazing, urban and residential development, water projects, forest regeneration, soil erosion, and air quality.

5. Recommend alternative management strategies to protect Sierra Nevada ecosystems, including watersheds and late successional forests and their associated species, and to assess whether reserves are necessary to maintain the

health of the Sierra forest ecosystems. Additionally, if the Science Team finds that reserves are necessary, to designate which lands should be included; recommendation of each alternative management strategy is to include both a discussion of the risks it would pose to the ecosystem and an economic analysis that evaluates impacts on jobs, county revenues, and timber supplies to local, state, and national markets.

6. Examine the Mediated Settlement Agreement for Sequoia National Forest relative to the management of giant sequoia groves and whether additional lands are needed to ensure the health and survival of the giant sequoia ecosystem.

Finally, H.R. 6013 called for a team of scientists to conduct the study with the following areas of expertise represented: forest ecology (old growth), forest ecology (managed forests), wildlife biology, forest economics, silviculture, hydrology, fish biology, forest fire management, forest entomology, range ecology, and risk analysis.

Additional Congressional Direction

Four legislators wrote the chief of the U.S. Forest Service to offer clarification of both H.R. 5503 and H.R. 6013. In their letter, which SNEP later used for clarification, they reemphasized that the scientific study of the Sierra Nevada should address the six objectives described in H.R. 6013 and that reports should be submitted for peer review before they are submitted to Congress.

Steering Committee Guidance

The Steering Committee, which oversaw SNEP (see "Administration"), further interpreted H.R. 5503 and H.R. 6013 in a charter to SNEP. In this document, the Steering Committee called for a two-part study:

1. An evaluation of available data, literature, assessments, maps, and related information to provide an inventory of old-growth and other associated ecosystems, including provisional strategies for management of these ecosystems.

2. An ecosystem study of the entire Sierra Nevada, including assessments, alternatives, and environmental, social, and economic consequences of provisional strategies.

The Steering Committee further clarified the assignment in stating that assessments are to include the following:

- A social overview of historic, current, and projected human influences and anthropogenic effects on the Sierra Nevada ecosystem.

- An economic overview of the current market and non-market economic effects of historic, current, and projected management scenarios.

- Resource inventories with an estimate of pre-Euro-American conditions that can be used as a benchmark to describe ecosystem changes; the inventories should evaluate the major geologic, climatic, physical, and biological conditions that influence ecosystem development within the Sierra Nevada.

- A special-feature assessment that identifies the remaining old-growth stands and the key features or definitions used to describe this resource.

- Examination of the Mediated Settlement Agreement, Section B, Sequoia Groves (Sequoia National Forest) and recommendations for scientifically based mapping and management of giant sequoia groves.

- Evaluation of the health status and sustainability of the Sierra Nevada ecosystems.

- Identification of the processes, activities, and other factors that affect the health conditions and trends of Sierra Nevada ecosystems (drought, fire and fire suppression, timber harvest and forest practices, disease infestations, livestock grazing, urban and residential development, water projects, forest regeneration, soil erosion, and air quality); a quantitative assessment of risk in each area must be included to the degree in which credible data exist.

- Assessment of the past, current, and likely future effects of water resource management strategies on aquatic ecosystems in the Sierra Nevada.

- Descriptions and analysis of the analytical models used in all assessments, including sensitivity analysis of the projected values.

- Research gaps and data needs.

In addition, alternatives were to include the following:

- A range of management scenarios for maintaining the health and sustainability of the Sierra Nevada ecosystems while providing resources to meet human needs.

- A wide range of themes or objectives; for example, alternatives could emphasize specific themes of (a) establishment of coarse- or fine-grain filter strategies (or combinations thereof) to enhance or maintain natural ecological values, (b) intensified zoning to emphasize featured uses or activities, and (c) natural values, recreational values, or commodity values.

- Environmental, social, and economic consequences, evaluated with regard to each alternative and using a wide range of criteria, including temporal and spatial effects.

The Steering Committee called for peer review of publications, products, assessments, and reports completed by the Science Team.

ADMINISTRATION

The various charges for SNEP gave direction for staff organization. Nonetheless, SNEP's administration, and the roles played by different groups, evolved over the course of the study.

Steering Committee

The deputy chief for the Forest Service was given authority to establish a science-based Steering Committee, whose job was to initiate and provide administrative guidance for the project. The Steering Committee elected its own chair from within the committee and included representatives from Forest Service Research, Washington Office; National Park Service; University of California; California Academy of Sciences; and National Academy of Sciences (table A4.1). The role given to the Steering Committee was to select the Science Team leader and the Science Team, to assume primary responsibility for public communications, and to provide overall guidance and advice to the Science Team throughout the study.

The role of the Steering Committee changed over time. It fulfilled the obligation of choosing team leaders (held by three different people) and ratifying selections for Science Team members. The Steering Committee initially played only a minor role, however, in interpreting the various charges for SNEP's assignment, in guiding the approach to the study, and in advising on public participation. After the first year of the project, the Steering Committee became more active and worked more closely with the Science Team. The Steering Committee handled the lawsuit that arose in the second year regarding public participation and Federal Advisory Committee Act (see "Public Participation"). Certain members of the Steering Committee became active reviewers of process and scope, emphasizing the need for explicit statement of assumptions, a practical approach to institutional realities, and the relationship of SNEP to other agencies, Congress, and the Administration. During the review of SNEP reports, the Steering Committee coordinated anonymous peer reviews.

Science Team

According to charge, the technical work of SNEP was to be conducted by an interdisciplinary team of high-caliber, nationally respected scientists with expertise in a wide range of biological, physical, and social sciences pertinent to the Sierra Nevada. Science Team composition grew in several phases during the first year. From an initial small team during the tenure of the first Science Team leader, the core Science Team eventually comprised eighteen Science Team members (so approved by the Steering Committee) and nineteen special consultants (see the lists in appendix 2). Special consultants served roles equal to those of designated Science Team members. This core Science Team comprised the leaders of SNEP projects, authors and coauthors of SNEP technical reports, and main participants in broad as well as specific dialogues about the SNEP strategic approach, direction, and progress. Science Team meetings were held monthly (most for two days) through the course of the project and attended by the core Science Team.

TABLE A4.1

SNEP administrative and science teams.

Steering Committee	Science Team
Chair Jim Space, Director, U.S. Forest Service, Pacific Southwest Research Station, Albany, CA *Former Chair:* Barbara C. Weber, then Director, U.S. Forest Service, Pacific Southwest Research Station, Albany, CA **Members** George Bartholomew, University of California, Los Angeles, CA Dennis Breedlove, California Academy of Sciences, San Francisco, CA Bruce M. Kilgore, Pacific West Field Area, National Park Service, San Francisco, CA Jeffrey Romm, University of California, Berkeley, CA Jerry A. Sesco, U.S. Forest Service, Forest Service Research, Washington, DC *Former Member:* Don C. Erman, University of California, Davis, CA	**Team Leader** Don C. Erman, University of California, Davis, CA *Former Team Leaders* Deborah L. Elliott-Fisk, University of California, Oakland, CA John Gordon, Yale University, New Haven, CT **Coordinating Committee** Don C. Erman, Team Leader, University of California, Davis, CA Constance I. Millar, Chair, U.S. Forest Service, Pacific Southwest Research Station, Albany, CA Deborah L. Elliott-Fisk, University of California, Oakland, CA David Graber, National Biological Service, Three Rivers, CA Douglas Leisz, Placerville, CA Rowan A. Rowntree, U.S. Forest Service, Northeastern Forest Experiment Station, Albany, CA *Coordinating Associate:* Michael Oliver, University of California, Davis, CA **Public Participation Committee** Jonathan Kusel, Chair, Forest Communities Research and University of California, Westwood, CA Susan Carpenter, Carpenter and Associates, Riverside, CA Sam C. Doak, Doak and Associates, Portland, OR Erin Fleming, University of California, Davis, CA Victoria E. Sturtevant, Southern Oregon State College, Ashland, OR **Science Team Members, Special Consultants, Associates, and SNEP Staff** See lists in appendix 2

200
VOLUME I, APPENDIX 4

In addition to the thirty-seven scientists who took primary responsibility for the broad SNEP project, a large and diverse group of associates played a critical if narrower role in the project (see list in appendix 2). These associates contributed technical information, reports, and reviews on one or several projects or disciplines. The associate scientists mostly did not participate in the broadest SNEP effort, nor did they regularly attend Science Team meetings but worked through a member of the core Science Team.

SNEP was directed by a Science Team leader, who shouldered executive responsibility for primary decisions about direction, scope, technical framework, philosophical approach, scheduling, and review of SNEP process and products. The Coordinating Committee (table A4.1), comprising six Science Team members including the team leader, provided strategic direction and executive recommendations and decisions on many aspects of the project. The Coordinating Committee met weekly (at times, daily), reviewed broad team approaches, approved direction and progress of Science Team projects, reviewed and recommended annual budgets for Science Team members, arbitrated conflict, interacted with the Steering Committee, and edited and coordinated production of the *Progress Report* and SNEP's final reports. The Coordinating Committee worked closely with the SNEP Public Participation Committee (table A4.1) and the public key contacts group in their efforts to involve the public with the SNEP process (see "Public Participation").

Project Working Groups

Science Team members, together with associates, staff, and select colleagues, formed several working groups during the course of the project. These ranged from technical groups addressing assessments (see "Technical Framework"), such as the Disturbance Group, the Watershed Group, the Institutions Group, to technical support, such as the GIS Group (see "Phase 3: Geographic Information System and On-line Availability," and appendix 3), to SNEP administration, such as the Public Participation Group (see "Public Participation") and the SNEP Editorial Group.

SCOPE OF SNEP

The philosophical approach taken by SNEP determined the way in which its projects were conducted and the nature of its conclusions.

Independence

In all direction regarding the project, independence of the Science Team and the scientific process was clearly stressed. The Science Team was administered within an academic context (Centers for Water and Wildland Resources, UC Davis), and many team members belonged to academic institutions. Several scientists were affiliated with public agencies (U.S. Forest Service, National Biological Service, U.S. Geological Survey, National Park Service, State of California Resources Agency), but within SNEP these members represented their respective research communities, not organizations.

Several other new or ongoing projects on the Sierra Nevada overlapped the tenure of SNEP, including the USFS CalOwl Assessment and Draft EIS, the state of California CERES program, the California Gap Analysis Project (GAP), the Sierra Nevada Research Planning Program (SNRP), and the California Rivers Assessment Program. SNEP directly coordinated with CERES (see Phase 3: "Geographic Information System and On-line Availability"), GAP, and the Sierra Nevada Research Planning Program but intentionally worked independently of the CalOwl Project, which was an agency assessment and plan under National Environmental Policy Act (NEPA) direction.

The nature of SNEP's funding further encouraged independence. SNEP projects were directly funded by Congress and, through congressional appropriation, the U.S. Forest Service. These funds were used as operating budgets for technical assessments, to support the SNEP GIS staff and facilities, to provide salary for support staff, consulting scientists, and some primary SNEP scientists, and to cover project overhead in facilities, printing, and accounting.

Other sources indirectly supported SNEP. Many SNEP scientists' salaries were covered by their respective organizations. Associate scientists contributed consultation and statistical and GIS advice and review, and uncounted hours were donated to SNEP projects by resource managers and specialists of agencies and departments in the Sierra Nevada. These latter included the U.S. Forest Service, National Park Service, Bureau of Land Management, state of California, counties, and California Indian tribes.

Process and Collaboration

SNEP's assignment put the Science Team on new ground; no previous assessments provided adequate models. As such, much of the team process and scientific approach summarized in this appendix and implicit in technical reports was newly developed as part of SNEP. Thus, SNEP's contributions are not just data, maps, and analyses, but new approaches to ecosystem analysis and bioregional assessment. One of the unexpected consequences from the approach SNEP took was an implicit collaboration and cooperation among federal, state, local, and private participants. Although SNEP maintained scientific standards and independence as indicated earlier, the critical involvement of people from many sectors meant that assessments and scenarios were not isolated scientific endeavors. The cooperation among team members and associates from different sectors within SNEP presages the collaborative teamsmanship that will enable successful management of Sierran bioregions.

Scientific Approach

SNEP attempted to maintain a scientific approach to team process, including candid presentation of the process. The SNEP team included scientists with differences of opinion, representing diverse schools of thought, ages, backgrounds, and experiences. Rather than minimize these differences in an imperative for team consensus, SNEP intentionally allowed them to flourish during team analysis and the review process. SNEP's intent was to highlight in reports and presentations the areas of team controversy and differing interpretation, describing the justifications, rationale, and assumptions behind interpretations. In so doing, SNEP hoped to demystify the scientific process and to clarify the nature of debate to users of SNEP's products. Although it would make easier reading to present unambiguous conclusions, in many cases, it would be false to imply consensus. By disclosing the process, we hope that the information we present will be understood in the context of the scientific process (including debate, uncertainty, fragmentary evidence) in which it was developed.

Peer Review

Peer review is part of the scientific tradition. SNEP's reports went through multiple cycles of review by different reviewer groups, the sum of which accounted for greater scrutiny than most scientists encounter in normal scientific journal or book publishing. The SNEP Coordinating Committee directed most of the review processes, except the anonymous reviews of the final reports, which were coordinated by the Steering Committee. All SNEP projects resulting in reports initially were submitted in proposal format, elaborating proposed rationale, justification, and methods. Before submission to the Coordinating Committee, these were reviewed by Science Team colleagues and then reviewed by the Coordinating Committee. Preliminary results of technical projects were presented to an external group of science reviewers at a Science Team meeting in May 1995, at which time critical comments were solicited.

Final reports were subject to review as follows: internal reviews by a minimum of five Science Team members, external review by three anonymous reviewers, and review by a variable number of public key contacts (see "Public Participation"). Review forms were used to track each manuscript. An editorial board of two SNEP Science Team members coordinated the review process by tracking review comments, assuring that review comments were incorporated in revisions, and granting final approval of revised manuscripts. Draft reports for which substantive comments were raised were brought to the attention of the Coordinating Committee, and appropriate actions (e.g., new authors added, workshops convened) were taken to bring the report to SNEP standards.

In addition to peer review of technical approach and content, SNEP conducted reviews with the public (see "Public Participation").

Assessment, Not Plan

SNEP's responsibility was to provide a scientific evaluation of trends and consequences, not decision making or planning. Throughout the project, the public often confused SNEP with a NEPA or California Environmental Quality Act analysis (such as CalOwl or FEMAT), which it was not. The primary difference is that, although both approaches undertake scientific analysis of conditions and trends, SNEP's recommendations for the future are nonbinding examples, not plans. SNEP was educational in nature: presenting new information, interpretations, and suggestions. With its strategies, SNEP presented a "grab bag" of tools, models, and suggestions for how to address some of the most important ecosystem problems confronting the bioregion. In most cases, SNEP's recommendations would not directly translate into on-the-ground plans but were intentionally conceived at a design level, although SNEP did consider aspects of management and institutional implementation. Any work done to translate SNEP's suggestions into real policy or management actions would entail further analysis of local implications, a task that was beyond the ability and responsibility of SNEP scientists.

The Science Team focused on technical analysis, assessment, interpretation, integration, and creative modeling. SNEP objectives were to unveil myths about resource conditions, raise red flags about problem areas, provide centralized and retrievable data and maps, interpret multidisciplinary information synthetically, and display in clear language potential designs to solve major problems in the Sierra. SNEP assessments attempted to be comprehensive and exhaustive; strategies developed were intentionally illustrative and representative. SNEP scientists strove to present material in a way that could be effectively passed to decision makers. Despite best intentions, the temptation to make comprehensive and exclusive recommendations was strong and unavoidable, and some bias undoubtedly remains in reports.

Data Compilation and Synthesis

Although a scientific assessment project, SNEP was directed by assignment not to undertake new or primary research. The Science Team therefore compiled preexisting data but reached deep for information beyond standard published scientific articles. Although SNEP scientists maintained a data-quality standard, they used information from agency files, consultations with experts and specialists, applicable evidence from studies in adjacent bioregions, projections from theory and simulations, historical files, and even anecdotes and historical photos. New simulation models were built in some cases (as in, for example, simulations of forest conditions), and new methods for evaluating conditions (e.g., variable riparian buffers, late successional forest categories). In the latter case, new data plots were installed and analyzed to validate the categories and ranks employed by SNEP.

SNEP scientists were requested by congressional charge to make evaluations about status and condition. Because of the generally poor data quality, the lack of preexisting information, the requirement not to do new research, and the short time frame to complete the work, making evaluative statements required each scientist to extend him- or herself. SNEP scientists were fulfilling their obligation by making professional judgment statements and inferences. For many, this was the most difficult and professionally challenging aspect of the project.

TECHNICAL FRAMEWORK

Several aspects of SNEP's assignment presented particular challenges to the team in developing a strategic technical approach. These included Sierrawide scale, interdisciplinary scope, lack of a "driving issue" and emphasis on integration, ecological versus social aspects in SNEP, poor data and scientific knowledge, time frame, assessment and policy alternatives, and role of public participation in the process. These are each considered separately (the latter in a separate section, "Public Participation").

Sierra-wide Scale

The geographic scope of the assignment remained a challenge through the course of the project. Even defining the outer boundaries for the study region remained a debate for over a year. The logical bounds of a Sierra region were different for almost every issue and discipline. Although this might not seem a significant problem, the imperative to integrate among analyses encouraged the Science Team to seek a "consensus" boundary. In the end, the team accepted a compromise boundary, recognizing that analysis of individual issues could modify boundaries without impeding integration.

For many issues, assessments and management were most approachable at scales below the Sierrawide level, for example, at the regional level. Nonoverlapping and hierarchic patterns of Sierran diversity created difficulty in approaching regionalization synthetically. In the end, the Science Team accepted diversity within the Sierra by not forcing "consensus" regional boundaries and recognizing that conclusions pertain to different hierarchic scales. In SNEP reports, authors point out issues relevant at different levels.

Interdisciplinary Scope

SNEP's assignments called for an interdisciplinary scientific evaluation. Various disciplines were named; SNEP added to these. Despite the attempt to cover all important issues, gaps remained. It became impossible to add scientists for every important discipline; some issues had to be evaluated by scientists whose primary work was not in the area of their direct expertise.

Large interdisciplinary teams function differently from small or individual efforts, leading to unexpected challenges. Large team size and diversity of composition—eventually about eighty active scientists—led to divergence of opinion on almost everything. Effective decision making, strategic planning, maintaining schedules, budgeting, and reporting became time consuming and unwieldy. Developing technical project groups and committees, and giving the Coordinating Committee executive power, helped to order the diversity and make progress.

Integration

Most previous bioregional assessments and landscape evaluations had at their core a single or a few crises or driving issues. The trend has been to start with these central issues (e.g., endangered owl, salmon, marbled murrelet) and expand to become more integrated ecological analysis. SNEP, by contrast, began as an integrated ecological study, with no central emphasis given in the charge. Although some key issues were highlighted (old growth, watersheds, wildlife), they were repeatedly set in the context of an integrated ecological assessment. Determination of priority and importance was left in the hands of the Science Team. In this, the team was aided by previous surveys of public and scientific opinion about priority issues in the Sierra Nevada (Sierra Summit, Sierra Now, Sierra Nevada Research Planning Program). These issues were merged with priorities derived from scientific experience and judgment.

Ultimately the challenge centered on how to do a truly integrated ecosystem study. The "whole" (Sierran ecosystem) could not be studied usefully only as a whole, but individual pieces dissected for analysis would lead to dis-integration. Further, scientific tradition conditions scientists to focus on narrow topics, small areas, controlled situations, and repeatable conditions and to work in small teams with scientists of their own discipline. Working at the level of system interconnections, considering relationships among topics, and seeing the whole as well as the parts remain as challenges for science as well as SNEP.

Ecological and Social Aspects

SNEP's charges stressed that social as well as ecological components were part of ecosystems, ecosystem sustainability, and SNEP analysis. Both the importance of this orientation and the uncertain implications of how to deal with it are not new with SNEP but nonetheless were recast in SNEP's attempts to define its mission and to understand what assessment standards to use and what broad targets to consider as appropriate futures for the Sierra. The imperative to assure ecological sustainability while providing human goods and desires (from the SNEP assignment) provided both a tension point and some guidance on how to assess trade-offs.

Data Quality and Scientific Knowledge

Despite an eagerness to achieve objectives that Congress requested, poor data quality and availability and limited scientific understanding simply did not allow the level of analysis Congress and the public might want. This reality influenced the way SNEP approached its charge, the nature of conclusions presented, the ability to achieve integrated assessments, and the way conclusions could be used.

Time Frame

Given the scope and complexity of SNEP, two and one-half years proved too short a time to complete the task. The interdisciplinary nature of the project, size and diversity of the team, enormous start-up time, need to develop a new GIS, lack of compiled information, inability of most scientists to devote more than part-time to the project, large geographic distances involved, and need for both analysis and integration all challenged the timing for completion of SNEP. Some projects, by the rudimentary nature of information, required new data gathering or information collection. Development of simulation models that integrated parts of the system were highly time consuming. Participation with the public absorbed scientists' time to a much greater degree than had been anticipated.

Assessment and Policy Analysis

The Science Team was challenged in determining how to integrate or dissociate assessments from development of management alternatives, how to define assessments, and what constituted appropriate policy alternatives. The allocation of time to these topics, the role of different individuals directing the efforts, and the challenge of integrating assessments with policy alternatives developed only slowly over time.

Technical Framework for Assessment and Policy Options

The Science Team divided the technical aspects of the project into three primary components: ecosystem assessments, analysis of management and policy strategies, and GIS database development (table A4.2).

Phase 1: Ecosystem Assessment. Phase 1 formed the primary emphasis of SNEP analyses and the bulk of Science Team efforts and final reports. Assessments were intended to address biological, physical, and social aspects of Sierran ecosystems and to link with policy strategies but not depend on

them. Assessments would meet agreed-on standards of explicit assumptions, risk assessment, statistical validity, and peer review.

SNEP conducted the assessments using a phase of conceptual dissection and analysis followed irregularly by several phases of synthesis. Although the "Sierra Nevada ecosystem" conceivably is divisible into a nearly infinite number of component parts and processes, the Science Team identified what it felt to be the most important parts for analysis, based on both the ecosystem standpoint and social priority. These included issues of biological and physical diversity, agents of change (disturbance forces), social components and human communities, and institutions (table A4.3). These elements, and the subsystems that the Science Team developed by combining several elements (e.g., watersheds, riparian communities, aquatic vertebrates and invertebrates), were subjected to in-depth technical analyses by project scientists and groups of scientists. These "assessment reports," published individually with author attribution in volumes II and III, are the primary analytical efforts of SNEP assessments.

Assessment of each ecosystem component was organized around five guiding questions:

1. What are current ecological, social, and economic conditions?

2. What were historic ecological, social, and economic conditions, trends, and variabilities?

3. What are trends and risks under current policies and management?

4. What policy choices will achieve ecological sustainability consistent with social well-being?

TABLE A4.2

Primary components of SNEP technical framework.

Ecosystem Assessments	Analyses of Management and Policy Strategies	GIS Database Development
Form primary focus of SNEP analyses and final report. Link with SNEP analyses of policy strategies, but do not depend on them. Meet agreed-on standards of risk assessment, data credibility, statistical validity. State assumptions, data sources, and methods explicitly. Address five assessment questions.	Form secondary focus of SNEP analyses and final report. Link problems identified in ecosystem assessments to possible solutions for improving health and sustainability. Depend on assessments for starting point (problems identified). Are intentionally illustrative, not comprehensive; provide thought-ideas, not detailed plans. Could not be implemented without further local analysis. Mostly address components of ecosystems (only a few attempt to be integrated at a regional level). Use diverse approaches for strategies, depending on issue, from quantitative simulations to verbal models. Meet agreed-on standards (public goals, potentially implementable, etc.).	Develop GIS database and maps to support SNEP assessments and policy stratagies. Provide access to file server and database post-SNEP for wide application by the public, other scientists, analysts, and managers.

TABLE A4.3

SNEP technical framework: ecosystem components in SNEP assessments.

Ecological Diversity	Agents of Change	Physical Diversity	Social Diversity	Human Resource Uses and Social Systems
Plant communities: general; riparian; meadow; oak woodlands; giant sequoia	Fire	Water	Population growth	Silviculture
	Insects and pathogens	Soils	Human communities	Grazing
	Floods and avalanches	Air	California tribes	Agriculture
Vegetation: forest structure and succession	Exotic plants and animals	Geology and minerals		Fire management
		Climate		Recreation
Species diversity: terrestrial vertebrates; aquatic vertebrates; aquatic invertebrates; insects, vascular plants; nonvascular plants				Special forest products
				Economics
				Institutions
Genetic diversity				Adaptive management
Significant areas				

5. What are the implications of these choices for ecological, social, and economic conditions?

Standards for evaluations of conditions and trends were derived from SNEP's operational definitions of health and sustainability.

Although ecosystem components were studied individually, the Science Team made a continuing effort to organize thinking at a higher, more integrated level. Where possible, assessments were linked (riparian with aquatic; vegetation with floristic diversity with forest structure; etc.) so that partial integration was achieved even during the analysis phase. Team presentations and whole-team reviews of draft papers provoked discussion among scientists and provided fertile ground for debate on fundamental topics and conclusions. This interdisciplinary debate proved healthy for the project as it led eventually to greater clarity of analysis and integration on many topics.

Once the detailed technical assessments were completed, efforts turned toward integration. Because scientists work more readily on individual projects rather than in integrated analyses, adequate time had to be left for this part of the project. This task proved to be extremely difficult. Volume I, our summary report, eventually became the vehicle for bringing about integration. This report was intended to synthesize, not abstract, the key integrating and synthetic priorities from the lengthy volume II reports. The discussions, workshops, and joint writing, reviewing, and editing for this volume produced a higher level of conceptual synthesis than had been achieved in the project previously.

Phase 2: Analysis of Management and Policy Strategies. Phase 2 was in the background of the project for the first year or so because it depended on results from assessments. Policy analysis initially focused on quantitative simulation models of commercial forest condition. This aspect was expanded through development of advances in models and use of data.

Emphasis on one approach, however, was met with debate in the Science Team when members found other issues to address for Sierra Nevada futures than those amenable to quantitative modeling of forest conditions.

Thus began a phase to broaden the scope of policy scenarios within SNEP. In the spirit of environmental think tanks (e.g., the Rocky Mountain Institute), the Science Team released itself from the constraints of mathematical modeling and considered diverse institutional approaches, thought-models, and fragments of components. In the end, SNEP presented a sample of ideas, each organized similarly, although methods, goals, and ecosystem components addressed differed among them. Finally, to address the concern that most scenarios were fragmentary and unintegrated, SNEP developed a few integrated scenarios for parts of the Sierra, which attempted to synthesize ecosystem components.

Ultimately, the team felt that *strategies* rather than *scenarios* more aptly describes the characteristics of the policy examples developed by SNEP, and *strategies* is the term used in the volume I chapters.

Phase 3: Geographic Information System and On-line Availability. The SNEP GIS Center was developed primarily to support SNEP inventories, mapping, assessments, simulations, and modeling efforts. A secondary goal was to make SNEP's data and data-management system available to federal, state, and local agencies, as well as various interest groups (e.g., university researchers, private industries, environmental organizations, and local communities) and the general public. The SNEP GIS Center collaborated and co-located with the state's CERES program to develop a system that would serve SNEP needs for independence during the course of the project yet could be integrated with ongoing programs in California after SNEP's completion. The SNEP GIS Center was also coordinated with the Alexandria system at the University of California, Santa Barbara, which serves as a storage location following SNEP's completion and before the system can be made more widely available via public media. SNEP information and some databases are accessible on-line via the World Wide Web.

For detailed explanation of the SNEP GIS, see appendix 3 in this volume.

PUBLIC PARTICIPATION

The Approach

The Sierra Nevada Ecosystem Project (SNEP) approach to public participation was based on adaptive principles. The Science Team encouraged active involvement of a diverse array of Sierra stakeholders to promote the broadest exchange of ideas and to promote a mutual learning process between scientists and the public. Specifically, SNEP public involvement was designed to be inclusive and participatory. It was also iterative, as it successively sought and responded to input from participants through a dynamic exchange. The approach was based on the premise that broad public involvement would improve SNEP's understanding of the Sierra Nevada and factors contributing to economic and social well-being, as well as assist in the development and refinement of scenarios for the Sierra Nevada.

The team's approach required both active participation from a diverse public and a willingness on the part of scientists to listen to the public and openly discuss different views. By interspersing periods of creative interaction with the public and focused consolidation and refinement among the scientists, the Science Team was able to adapt to new ideas and information provided by the public as well as inform the public of its progress. This productive interplay allowed SNEP to develop an assessment that combined the rigor of a scientific approach with the grounded knowledge and practicality afforded by public input.

Participation

To ensure an inclusive process, the SNEP team focused on three distinct types of public groups: key contacts, collaborative place-based groups, and the general public. The public involvement strategy included activities for each of these groups because they brought unique skills and knowledge to the SNEP assessment process.

The charter for SNEP recommended that the team rely on a group of *key contacts* to help accomplish project objectives. The initial key contact group consisted of individuals who had participated in previous planning and evaluations of the Sierra Nevada (e.g., Sierra Summit Steering Committee, Sierra Nevada Research Planning Team). Additional individuals were added to the group as the team identified regions or areas of interest that were not represented. Members of the key contact group generally had considerable knowledge of and experience with Sierra Nevada issues. The key contacts group totaled approximately seventy individuals representing various interest groups and scientific or other perspectives within the communities of interest of the Sierra Nevada.

Early in the public involvement process, a subset of key contacts were self-selected as a work group to advise the SNEP team on public involvement strategies. The *key contact work group* consisted of about a dozen people who assisted the team with planning public meetings during the final year of the project. Groups with a diversity of interests were represented in the work group, including recreation groups, public agencies, the timber industry, and the environmental community.

Place-based collaborative groups, which focus efforts in communities "placed" in the Sierra, were selected as focal points for SNEP's local public participation activities. These groups were selected because they represented a diversity of perspectives and a high level of general understanding of natural resource issues. Additionally, the team felt these groups could effectively contribute local and regional knowledge and act as catalysts for local public involvement. Collaborative place-based groups can be broadly defined as bioregional, community, or watershed-based groups with diverse interest representation that meet to discuss local resource management and well-being issues.

SNEP sought collaborative groups in three regions based on variations in resource-dependence, economics, development pressures, and other variables: the northern Sierra, the west-central Sierra, and the east-central Sierra. Only two groups were chosen, however: the Quincy Library Group in the northern Sierra and the Coalition for Unified Recreation in the Eastern Sierra (CURES) in the east-central Sierra. A high level of conflict and the absence of a collaborative group with broad enough interest representation prevented SNEP from working with a place-based group in the west-central Sierra.

The *general public* includes all other individuals not specifically included in the key contact or place-based groups. Although limited resources constrained SNEP's work with the public, working relationships with both the key contacts and the place-based groups helped to draw and focus general public interest and participation. Three meetings were held to which the general public was invited.

Implementation

The SNEP public participation strategy consisted of a multi-stage approach involving newsletters, an open letter to the public, meetings and workshops, and focused public reviews of draft assessments (a list of all individual public involvement meetings and more general public interactions is provided at the end of this section).

Newsletter. Four issues of a newsletter, *SNEP Update*, were used to provide general information on project activities and preliminary findings. Each issue included discussion of public involvement activities, including calls for public input and announcements of public meetings. Newsletters were mailed to key contacts and others on SNEP's mailing list, which totaled close to 3,000 names, and was made available at all public meetings, workshops, and other meetings attended by team members.

Open Letter. An open letter to the public was prepared requesting information and calling for public contributions to scenario development. The letter was printed in the March 1995 issue of *SNEP Update*. It was also widely distributed via mailing lists provided by key contacts and the California Department of Forestry and Fire Protection. From this outreach effort, a total of forty-one submissions from the public were distributed to the Science Team.

Meetings and Workshops. A series of public meetings and workshops were conducted with collaborative groups (and communities of place), key contacts (largely communities of interests), and the general public.

Two public meetings were held within the geographical areas of each of the two collaborative groups. These meetings were co-hosted by the collaborative groups, which made arrangements and ensured that the broader public was invited. After the first meeting in the east-central Sierra, a special planning meeting was held with a subset of members of the CURES group to plan the second one. In the northern Sierra a member of the key contact group facilitated discussions and arrangements between the SNEP team and the Quincy Library Group. A single public meeting was held in the city of Jackson in the west-central Sierra during the summer of 1995 without the aid of a local collaborative group.

These local meetings were attended by a subgroup of the Science Team representing a diverse range of disciplines, including areas of particular interest to the collaborative groups. Each meeting had a different complement of scientists and was initiated with an introduction to SNEP's mission and general progress to date. Brief presentations were made by members of the Science Team on approaches and progress within their individual assessments. The last half of these two- or three-hour meetings was dedicated to informal questions and answers and open discussion among scientists and public attendees. The second meetings in both the eastern and the northern Sierra also included interactive demonstrations of some of SNEP's computer-based geographic information system (GIS) data. Notes were taken at each meeting to ensure that questions and suggestions from the public were captured, and these were later shared with the full team.

The first public meeting was held in June of 1994 with the release of the SNEP Progress Report. There was limited interaction between the Science Team and the public beyond a formal question-and-answer session. The first SNEP team meeting with the key contacts took place in November of 1994. At this meeting the team learned the importance of public access to scientists: breaks in many instances proved more valuable than the presentations themselves, as participants took the opportunity to discuss issues with scientists directly. Two additional large public meetings were held along with a separate workshop with the key contacts. The key contacts

work group helped plan these meetings, which allocated considerable time for interaction between scientists and the public. The key contacts work group was instrumental in providing ideas on how to maximize interactions between SNEP scientists and the public. The public meeting held in February of 1995 focused on introducing the approaches used by scientists in the assessment and discussions of preliminary findings. The full-day meeting began with formal presentations by some of the scientists, including questions from the public. Nearly three hours of the meeting were dedicated to an open workshop format in which attendees were able to engage in discussions with scientists at tables organized by resources and disciplines. Included in this arrangement was an area dedicated to interactive demonstrations of some of SNEP's GIS data. Note takers were stationed at each table to capture the questions and suggestions offered by the public.

In June of 1995 a special workshop was held with the key contacts to solicit ideas regarding the development of policy scenarios. During this workshop, the key contacts were briefed on a list of possible scenarios based on ideas from the public, scientific models, and the team's resource assessments. Attendees were then divided into small groups composed of both scientists and key contacts. Led by SNEP facilitators, the groups discussed concerns and offered suggestions regarding scenario development. Notes were taken on poster sheets. Representatives from each group summarized their discussions to the full group. The dialogues captured were used by the Science Team to expand and refine the development of a suite of scenarios.

The final public meeting, in September 1995, was scheduled to provide sufficient time to incorporate public comment gained during the meeting into the final development of scenarios. This meeting offered an opportunity for the public to understand and evaluate the range of strategies developed to date and for the SNEP scientists to listen to the public's concerns, insights, and suggestions. Scheduling additional time to incorporate public comment allowed the SNEP team greater opportunity to fashion strategies that incorporated local expertise and reflected public concerns. The round-robin type of interaction in which the public conversed with scientists face-to-face—a style first suggested by the key contacts work group for the February public meeting—was repeated in this meeting. Following a few formal presentations by SNEP scientists, participants were given the opportunity to discuss scenarios and findings directly with scientists at tables organized by strategy focus and general resource area. As with previous meetings, notes were recorded at each table to capture the questions and suggestions offered by the public, and these were circulated to the team shortly thereafter.

Reviews. Key contacts and place-based groups also participated in a focused review of SNEP assessment reports in late summer of 1995. Draft assessments were subjected to blind peer reviews and were simultaneously sent to key contacts and place-based groups, on request, for their review and comment. Key contacts and place-based groups asked to coordinate public review of these drafts and were permitted to circulate the draft subproject reports to whomever they chose. In order to limit the number of separate comments on each report, the key contacts and place-based groups were responsible for summarizing responses and returning them to the team within the same time period given to peer reviewers. In a process similar to a formal peer review, team scientists used comments received from the key contacts and place-based groups to inform subsequent revision of subproject reports. Interestingly, though there were extensive requests for individual reports by key contacts and place-based groups, there were only a limited number of reviews returned to the team.

Other Interactions. The formal public involvement strategy just detailed was supplemented by a variety of other interactions between individual scientists on the SNEP team and the public. Interactions were often intended to either inform the public of SNEP or gather specialized knowledge, but they often accomplished both. These included meetings with agencies, private industry, county supervisors, and interest groups, a series of workshops with local experts to assess community capacity and well-being, and other workshops to identify and map late successional forest types.

SUMMARY

The Sierra Nevada Ecosystem Project is drawing to a close, though it is not complete at the time of this writing; nonetheless, some preliminary conclusions can be drawn about the efficacy of the adaptive process employed. First, most scientists, including those who were initially skeptical of interaction with the public, found the public involvement process both instructive and valuable. Many scientists were influenced in a variety of ways by public interaction, and near project end virtually all scientists were positive about exchanges with the public. The ease with which the public involvement team was able to draw scientists to public meetings toward the end of the project compared with the beginning is evidence of this. Further evidence is the nature of exchanges at public sessions: scientist interaction with the public shifted from being didactic and somewhat defensive in early sessions to explanatory and encouraging of mutual exploration of complex issues in the later sessions.

Secondly, though it is impossible to pinpoint specific "public" ideas that influenced scientists' work, it is clear that public involvement influenced the work of the team. Numerous times in SNEP team meetings, a scientist would reference a public comment to reinforce a point or make clear that the issue under discussion must be addressed to respond to public concern. The focus on institutions in SNEP, which emerged late in the project, was driven by a small number of scientists on the team as well as by continued comments and questions in public sessions. Designing a fuels-reduction strategy was reinforced by public comment and interaction with the Quincy Library

Group, which had done considerable thinking on its own on this subject. Identification of areas of late successional old growth and determination of community capacity could not have been done without the help of numerous agency and local experts, respectively. The scientific assessments may not have been changed dramatically through public involvement, but interaction with the public often influenced how data were presented and conclusions drawn and, perhaps most profoundly, influenced the development of scenarios.

Thirdly, the adaptive process itself had a significant effect on the involved public, in both their perceptions of the science project itself and their relationships with one another. Individuals who initially felt the project was a waste of time later expressed a genuine concern that the best possible science be used to address the complex social and resource issues in the Sierra Nevada. There was general acknowledgment that much needed to be learned and that scientists were essential in facilitating this learning process. Virtually all participants appreciated being a part of the process and praised the openness of the scientists in listening to their viewpoints. Perhaps most importantly, people who had long been sitting on opposite sides of issues agreed that resolution of complex resource management issues would be achieved only with them working together and not against one another. There appeared to be broad agreement among these participants to continue the dialogue begun in this adaptive process.

Summary of Public Interactions

General public and key contact meetings or workshops:

- June 15, 1994, Steering Committee meeting

- November 21, 1994, Steering Committee/Science Team/ key contact meeting

- December 7, 1994, public planning meeting with CURES work group—Sam Doak, Don Erman, Jonathan Kusel, John Menke, Connie Millar, Bill Stewart

- December 8, 1994, meeting with Key Contact Planning Group—Jonathan Kusel and Public Involvement work group, Susan Carpenter, Sam Doak, Vicki Sturtevant

- December 12, 1994, Quincy Library Group (Quincy)—Joan Brenchley-Jackson, Sam Doak, Norm Johnson, Jonathan Kusel, Bill Stewart

- January 19, 1995, CURES planning meeting (Mammoth Lakes)—Sam Doak, Jonathan Kusel

- February 4, 1995, public workshop for MSA Giant Sequoia work group—Debbie Elliott-Fisk and MSA work group

- February 9, 1995, meeting with Key Contact Planning Group—Jonathan Kusel and Public Involvement Work Group

- February 21, 1995, public workshop (Davis)—Science Team and associates

- February 23, 1995, conference call with Key Contact Planning Group—Jonathan Kusel and Public Involvement Work Group

- February 1995, CURES east-side public workshop—Sam Doak, Tim Duane, Rick Kattelmann, Jonathan Kusel, John Menke, Connie Millar, Vicki Sturtevant

- March 1995, call for public input into scenario development—Harrison Dunning

- March 17, 1995, trends of fish, amphibians, and aquatic habitats, UC Davis—Peter Moyle

- April 11, 1995, Quincy Library Group public workshop — Joan Brenchley-Jackson, Sam Doak, Tim Duane, Jo Ann Fites-Kaufmann, Jerry Franklin, Norm Johnson, Rick Kattelmann, Jonathan Kusel, John Menke, Bill Stewart, Vicki Sturtevant

- June 22, 1995, key contacts workshop to discuss scenarios—Science Team

- July 13, 1995, west-central Sierra meeting (Jackson)—Larry Costick, Mike Diggles, Dave Graber, Greg Greenwood, Jonathan Kusel, John Menke

- July 25, 1995, meeting with Key Contact Planning Group—Susan Carpenter, Sam Doak, Jonathan Kusel and Public Involvement Work Group

- September 20, 1995, general public meeting (Sacramento)—Science Team and associates

Presentations and Workshops

- September 1993, Environmental Sciences Policy and Management, UC (Berkeley)—Debbie Elliott-Fisk and Don Erman

- November 1993, Resource Conservation Districts (Mark Hicks and Julie Spezia)—Debbie Elliott-Fisk

- December 2, 1993, Cooperative Snow Survey Conference (Tahoe City)—Rick Kattelmann

- December 1993, Sierra Alliance—Debbie Elliott-Fisk

- December 1993, Resources Agency satellite interactive teleconference—Debbie Elliott-Fisk

- February 1994, TUCARE—Debbie Elliott-Fisk

- February 1994, meeting, Human Dimensions—Science Team

- February 8, 1994, eastern Sierra public (Lee Vining)—Connie Millar

- March 1994, USFS PSW Science Forum (Albany)—Connie Millar

- March 29, 1994, Inyo National Forest (Bishop)—Connie Millar

- March 31, 1994, Lake Tahoe Basin Management Unit—Connie Millar

- April 7, 1994, White Mountain Research Station (Bishop), —Rick Kattelmann

- April 22, 1994, Toiyabe National Forest (Bridgeport)—Connie Millar

- April 26, 1994, Transportation/Roads Workshop—John Menke

- June 1994, Eldorado National Forest management team—Doug Leisz

- July 16, 1994, Sierra Nevada Alliance annual meeting (Mammoth Lakes)—Connie Millar

- September 1994, county planners—Tim Duane

- September 21, 1994, California Biodiversity Council (Yosemite)—Don Erman

- October 1994, El Dorado–Amador Forest Forum—Doug Leisz

- October 10, 1994, Sierra Nevada Industrial Forest Land Owners: California Forestry Association—Don Erman, Harrison Dunning, Norm Johnson, Jonathan Kusel, Doug Leisz, Connie Millar, Rowan Rowntree, Bill Stewart

- October 21, 1994, Sierra Communities Council—Don Erman

- October 28, 1994, key contact members representing environmental interests—Don Erman, Jonathan Kusel, Dennis Machida

- November 1994, California Cattlemen's Association—John Menke, Bill Stewart

- November 1994, Cooperative Snow Survey Conference (Asilomar)—Erin Fleming

- November 1994, USFS–Sequoia National Forest tour for Regional Forester Lynn Sprague (MSA tour)—Debbie Elliott-Fisk

- Fall 1994, University of California Extension Ecosystem Conference—Don Erman, Norm Johnson, Connie Millar

- February 3, 1995, Western Section of the Wildlife Society, annual meeting—Don Erman

- February 3, 1995, MSA signatories, MULC, and associates—Debbie Elliott-Fisk and MSA work group

- February 23, 1995, government conference on the environment—Mike Oliver

- March 3, 1995, California Licensed Professional Foresters Association—Don Erman

- March 8, 1995, Resources Agency and department administrators—Tim Duane, Don Erman, Jonathan Kusel, Connie Millar, Bill Stewart

- April 26, 1995, University of California, Division of Natural Resources, Continuing Conference on the Environment (Granlibakken, CA)—Mike Oliver

- May 25, 1995, Regional Council of Rural Counties (Sacramento)—Don Erman

- June 1995, U.S. Forest Service regional managers (Sacramento)—Mike Oliver

- July 15, 1995, Society of American Foresters: Riparian Grazing—John Menke

- July 17, 1995, California Wool Growers/National Lamb Feeders Association—John Menke

- UC Division of Agriculture and Natural Resources Council of Deans and Directors—Debbie Elliott-Fisk, Don Erman

- Executive Council on Biodiversity—Debbie Elliott-Fisk

- Sierra Summit Steering Committee—Debbie Elliott-Fisk

- State Senate Committee on Natural Resources—Debbie Elliott-Fisk

- California Forestry Association, annual meeting—Debbie Elliott-Fisk

- Quincy Library Group, consulting on model of late successional forests—Jo Ann Fites-Kaufmann, Jerry Franklin

Case study workshops were held to assess the accuracy of the experts at the county level, working with community experts (Sam Doak and Jonathan Kusel): April 3, 1995, Portola; April 4, 1995, Sierraville; April 5, 1995, Quincy; April 7, 1995, Graeagle; April 12, 1995, Chester; and April 20, 1995, Greenville.

Social assessment workshops were held at the county level (Sam Doak and Jonathan Kusel):

- March 27, 1995, Kern County (Bakersfield)

- April 4 , 1995, Sierra County (Sierraville)

- April 5, 1995, Plumas County (Quincy)

- April 13, 1995, El Dorado County (Placerville)

- May 3, 1995, Mono County (Mammoth Lakes)

- May 4, 1995, Inyo County (Bishop)

- May 4, 1995, Placer County (Auburn)

- May 5, 1995, Greater Lake Tahoe Basin (South Lake Tahoe)

- May 8, 1995, Amador County (Jackson)

- May 9, 1995, Calaveras County (San Andreas)

- May 9, 1995, Tuolumne County (Sonora)

- May 10, 1995, Madera County (Oakhurst)

- May 10, 1995, Mariposa County (Mariposa)

- May 11, 1995, Fresno County (Fresno)

- May 11, 1995, Tulare County (Tulare)

- May 16, 1995, Lassen County (Susanville)

- May 18, 1995, Butte County (Paradise)

- May 22, 1995, Yuba County (Brownsville)

- May 22, 1995, Nevada County (Nevada City)

- May 24, 1995, Tuolumne County, second meeting (Sonora)

- May 1995, Nevada County, second meeting (Nevada City)

- May 1995, Butte County (Oroville)

- June 1995, Sierra County, second meeting (Sierraville)

FACA

SNEP is excluded from the regulatory actions of the Federal Advisory Committee Act of 1988 because it was initiated by congressional action and is conducted as a report to Congress. This assertion was challenged in a lawsuit, *California Forestry Association v. U.S. Forest Service*, which charged that SNEP was in violation of FACA. District Court Judge Charles Richey concluded in his decision of December 22, 1995, that SNEP did not violate FACA. In arriving at its decision, the court discerned that the congressional intent for SNEP made clear that the project would report to Congress and that both the Forest Service and SNEP subsequently conducted the project in a manner consistent with this interpretation. The fact that SNEP was initiated to provide information and analysis, not a plan for proposed management action, was considered by the court a distinction without a difference, because the Forest Service plans would likely derive, at least in part, from SNEP's report. Judge Richey ruled not only that FACA did not apply to SNEP but also that the Forest Service may use SNEP's final report without fear of violating FACA.